# 40 Years Afore The Mast

# Volume 2

## A collection of my writing on Helicopters 1975-2015



For information on bulk purchases, academic sales or textbook adaptations, please contact Eagle Eye Solutions, LLC. (www.eagleeyesolutionsllc.com)



Library of Congress Card Number -

ISBN -xxx

Manufactured in the United States.

Published by:

Eagle Eye Solutions, LLC
P.O. Box 27, Charlotte, VT 05445 USA
Phone1-800-653 7483 (USA)+
email:shawn.coyle@EagleEyeSolutionsLLC.com
Web www.EagleEyeSolutionsLLC.com
Printed in the United States of America.
Publishers Cataloging in Publication Data
Coyle, Shawn C
40 Years Afore the Mast Volume 2
First Edition
1. Books - United States - Aviation 1. Coyle, Shawn, 1950 -
II Title - 40 Years Afore the Mast Volume 1 2018
III Title - 40 Years Afore the Mast Volume 2

# PREFACE

## AVIATION HAS BEEN MY LIFE

I began life at an early age

My mother told me that about age 4, I wanted to be a pilot. I obtained my pilot's license at age 17 (thank you Royal Canadian Air Cadets) before I had a driver's license and it was all downhill from there!

Royal Military College of Canada for an Engineering degree, the Canadian Air Force for jet and helicopter training, Empire, Test Pilot School all set me up for a great adventure!

Test flying in the UK and Canada preceded teaching at the US Naval Test Pilot School, the original International Test Pilot School at Cranfield, National Test Pilot School in Mojave, as well as other minor courses. Working as an Engineering Test Pilot for Transport Canada exposed me to a world of great importance to aviation safety, and even more poorly understood than experimental flight testing.

I've had the great pleasure of working for many outstanding people, but would like to single out John Maris, a true genius.

The helicopter has evolved to a wonderful tool for a wide variety of daily tasks, ranging from news reporting to dramatic rescues and airborne ambulances. Yet many parts of its operation and use have defied detailed understanding.

I have been extremely fortunate to have the opportunity to study and understand these machines, and more lucky to not only teach others about them, but to have some modest gift in writing about them.

### WHY DID I WRITE THIS BOOK?

Aside from the persistent , but pleasant urging from my wife... (Whom I thank wholely)

The answer eluded me for a while. Sharing my experience was part of the reason, but finally I realized that there was no single source for this knowledge.I have enjoyed flying helicopters, and doing a myriad of things that can only be done with helicopters, and wish that others can continue to do those same type of things with increased knowledge and greater safety.

## WHY TWO VOLUMES

There are two 'books' for several reasons.

One book would be huge!

Volume 1 has accident analysis and pilot and company reports,

Volume 2 has the other columns. It was a more or less natural 'split'.

### STANDARD DISCLAIMERS

The view expressed here are purely personal and definitely unofficial. They do not represent the views of any previous employer or any professional organizations or publication with which I may be affiliated.

There are many techniques and methods in these books. These are the result of observations and experimentation while flying in a wide variety of helicopters. These techniques may not be appropriate to all types of helicopters, nor for all skill levels of pilots or ambient conditions. For this reason conditions are given only approximately. In some cases, specific advice is given to avoid what turned out to be close calls for me. This advice is meant to prevent others from re-inventing the wheel, or being embarrassed. I can make no claim for these maneuvers working at all times for all helicopters - the reader is reminded to take care and be responsible for their own actions and remaining within the limitations in the Flight Manual. Good judgment of what is safe and unsafe must be left to the properly trained individual.

Obviously nothing in this manual should be taken as superseding any procedures mandated by various State rules and regulations, aircraft or equipment manufacturers limitations or company operating manuals.

While the author and publishers have exhaustively researched the subject to ensure the accuracy and completeness of the information contained in this book, we assume no responsibility for errors inaccuracies, omissions or any inconsistency herein. Any slights of people or organizations are unintentional.v Terms Used

## *Political Correctness*

There is no intention to demean members of either (any?) sex by the use of gender–related pronouns. Men can fly helicopters just as well as women*
*and I didn't put this in to gain sales from the Whirly Girls either.""

## *Dedication*

This book is dedicated to all the designers who turned concepts into designs, all the engineers who turned designs into useful bits of machinery, the skilled workmen who turned those bits of metal into living objects, all the dedicated mechanics who kept those machines breathing. I would like also to thank all those who passed on their ideas and knowledge, both instructors and students that I have learned so much from.
And to all those who let me control their machines, my eternal thanks.To Mike Reyno, The publisher of Vertical magazine- thank you for all you've done to put me (keep me) in print.
Finally, I would again like to thank the Grand Aeronautical Engineer and Grand Chief Pilot, from whom all ideas and concepts flow, and who has never made a mistake.

## *It's Been a Grand Flight so Far*

And It's not over

# FOREWARD

If you're a helicopter pilot, there's a good chance you're familiar with the name of Shawn Coyle.

Shawn's book "Cyclic and Collective" has been a bible to a generation of helicopter pilots. Smart and practical and suffused with humour, it's a rare example of educational material that's actually fun to read. Shawn presents complex technical and aerodynamic concepts in a way that is not only easy for pilots to understand, but more importantly, directly relatable to their experiences in the cockpit.

When my wife, Linda, and I started *Vertical* Magazine in 2002, we wanted to provide people in the helicopter industry with content that would have a positive impact on their real-world operations. Shawn's expertise and conversational writing style were exactly what we wanted for our readers, and we're so grateful that he signed on with us as a contributing editor.

This volume, *40 Years Afore the Mast*, includes a number of articles originally published in *Vertical*. Overwhelmingly, they're as timely and useful today as when they were first published. Whether or not you caught them the first time around, you'll be glad to have them collected in one convenient reference, along with many other insightful essays.

Shawn is a professional who writes for a professional audience, and I have no doubt that many readers of this book will have likewise spent many decades "afore the mast." However, I hope that *40 Years Afore the Mast* also reaches many brand-new helicopter pilots — the young men and women who will shape our industry in the decades to come.

At *Vertical*, we believe that making the helicopter industry better and safer begins with knowledge… and when it comes to knowledge for pilots, there's no one better than Shawn Coyle to impart it.

Mike Reyno

Editor and Publisher

Vertical Magazine

**CHAPTER 1** # *Operational Requirements vs Technological Capabilities*

**AGARD** NATO;s Advisory Group For Research and Development

This was written in 1984, long before GPS was a viable Navaid. Aside from that, much of it is still relevant!

*Comment: This paper discusses the lessons learned in the wartime use of helicopters, and the impact that modern technology can have on what have become common themes.*

Lessons learned, the constraints on helicopter operations, and the requirements of the battlefield helicopter are integrated to show where technology would better serve the operators. Performance monitoring, handling qualities and radio communications examples are presented, and a brief outline of how existing technology could be used to update an existing helicopter is made.

## *Introduction*

That the helicopter is poised to undergo as dramatic an advance as the fixed wing aircraft did in changing from piston to jet engines should be obvious to every person in this room, even without the projections of what LHX or JVX will look like or the fanciful cinematics of "Blue Thunder" or "Airwolf". The helicopter is coming of age.

The helicopter's image as a relatively fragile, underpowered device useful for hauling troops, cargo or casualties is gradually being removed, Developments in the technologies of structures, composites, and engines have overcome many previous shortcomings and the helicopter is about to become a device whose uses may well be limited solely by man's imagination.

## *History*

The whole history of aviation has been one of development based on knowledge. Often this has been hard won and many have paid with their lives for lack of knowledge. Rotary wing aviation unfortunately has not been immune to this costly way of learning, and many of today's advances owe their impetus to the shortcomings of the past. The improvements in airframe design and powerplants and the use of composite materials, for the most part, are logical extensions of the things we have grown familiar with. They present no great leap of knowledge nor difficulty in application. This is not the case in electronics. Even the most expert are having difficulty in keeping up with developments and no one can forsee all the possible uses for many new items. That electronics will do almost anything we ask is not the problem. What do we want done and how much we want to do is of far more importance.

The main improvements that electronics have provided for the helicopter have been in the area of night and bad weather operations. These two areas show up all too readily man's shortcomings, and here electronics has extended capabilities. Wars do not stop at night, nor on account of rain, and up to now this has been a crippling limitation of the helicopter. Yet before we get too deeply into the improvements possible with technology it is necessary to review some of the other, non-technical lessons that have been so dearly learned in the past. While the helicopter has been used in warfare for only a relatively short time in comparison with fixed wing aircraft, many lessons can be learned from WW II, Korea, Malaysia, Algeria, Vietnam, Yorn Kippur and the Falklands conflicts.

## *The Lessons of War*

Briefly and by no helicopters in particular aspects: means completely, the history of aviation in a combat environment seems to point tosome general and interesting

- Operations are conducted beyond what the original design intended in terms of weight, and to a lesser extent,role.
- Unit level modifications are the norm not the exception.
- Periods between overhaul are extended
- Personnel, both operators and maintainers, are pushed to limits of endurance
- Operators and maintainers have low experience levels

To a greater or lesser extent, all of these aspects have been present in the previously mentioned conflicts, and interestingly enough, have parallels in the development in fixed wing aviation. There is no reason to suspect that they will be missing from the next war, and if we can use technological improvements in such a way as to focus on these lessons learned in the past, we may make a significant improvement in our operational capabilities.

## *Rules, Limitations and Physical Laws*

During peacetime the operation of any aircraft is subject to a never ending number of rules and regulations, and operating limitations. Broadly speaking these items break down in the following way:

### Rules and Regulations

Those regulations set out by authorities to govern the c9nduct of peacetime operations in a safe and orderly manner.

As every pilot will tell you, there are many rules that you can break with impunity. It is expected that many of the numerous rules and regulations governing day to day operations will be gratefully thrown out when a war comes along. Rules cannot cover the variety of situations encountered in peacetime, and to slavishly follow them in war would be folly of the highest order.

### Aircraft Limitations

The restriction of an aircraft parameter, such as weight, speed, engine power etc., to permit safety of flight, long life and continued use at an acceptable maintenance penalty.

Likewise, limitations are placed on helicopters to preserve them. Speaking from personal experience, it is not difficult to exceed some of these limitations and not know it, or to exceed them with small or no consequence. It only takes one transmission overtorque, with a subsequent discovery that all it means is checking the oil filters, to realize that a healthy margin of safety is built into many components. In my test flying career, I have become more aware of the allowances made for inadvertent excursions beyond the limitations published for the operators.

For example, there is almost no way of determining the effective weight (aircraft plus underslung load) of a helicopter without resorting to cumbersome and imprecise charts. The UH-60, for example, designed to be able to achieve a rate of climb in the hover on a 4000 foot pressure altitude, 95 degree F day, has been flown at 50% above its original design weight. While few would argue with having this sort of capability, consider the consequences - the operational pilot seeing this sort of demonstration now realizes that he can overload his UH-60 with impunity. As previously discussed, there is a very strong possibility that given a war environment he is going to overload the machine anyway, so now caution can be thrown to the winds. Unfortunately there is a third set of constraints, often ignored and much less forgiving, that the operational pilot is about to face, one that he cannot ignore, like rules, or stretch, like limitations.

### Physical Laws

The laws of aerodynamics, performance, thermodynamics and strength of materials.

There are already numerous examples of what happens when people attempt to break some of these laws - one of the most common being performance required exceeding performance available from the engine. Some services have reacted to accidents of this nature by regulating that prior to every sortie, performance must be calculated using the various charts.

As one of the first casualties of a war is the regulations, and as the charts aren't light in weight or easy to use, the operational pilot is put in a very unenviable situation. Suitable technological application in this area would eliminate this problem, however, adequate guidance beyond the limitations prescribed for peacetime operations must be given. For example, it is feasible to put all the performance charts of a helicopter into a microprocessor, which would certainly eliminate the problem of carrying around all the charts, and probably give more a curacy at the same time.

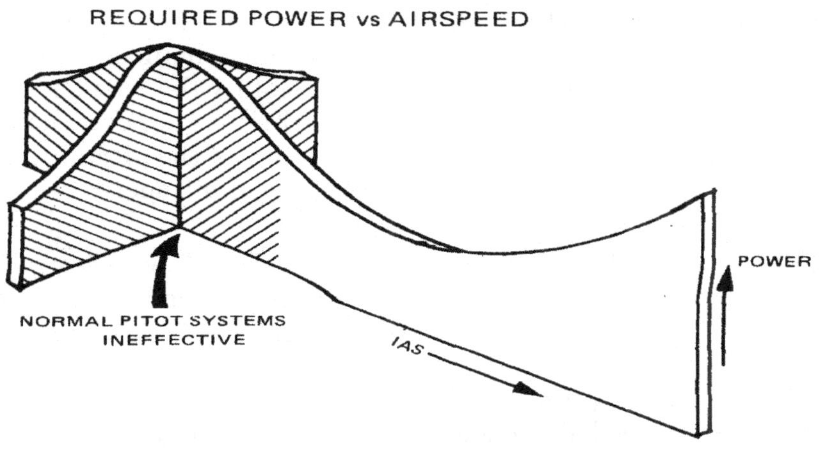


**Figure 1-1 Power Requiems, Pitot Statics and Low Airspeed**

If such a microprocessor were to be hooked up to sensors in the aircraft: such air temperature, pressure and radar altitude, a low airspeed sensor and engine conditions such as torque, temperature and RPM, it would be possible to automate the performance calculation process. The very large change in power required versus airspeed in the area where current pitot static systems are ineffective is graphically demonstrated in Figure 1-1 on page 3. with such an automated system the pilot wouldbe able to instantly. determine if he had overloaded his machine (useful in peacetime to satisfy the authorities) and also determine if he has sufficient power available for the more critical wartime situation. Such technology has existed for at least five years, and an example of an attempt to put it into a helicopter is shown in Figure 2. Unfortunately this equipment did not proceed beyond the demonstration phase. There is clearly an operational requirement for this equipment, and the technology has been available, but it has not been harnessed.

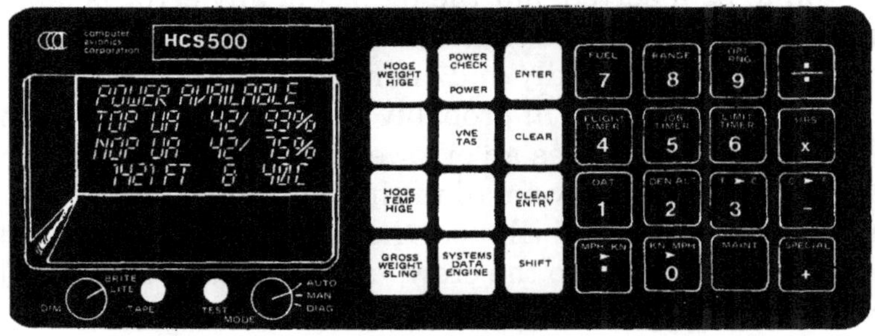


**Figure 1-2 1980's era Helicopter Performance Computer**

It would be relatively easy to program such a device to cater for the wartime scenario. Given that limitations are going- to be exceeded, the computer could say what capabilities exist for the conditions. It could, for example, take into account flight control margins for hovering out of wind, or allow for increased weight when it is possible. Rather than leaving the pilot to "suck-it-and-see" in an overloaded aircraft, some precise guidance could be given. The_ penalty for failing the "suck-it-and-see" test is very high. Laws, especially physical laws, cannot be broken repeatedly without a very high penalty.

## *The Other Lessons*

Unit level modifications are going to be the norm, not the exception, as the personnel most affected by shortcomings in material and equipment cannot and will not wait for the official answer to their problems. How this can be improved upon is not an easy question to answer and is beyond the scope of this paper.

The other lessons gleaned from the past should also have an impact on how we use our technology. It has been gratifying to see more and more "on condition" maintenance being demanded and built into helicopter designs, however, do they take account of the very strong possibility that the normal operating limits will be exceeded? Are there data recorded to see exactly what limits were exceeded and for how long? Has anyone thought about how this will impact the long-term life of the aircraft concerned? This will not only have an impact on wartime availability, but also on peacetime operation, when perhaps not all that should be reported is in factreported.

That everyone is worked to the limit of their endurance in a war is a fact that all who design, build or test military equipment should be well aware of. What it means is that the system that worked so well in the lab or in set field exercises may be too complex or too time consuming to be worthwhile in a war. In addition, it is worth considering the factors of mans adaptability, and his desire to make things work. That man could fly some of the early helicopters and perform some of his magnificent feats of flying in them is surely the only proof that is needed of his adaptability. New equipment often needs a long hard look by the skeptical to see if it really is progress. An inertial navigation system with superb accuracy but with a 10 minute warm-up time is not only a hindrance if you want to take off in a hurry, it could be a liability if it is the only system you have. The increased capabilities that electronics have bequeathed on the helicopter were mentioned previously, and the prime areas affected are night and bad weather operations. Previously these had afforded tired crews at least some chance for a rest. Unless adequate provision is made for around the clock manning for aircrew and ground crew, the advantages gained will be for naught. Tired people make more mistakes and faster computers will only accelerate the gravity of themistakes.

## *Murphy's Law*

No endeavor of mans is immune to this law. War may amplify it, due to hard use of equipment and the inevitable fog of war, but even the best engineering will not make it go away. It certainly did not disappear with the advent of the microprocessor. However, wars do not stop because the circuit breaker blows, or because the voltage levels are not right or because the operator inputs wrong information. For example, with a means of distributing information the overall number of errors may decrease slightly, for a given amount of information to be inserted, but the impact of any error is magnified many times. Consider a totally integrated cockpit that has a cassette device for the input of data. Due to the volume of information required, for example, friendly and enemy troop positions, code words, call signs, frequencies, and so on, the compiling of data will probably be done by someone other than the pilot or crew. Without this system, if one person makes an error entering a grid reference in a navigation system the consequences of the error are probably small in the overall picture. If one person makes an error in a data cassette that a whole formation will use, the results could be much worse. At the least, a means of verifying data should be available to the crew, and a suitable means of completing the mission after multiple failures should be high on the priority list.

The low experience levels of the operators and maintainers are also cause for concern. At present it takes a relatively short time to train a helicopter pilot, in comparison with his fixed wing counterpart, as most helicopters have been little more than engines, airframes and at best a rudimentary armament system. More complex helicopters require more lengthy training, more specialized pilots and more specialized ground crew. As we have not yet started genetically engineering pilots it is well to remember that pilots are no better nor worse than they ever have been, It is not enough to cater for the mythical and non-existent "average" pilot, as by definition, half of the pilots will be below the mark. Having trained and equipped the future aviator at great cost can we afford to put him at risk in the same fashion as the cheaply trained and cheaply equipped?

## *A Review of the Characteristics of Helicopter Predations*

At the risk of offending many who are intimately familiar with helicopter operations in the land scenario, a review of the items that separate helicopter operations from those of our fixed wing brethren is necessary. These include, in the main:

**Operations From Remote, Austere Locations**

- Weather information is either limited or non-existent.
- Navaids are extremely limited, and air traffic control is almost non-existent (there are also no runways on which to align the compass).
- Communications are mostly to and through Army networks. Knowledge of elevation, variation and so on is limited to what is shown on the maps available,
- Operations are conducted in small groups, and the supported units are widely scattered.
- Operations are conducted in conditions of poor visibility.
- Flexibility of Operation
- The crews must be expert in reconnaissance, observation, artillery fire control, anti-tank operations and numerous other army related specialties, often simultaneously.
- Response time to different tasks must berapid,
- Numerous radios must be monitored and different call signs and even different jargon must be used on each differentradio.

**Continuous Performance Monitoring**

- Torque limitations.
- Engine speed and temperature limitations, Low airspeed flight envelope.
- Low altitude flight with very limited terrain clearance.

There are obviously too many of these to be dealt with completely in this brief discussion, however, some of the implications of these problems should be considered. Let us look at the impact of these aspects on only one new type of system. Personally, one of the pieces of avionics I would like to have in any helicopter is a Doppler navigation system, so for the purposes of illustration let us look at a Doppler navigation system.

For operation at low speed or in reduced visibility it gives the ability to observe groundspeed and eases the task of navigating. It is to date the only navaid that I am aware of that will permit an accurate zero groundspeed IFR hover, yet it requires very precise inputs from the magnetic compass to be of any use in navigation. How will the accuracy of the compass be checked when operating behind a barn one day and in a village the next? Even more interesting, how will the magnetic variation be checked for the area of operation? How long will it take to program the system, and can it be done without starting the engines orAPU?

A Doppler navigation system has been used here as it is a personal preference, however, any navigation system is only as good as the person who is using it. It will not show errors in entry, it will not correct mistakes, it will not relieve the operator from checking it, and most important, it will never replace a man with a map. The best that any navigation system can hope to do is to assist in navigation. It will permit the operator to perform another task, such as observe the enemy or fire weapons, instead of constantly referring to a map, but it will not permit him to stop navigating, It certainly will not let the crew be ignorant of the principles and practices of navigation,

There have already been examples of human error defeating very complex, triplicated navigation systems, and these have been without the complications of fatigue, pressure or confusion that will be prevalent in war. Navigation systems are needed, as the job of navigating at night or in bad weather is difficult, Even in these conditions however, it is still necessary to update the system by some other external means. Navigation systems must not be made so excessively complex as to be too difficult to use or understand, nor must they be treated or advertised as replacing maps. Even moving map displays will still require checking against the ground, which presupposes a minimum skill level at map reading. Any device designed to replace the printed paper map should also be capable of displaying at least as much information and to the same resolution as a map held 18 inches (0.5 meter) away from the eye.

There is an operational requirement to assist in navigation, but there is no requirement to make the operator a slave to the technology.

**Performance Monitoring and Handling Qualities**

Moving on to performance monitoring and handling qualities, it is interesting to note the number of engine instruments in fighter cockpits and the number in helicopters. It is also interesting to note that not only are the critical instruments that require monitoring in helicopters more numerous, but they all appear to change simultaneously. (See Figure 3)

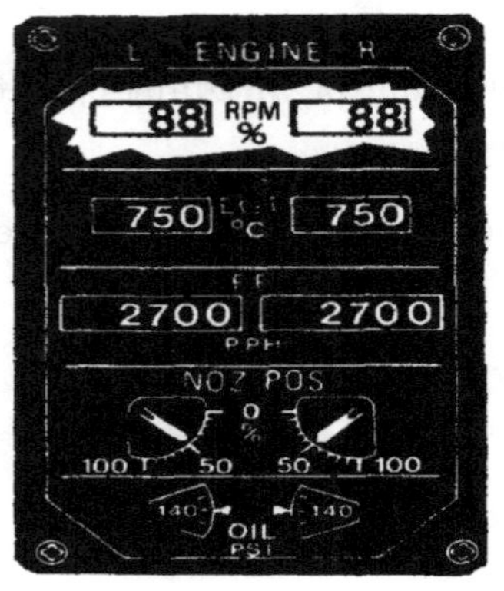


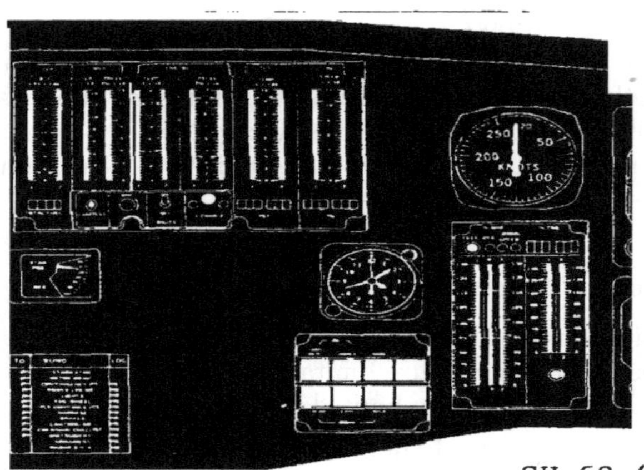

**Figure 1-3 F-16 (left) vs SH-60 Engine Instruments**

The requirement to monitor so many engine parameters simultaneously must be questioned. Each of the parameters concerned can be justified on the basis that it is vital to maintain the longevity of the component, and has historically always been in helicopters, yet why do we not have transmissions that can handle all the power that the engine can put out, and which do not require a separate indication? Why do we not have a single indication that will tell if the engine is performing satisfactorily, and if the power required for the ambient conditions and at other sites en route is sufficient? Why do we not have more collective lever designs like that of the Gazelle, that incorporate changes in force? Without having to look inside, the pilot is able to pull to a position that is defined by a tactile stop, (that is easily overcome), and to know that no limitations will be exceeded. This is very handy in rapid reaction situations. As air to air combat between helicopters becomes more probable such a feature will be essential.

Helicopters have been saddled with handed down technology for too long, and it is only recently that this mold has been broken. The first generation of helicopters to be fitted with low airspeed sensors has just emerged and it promises to revolutionize the way helicopters will be used and what low airspeed envelopes will mean. The next step is to integrate them into the previously mentioned performance computer which will be able to predict to the pilot what maneuvers he will and will not be able to perform. For example, current low velocity limitations are most rudimentary and are given as side and rear wind speed limits. Often these have no mention of the effect of weight or density altitude, or if they do mention them require the use of cumbersome graphs. Side and rear wind limitations are based for the most part on having sufficient yaw or pitch control to maintain a desired flight condition.

This is not a limitation in the terms of the definition given previously, but it is rapidly approaching being a law.

Like any other aerodynamic variable, the amount of thrust available from a tail rotor or the amount of pitching moment available from a main rotor will vary, at constant RPM and angle of attack, with density altitude. What may be an adequate margin at sea level may not be adequate at greater altitudes. For the most part, no direction is given to the operational pilot on this matter, and the result is another attempt to break a physical law. By using a low airspeed indicator it would be possible to warn the operator when he is approaching an area of inadequate yaw control before he gets himself into trouble. Again, as it is very likely that the helicopter will be operated beyond the peacetime limits, information in this area is also needed. The technology has existed for some time to obtain low airspeed information, but those helicopters that use such equipment do not use it for anything related to performance or control margins.

## *Integrating The Talk Show*

Communication is one other area of great difference between fixed and rotary wing aircraft. It is not uncommon for an Army helicopter to have four or more radios. The agencies that a helicopter may have to talk to are shown in Figure 4.

A breakdown of the radio types is given below and should be taken as being a minimum fit.Not only

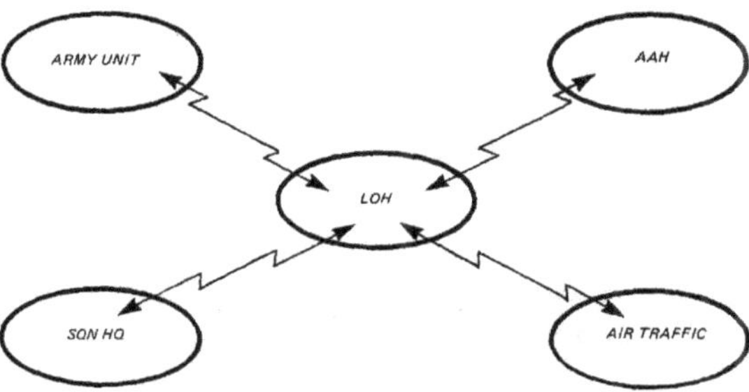


**Figure 1-4 Typical Radio Network oft Light Observation Helicopter (LOH)**

is there a proliferation of radios, but there are different ways of talking on each one and to further complicate the matter the same aircraft may often have different call signs on different radio nets. To say that handling he various radios in a battlefield helicopter is one of the more difficult tasks 1s a large understatement. Until recently this has had to be accomplished with different radio control heads and inadequate intercommunication facilities that required the radio volume to be set at the radio, and that required hands off the flight controls to change transmitters and frequencies.

Recent developments in cockpit design have improved some aspects of this problem, however, they have led to another problem where perhaps we can take some very good lessons from the fixed wing community. Using the AHIP and SH-6O as examples it is interesting to note how all the controls on the cyclic and collective have been positioned for the thumbs to use; none have been positioned for the other digits. This first attempt at Hands On Cyclic and Collective (HOCAC) is long overdue, but there may be room for further improvement. Compare this with the F-18 where the controls have been more equitably divided. Surely more use of the other, equally dexterous, digits of the pilot's hands could be found without much more effort. Figures 5 and 6 show these differences.

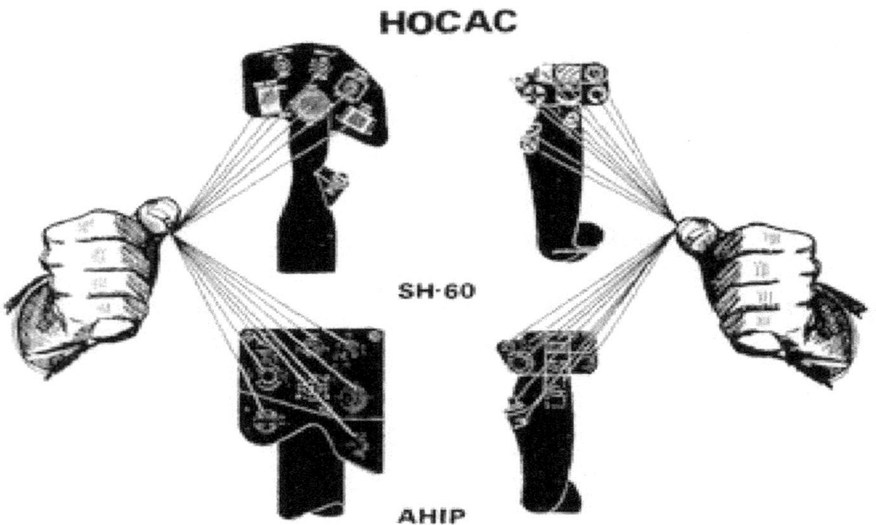


**Figure 1-5** **Hans On Cyclic and Collective (HOCAC) for SH-50 and OH-58D. Compare to F-18 Below**

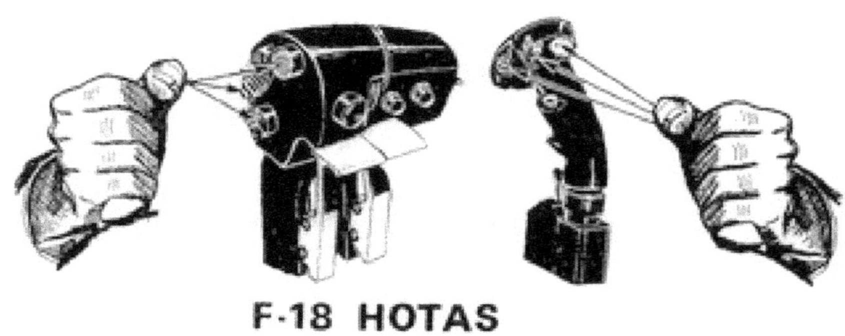


**Figure 1-6** **F-18 Hands on Throttle and Stick (HOTAS).**

Returning to communications, careful control of technology is required to truly reduce the workload of the operators. Prior to analyzing what is or is not progress in radios, let us look at what we have at present. Radio packages seem to fit into two categories, those with preset channels and those without. For an operational pilot faced with a suite of radios, his actions are relatively simple. To change frequencies he either moves the preset channel knob to another channel, or if he has no preset channels he dials up the new frequency. To change the transmitter he simply changes the position of the selector, and to select any receiver he merely changes the position of the appropriate switch. To see what frequency he is transmitting on he need only look at the control head of the radio concerned. This system has its shortcomings, mostly in the panel space it takes up, however, it is simple to operate and exceptionally easy to learn to use. Any technological change should, if at all possible, improve on the situation, and certainly should not either take up more panel space or, more important, require more steps to preform a task. As we shall see this is not always thecase.

Two examples of radio controllers and intercom systems are given to illustrate the point. One is a definite improvement, the other is in my opinion almost a retrograde step.

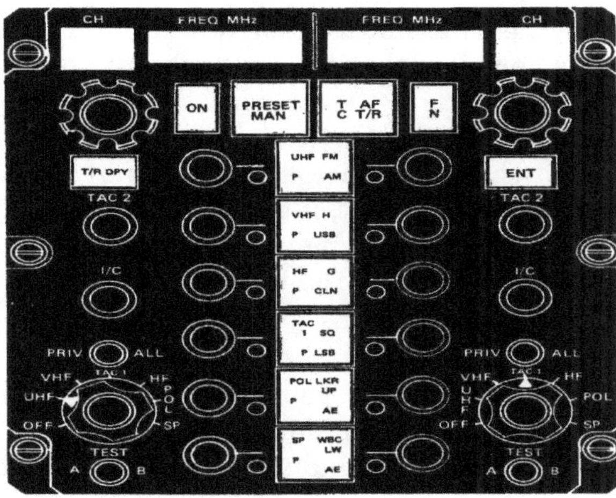


Figure 1-7 **Retrofit Radio Package for Observation Helicopter**

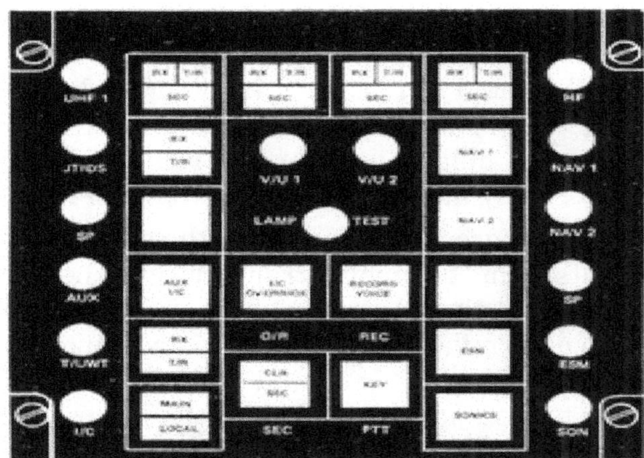


Figure 1-8 **Radio Controller for ASW Helicopter**

The first case involves retrofitting of a radio package for a light observation helicopter to include six. radios. This is shown in Figure 7. The exact details of this controller have been detailed in a previous AGARD paper (AGARD Guidance and Control Panel Proceedings Number 329, Paper 19; Communications Management - A Vital Link). An operational pilot who tried the system commented that it took ten minutes of instruction to learn how to use it. It is simple, it looks like a.radio and it is easy to change fixed and preset frequencies with this system. The drawbacks are that it only displays the frequencies of the radios selected for transmission on each side, (given that panel space was limited this was an acceptable shortcoming), and that it requires hands off the flying controls to change frequencies or radios.

The second system, shown in Figure 1-8 on page 9, was admittedly from a prototype anti-submarine warfare helicopter, however, that does not mitigate the bad features of its design. It was designed for a single pilot operation aircraft, with two rear cabin crew, and each station featured 18 pushbuttons and 14 rotary volume controls. The rationale for the proliferation of pushbuttons was that they were inherently more reliable than rotary switches.

The display was blank until a pushbutton hadbeen pressed.T he logic was arranged so that the first press of the button brought the set to receive, the second push placed it in transmit/receive and the third push turned the radio off again. Changing transmitter took a minimum of three pushes of buttons, if itwas done correctly the first time. After all of that the controller did nothing more than select radios for transmitting and adjust volumes. Changing frequencies still had to be done through a Controller Display Unit (CDU) and took a minimum of five further steps. If the CDU happened to be on another function the pilot was not able to see what frequency e was transmitting on. This second system clearly demonstrates many things, but most important, it shows that a minor technical decision (use pushbuttons as theyare more reliable) can have a tremendous impact on the usefulness of the system. The operational requirement was subordinated to the technological requirement.

## *Updating the Mature Helicopter*

Putting together a package of advanced technology is not easy, especially when starting from scratch on a new design. There is always the demand to put a quart in a pint pot and demonstrate improvements in performance, fuel consumption, noise, maintenance and the whole host of other measures of a product. Rather than pursue this avenue, I will attempt to show how a retrofit to an existing helicopter can significantly improve its safety and capabilities, while reducing pilot workload. The devices chosen for the mock retrofit are existing technologies and represent a minimum amount of risk. The helicopter chosen is the venerableUH-

No changes to the engine, airframe or rotor are considered as they are independent of the electronics and in any case represent only a minor change in the existing order of things. Items that are changed are those that will reduce pilot workload while improving capabilities. In addition, no attempt will be made to include such items as MLS or tactical approach aids.

To assist in flying the helicopter a simple AFCS should be installed. It should include an attitude hold feature in pitch, roll and yaw, and permit rate damping when maneuvering. Each lane should be de selectable, i.e. a malfunction in the pitch channel should still permit the roll and yaw channel to operate. To maintain simplicity, it should not feature any altitude hold, turn to heading or other modes.

Performance monitoring and computation would be greatly enhanced by the addition of a computer, as previously described. This would require inputs from the engine, transmission, the low airspeed sensor, the radar altimeter, the cargo hook and the Doppler navigation system. With the appropriate information in its memory, it would be able to determine if power required was likely to exceed power available, or if any control margins were being approached. It should of course be capable of computations well beyond the normal published limits to cater for the wartime case. Figure 9 shows basically how this could be integrated.

To assist in navigation, a Doppler navigation system should be added, however, it should have a limited number of waypoints, and simple controls. It should require only battery power to insert information, and have a suitable instrument panel display of groundspeed, drift, and at low speed, a set of cross hairs for hovering. The display should be to the right of the radar altimeter

If not already fitted, a radar altimeter should be installed, and situated immediately to the right of the attitude indicator.

The radios should be replaced to minimize the work required to change not only frequencies, but also transmitters. This should be possible with hands on the flying controls. The flying control grips may require slight modification to permit this. The frequency currently being transmitted on should be displayed in front of each pilot on the instrument panel. ·

Finally, the pilots seats should be made comfortable enough to permit eight hours of flying to be done each day without crippling the pilot.

## SUMMARY

In summary, the lessons of previous conflicts have taught us many things about the helicopter and its shortcomings. Many of these lessons have been absorbed, and advances made, however, the electronic explosion presents an opportunity to correct many of the recurring themes that may have slipped through the cracks. The danger lies in letting technology do everything, when a man is capable of performing many functions with equal ease. Future helicopters must not be technological showpieces just because technology has the capabilities, but should have only sufficient technology to do their mission, driven by a firm operational requirement.

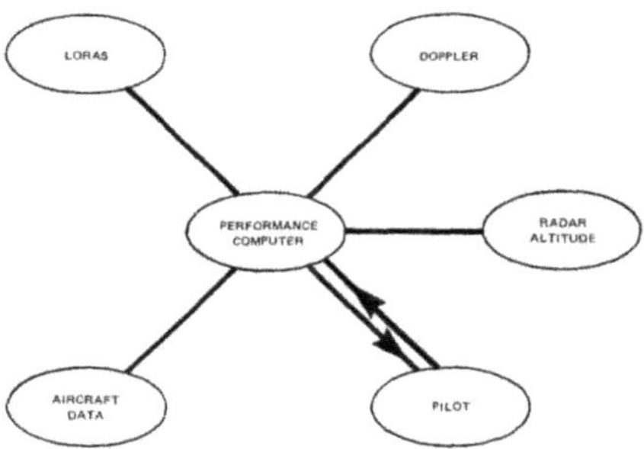


**Figure 1-9 Integration of Sensors**

# CHAPTER 1 *Civil Certification Part 1*

**Vertical** October / November 2009

*Comment: In part one of helping pilots understand airworthiness requirements, we examine the basis for these regulations, issues with STCs and TSOs, and the differences between parts 27 and 29*

## *Understanding Airworthiness*

All commercial pilots should be intimately familiar with the operational regulations that govern the way they operate. The regulations that govern how helicopters are designed and tested for airworthiness are less well known, but have an equally large impact — although this may not be immediately obvious. I'm safe in saying that airworthiness regulations are not well understood: I was a pretty experienced test pilot when I started working at Transport Canada, and it still took a year's on-the-job training to start to understand the basics of civil certification. When I left after five years, I thought I was pretty well-versed in all the more subtle aspects, but I'm still running into interesting complexities. As such, this new series will only scratch the surface of the subject, so don't take any of it as the complete gospel truth. The next few columns aren't intended to make civil certification test pilots out of both my loyal readers, but should give you an insight into how limitations in the flight manual are derived, what is required from a technical standpoint — and what isn't — and areas where there are holes in the certification we should be aware of.

## *An Imperfect World*

Why do we have airworthiness certification? It took awhile, but I finally realized that despite what marketing folks (and occasionally pilot evaluation reports in magazines like this) might say, there is no perfect design. There's also no perfect operator, no perfect maintenance organization and no perfect certification or regulatory authority. Think about it for a second: if any of these were perfect... they'd be the only ones. If aircraft were perfectly designed and manufactured, would they need airworthiness approval or maintenance? As we are stuck on this less-than-perfect plane of existence, we've attempted to develop a series of steps to keep us safe. Good design is the first step, and meeting the requirements laid out in the regulations is the next. But, what exactly is the legal basis for airworthiness rules? In a legal sense, airworthiness rules come from one of the few parts of the United Nations that actually does something useful — the International Civil Aviation Organization. ICAO was set up shortly after the Second World War to allow air transport to operate internationally. A set of broad rules covering personnel licensing and airworthiness (among other things) were established, and countries signed up to abide by those rules. There are a host of these rules, and the adventurous reader is encouraged to look up items of interest at the ICAO website (www.icao.int). The general idea is that these rules permit aircraft and crews to operate internationally. More specifically, the airworthiness annex basically says each country will create a set of airworthiness requirements. Naturally, for many years, each country had its own regulations, with little in common. This made it difficult for manufacturers to get their equipment approved outside the country of origin. To combat this, a series of bilateral agreements between countries (Elbonia and Nefarious, for example) allowed an aircraft certified in Elbonia to be approved in Nefarious without repeating the expensive process. Now, thanks to a lot of work, harmonization groups have minimized the differences and airworthiness approvals between different countries are much less expensive and time-consuming. However, each country still has the option to apply their own differences: Canada for example, has a thing about flight in snow (I can't imagine why). So, each country will set up their own rules for certification, and most model theirs on the system in the United States. For helicopters, the parts of U.S. Title 14 of the Code of Federal Regulations (14 CFR) that are of interest are Part 21 (general [an over-arching part covering a variety of items]), Part 27 (covering "normal" category aircraft up to 7,000 pounds maximum internal weight), and Part 29 (covering transport category aircraft: anything above 7,000 pounds or nine seats). A host of other parts govern engines and maintenance.

## *Differences and the Dividing Line*

Why the difference between Part 27 and Part 29? In simple terms, if you were operating a small, single-engine helicopter carrying only a few passengers, it would be unreasonable to expect the same level of safety as if you were carrying 20 passengers on an airline-style operation. The dividing line for helicopters is more than nine passengers — this puts the body count up to a point where widespread front-page headlines would follow a crash. Less than nine passengers... not so much. While this may seem pretty brutal, if we were to apply the higher level of safety to small helicopters, they'd never get off the ground, and a lot of their benefits would be lost. An interesting aside here: the FAA's mandate is to write the minimum legislation necessary for safety. It's a fascinating approach, which begs the question: how do you know it's the minimum? After some reflection (in several glasses of single-malt Scotch) it became clear (the question, not the Scotch): you'll only know it's the minimum because you'll go below it every now and again, and as long as the accident rate isn't too high, and the nation as a whole is benefiting, things are okay. When the accident rate gets too high, or the political pressure starts getting too much, then a change in the rules might be contemplated. Both Part 27 and Part 29 have the same structure, and their respective performance requirements are in nearly the same section numbers. Perhaps the difference in the level of safety is best illustrated by comparing the same section in the two different regulations. Section 1309 in both parts is one we'll spend more time on later, but as a comparison, look at the wording difference between them in table at the top of the page. Believe me, it takes quite awhile to digest the importance of these subtle differences in wording. There is a very large advisory circular for fixed-wing transport airplanes (Part 25) that deals only with Section 1309, and that is used for guidance in certifying Part 29 helicopters. But, we'll deal with advisory circulars in a later column. Of more immediate interest, these differences mean that Part 29 (transport category) helicopters operate to a higher standard of safety. For example, the height-velocity curve for Part 29 helicopters with more than nine passengers is a limitation, not a performance curve (more on that in a later column).

Changing Requirements

While our safety record can always stand improvement, it's pretty safe to say that flying helicopters is no longer as dangerous as it once was. One reason for this is improved requirements — which are amended frequently. Amended requirements, though, cause a small problem for those making new additional equipment. Obviously, it's not feasible to do a complete recertification of a helicopter just because you want to attach some new piece of equipment to the airframe. So, the process of a supplemental type certificate (STC) was evolved — that way, if you want to add a new air conditioner system to an airframe, you only need to show compliance with the appropriate part of the requirements, not all of them. An STC amends the original certification, and the flight manual supplement amends the original flight manual. You need to know the changes well, as they may change limitations and procedures for your helicopter. But, what if the "appropriate" requirements have changed since the helicopter was originally certified? The Bell 206 series has been around since just slightly after the dawn of time, yet new things are still being added to them: should the developer of those new items have to design to the latest set of rules? It would seem reasonable, until you realize the basic airframe may not be capable of meeting the new rules. Seats are a good example — the latest seat crashworthiness requirements are a welcome improvement. So, if you wanted to put new seats in an old Bell 206, it would make sense to build them to the latest standards. Unfortunately, the underlying structure of the airframe may not be able to handle the forces the new seats would place on them in a crash — because the original structure was made to earlier, less stringent standards.

## *TSO'd Equipment*

This leads nicely to another point that is not well understood: technical standard order (TSO) approved equipment. Receiving a TSO approval means a piece of equipment has passed a series of tests that shows it is safe to install in an aircraft. The tests are typically for altitude and temperature, and vibration and electrical safety (known as "shake and bake" tests). It does not mean you can simply plug the item into the instrument panel, as the installation of TSO-approved equipment may be a complicating factor. For example, installing a TSO-approved GPS that interfaces with the existing horizontal situation indicator navigation display requires that the switches and relays work properly, often a very complex job. In simple terms, a TSO-approved piece of equipment means it is capable of being installed, not that the installation will be satisfactory. It's never as simple as just plugging the box into the dash. Just as operational rules play a part in the overall safety net, so do certification requirements. It could be argued that they are written in blood: landing gear strength requirements for sustaining a drop from a certain height are a good example; they came about because some airframe somewhere didn't survive a heavy landing. The same is true for things like fuel tank strength and survivable seats. In short, you may not immediately see the results of the airworthiness requirements, and there is no need to be intimately familiar with the rules themselves, but you should be aware that they will affect you. In the next column, we'll look at the flight manual and performance charts.

**TABLE 1.**

| **Part 28.1309** | **Party 29.1390** | **Remarks** |
|---|---|---|
| (c) The equipment, systems, and installations of single-engine rotorcraft must be designed to minimize hazards to the rotorcraft in the event of a probable malfunction or failure. | (b) The rotorcraft systems and associated components, considered separately and in relation to other systems, must be designed so that —<br>(1) For Category B rotorcraft, the equipment, systems, and installations must be designed to prevent hazards to the rotorcraft if they malfunction or fail. | Notice also how Part 27 only requires hazards to be minimized, but Part 29 requires preventing hazards.<br>Part 27 assumes that a system may fail (probable failure), while Part 29 assumes the system will fail at some point in time. |

# CHAPTER 2 *Civil Certification Part II*

**Vertical** December 2009 January 2010

*Comment: In part two of helping pilots understand airworthiness requirements, we examine the legal basis for flight manuals, flight manual supplements and the differences between the performance and limitations sections.*

ORIGINALLY TITLED *WE'RE NOT WORTHY PART II*

In my previous column, mention was made of airworthiness requirements being written in blood. Such is the nature of rules and regulations. But, the other truth is that we can only work with what we know, and can only fix what we know didn't work before. For example, in the fixed-wing world, the Airbus A320, the first fly-by-wire airplane, did not meet the strict requirements of the existing regulations when it first came out. It took a while to work out the "special conditions" that proved it met the spirit of the regulations, and then it took longer to get new regulations for it written into the rulebook. Put another way, there is no one currently working on the rules for anti-gravity-powered aircraft.

With that in mind, this column will look at civil flight manuals. Flight manuals are a very interesting subject. They form the regulatory basis for how to operate the helicopter, but definitely don't tell you how to fly it, because some knowledge of helicopter flying is assumed (more on that later).

## *THE LEGAL BASIS*

The certification requirements (United States Federal Aviation Regulations Part 27 and Part 29) have some detailed regulations that specify what has to be in the flight manual. But, it's not just nice-to-know information — there's a legal basis for the flight manual's limitations section that can be traced to the airworthiness certificate/certificate of airworthiness (CoA). {Comment: I'm assuming that the terms "airworthiness certificate" and "certificate of airworthiness," are just a different means of reference by different countries — as they seemed to be used interchangeably in the original draft. If not, I've mucked up a lot here by combining them!

This diminutive piece of paper (the CoA) states, something to the effect, that the aircraft must be operated and maintained in accordance with the type certificate data sheets (TCDS). This means the limitations section of the flight manual is based on the limitations found in the TCDS. You can find this by going to any of the regulatory agencies' websites. But, be aware the flight manual also contains more details about the limitations than can be put in text of the TCDS.

It is also important to note the wording at the beginning of the limitations section of the flight manual, which effectively states that it is mandatory to obey the limitations. The implication is you will have invalidated the CoA if you do not obey the limitations, because you have not obeyed the limitations of the TCDS.

This means, for instance, if you load a helicopter beyond its maximum certificated weight, you will invalidate the CoA (and probably your insurance). This is because the structure was only tested to that maximum weight, and additional weight beyond that will impose unknown loads on various parts of the structure, such as the landing gear, which then may not be able to handle the extra loads in a heavy landing. Performance is also based on that maximum weight; so exceeding it could bring up any number of hidden issues (e.g., drag on the blades may rise in a sudden and non-linear fashion if blade pitch is increased to hover with this additional weight at high altitude).

The manufacturer is not required to state the reasons for the limitations, and the pilot's job is not to second-guess the reasons, just to follow the limits.

In some instances, you may have inadvertently exceeded some limitations (I was certainly guilty of that in my younger days) and saw no immediate adverse effects. But, you don't know the possible long-term, cumulative effects that have been taking place. On the Bell UH-1N Twin Huey I flew in the Canadian Air Force, we seldom looked at the performance charts, and would blithely claim that if it could hover at 100 percent torque, we were within limits. One day I looked at the hover performance charts and was shocked to see how much over weight we had been. I suddenly realized why all our helicopters were having problems with transmission mounts cracking prematurely!

There are also some limitations that aren't immediately obvious as limitations. For Part 29 helicopters with more than 10 passenger seats, the height-velocity (HV) curve that defines the safe takeoff profile is in the limitations section, not the performance section, as it would be in most smaller-seating-capacity machines. This has caused quite a few problems — and if you're still operating in the HV curve in your Bell 212 with a load of passengers, then you're putting yourself, and your company, into a large liability situation if there is a crash. (It's a limitation, so remember what happens to your CoA and insurance if you break it.)

## *Performance vs. Limitations*

It's important to be aware of instances where the HV curve is in the limitations section, not the performance section of the flight manual. An example from my own past occurred while I was working at Transport Canada as a certification test pilot. The folks in the standards section contacted me after they'd received a letter from a foreign airworthiness authority, whose people had often seen a Canadian-registered helicopter operating in their country and performing a towering takeoff to 100 feet before accelerating to forward flight. This authority wondered where the approval for this maneuver had been awarded. Armed with the flight manual, I showed the standards folks that this was clearly a prohibited maneuver, as it violated the HV curve, which, for this model aircraft, was in the limitations section.

A phone call was placed to the operator's chief pilot. He said they had tested this maneuver and it was safe. Further questioning revealed there had been no formal records kept of the testing, nor any report produced. Also, the operator had been using the very liberal transient limits of the engines for this test, and transients are not permitted to provide any performance benefit in testing — they are for unusual situations, not normal use. Topping it off, the operator had slightly bent one of its aircraft during its "tests." After more discussion, it was decided this maneuver would no longer be performed.

Of course, the story doesn't stop there — do they ever?

It turned out these helicopters were being used extensively for medical transport, and there were many hospitals where the towering takeoff was the only way to get out of the facility. This was a real dilemma. Fortunately, I knew, from my time in the United Kingdom, that this model had a flight manual supplement for Category A performance. The air ambulance version also had a natural limit on the number of "passengers." After a few phone calls to the airframe manufacturer a solution was found. A new flight manual supplement for less than nine passengers was produced, moving the HV curve to the performance section and making it legal for the air ambulance versions to do towering takeoffs.

As an aside, this particular operator had tried to use a comparison to another, slightly smaller Part 29 helicopter, saying that because the HV curve for that machine was in the performance section, the same must hold true for this larger aircraft. It was pointed out that the smaller helicopter's standard configuration was for less than nine passengers, and that it had a flight manual supplement for 10 passengers that moved the HV curve to the limitations section.

Why, you might well ask, is the HV curve in the limitations section for the larger passenger capacity? The simple but honest answer is body count. A higher level of safety is demanded for a higher number of passengers because of the headlines a crash would produce.

## *Flight Manual Supplements*

When the original helicopter design is modified in a substantial way (a change that will affect performance, handling or systems such as the electrics), it's necessary to revise the certification... but not completely — only as far as that modification affects the helicopter.

Let's say we're going to add a bleed-air powered air conditioner to a turbine helicopter. The company that first does this modification has to do all the engineering work for the installation and have that approved. Obviously, because it's internally mounted, the air conditioner wouldn't affect handling, but it could affect performance (bleed air has to come from the turbine engine, and that raises the turbine outlet temperature measurably).

Since the modification company probably doesn't have the resources to completely revisit all the performance charts in the flight manual, there may be a limitation that the air conditioner be switched off for hover, takeoff and landing. This way, the original performance charts are still valid. The normal procedures section will also be modified to add a line in the pre-takeoff section to ensure the air conditioning system is off. These changes have to be incorporated into any checklists the operator uses, as they modify the original helicopter.

So, if you're flying a new helicopter for the first time, you need to spend some time reviewing the supplements in the back of the flight manual to ensure you understand what might be different from the baseline. This assumes you've already read the basic flight manual and/or are familiar with the model.

As the first article in this series mentioned, my intention is not to make both readers of this column into certification experts — the twists and turns of the regulations are responsible for most of my graying hair, so I wouldn't wish that on anyone else — merely to make you aware there is a lot that goes on behind the scenes as part of the continuum of safety. This is why following the requirements can be so critical, even if it doesn't seem like it at the time.

In our next column, we'll deal with performance, including looking at why the civil helicopter flight manual has the charts it has, and what are some of the shortcomings of those charts.

# CHAPTER 3 *Civil Certification Party III*

**Vertical** February/ March 2010

*Comment: In part three of helping pilots understand airworthiness requirements, we examine "approved" civil performance charts and the inherent confusion/complications with them*

It will probably come as a surprise to most of you that the civil airworthiness authorities have absolutely no interest in certain aspects of your helicopter's performance, including how far it can travel. You'll note I said "airworthiness" — the operational side of the authority takes an inordinate interest in, things like, those who run out of fuel short of their destination. (I wish the two sides would get together and sort this out... meanwhile, I'll provide a solution in the next article for those interested in solving the running-out-of-fuel problem, regardless of what the authorities think or do.) The regulatory authorities are interested in safety: first of all, safety for those on the ground, so they don't get smote by falling aircraft or objects; secondly, safety for those who are paying to fly on an aircraft; and, lastly, safety for the crew of the aircraft. To ensure these priorities of safety, the authorities will make sure the performance of an aircraft is displayed. And, how far your aircraft will travel through the air is not so much a matter of safety as it is a selling point for the aircraft manufacturer or operator. The performance the authorities are going to insist on knowing is related to safety only. Conversely, most manufacturers provide more performance data than required by regulation, both for marketing reasons and because they want their machines operated with confidence and safety, too. The authorities indicate the performance that is "approved" (required by regulation) by adding words such as "FAA (Federal Aviation Administration) approved" to those charts that are required. These will appear in the performance section of the flight manual — but it's important to note that not all charts in that section need to be "approved." From a safety point of view, if we look at fixed-wing airplanes first, the important things are takeoff and landing distance, and rate of climb. As we get to multi-engine airplanes, performance following failure of one engine (one engine inoperative, or OEI) becomes important — whether you can stop safely following an engine failure prior to takeoff, what sort of climb gradient you have OEI and so on. For single-engine helicopters, the performance measurements that directly impact safety are hover performance and rate of climb. If you have two engines in a helicopter, then, just like the fixed-wing world, things become slightly more complex.

## *THE PERFORMANCE CHARTS*

Of all the performance charts included in most civil helicopter flight manuals, we should take a look at four key ones: power available, hover performance, in versus out of ground effect, and rate of climb; along with the reasoning behind each of them.

. Power Available. When helicopters first started, there were only piston engines to power them. Unlike their later turbine-engine brethren, which have temporary exceedance capability, it's difficult to get much more power out of a piston engine for short periods of time. Thus, one of the performance rules is that the manufacturer can't take advantage of exceedances to get better performance charts. Turbine engines are different from piston engines: they can appear to work well, but not put out the performance they should. Conversely, they can put out more power than they should (i.e., more than the minimum specification). This has resulted in a requirement for the pilot to be able to determine the power available from his or her ship's turbine engine, in comparison to the specification engine. This is one of the first charts in the performance section of the flight manual — and one you should know how to use, so you can know whether you will have at least the power output that the rest of the charts are based on. The complications this chart has will become clear in the "Problems" section later. 2. Hover Performance. Obviously, given ground effect, the closer you can hover to the ground, the more the rotor can lift. But, being able to hover at inches above the ground using all the power available is of little use if you can't make it to forward flight. This has given rise to a little known part of civil helicopter performance certification: the fixed-collective takeoff to determine hover performance in ground effect. The fixed-collective takeoff works like this: there is a height above ground from which the helicopter can hover and transition to forward flight, with no wind, over a smooth, flat surface, without using any additional power. When the helicopter is close to passing through translational lift, it will dip down toward the ground, and, for certification purposes, the pilot cannot use additional collective to stop the descent. The hover height chosen to start from needs to be high enough so that when the helicopter dips, it won't hit the ground. Obviously, the manufacturer will want this height to be as low as possible, and will try several heights before settling on the one that allows for less than perfect technique and is easy to judge. This is why there is only one hover-in-ground-effect (HIGE) height in most civil helicopter performance charts. For example, the "standard" Bell 206 on low skid gear has an IGE performance hover height of two feet above ground level. When high skid gear is added (a separate flight manual supplement with a separate hover height), the hover height becomes five feet. The reason is that the height loss passing through translation is greater with high skid gear in place than with low skid gear. 3. IGE vs. OGE. There is a requirement for IGE performance, but not all helicopters require hover out-of-ground-effect (HOGE) performance charts. Check your flight manual to see whether your OGE performance is approved or not. At the same time, note the HOGE height shown, it might be quite a lot higher than you would expect. And, if you try to demonstrate HOGE performance by climbing vertically, you might be surprised that your helicopter can't do it. This is because HOGE charts can be based on flying in to the hover from forward flight — which can often result in better performance than by climbing vertically. I suggest you try this to see how your helicopter compares to the manual, so you're not surprised later. 4. Rate of Climb. For most airplanes, rate of climb is important for climb gradient reasons in instrument conditions. Helicopters have also inherited this requirement, even though our rate of climb at the best-rate-of-climb airspeed, known as Vy (typically between 50 and 70 knots in most helicopters), provides that if the helicopter can hover, it has such a large climb gradient that we easily meet any instrument flight rules climb gradient requirement.

## *The Problems with Civil Performance Charts*

Earlier, we mentioned that turbine engines can be either above or below specification performance. If the engine is below specification, you're not going to get the performance shown in the flight manual, but you'll have no idea how much less payload or performance you're going to get. Since payload keeps the mortgage and other loan payments covered, it's quite important. Know how to keep your engine up to spec! What if your engine is above spec? (Most of them are, some by quite a large amount.) There are several problems with this — the first is that since you can't use that extra performance with the current charts, you're denying yourself payload (and the extra income it might provide). The second is that nearly all the charts I've seen don't tell you what you need to know. The charts are titled "hover capability" and merely tell you if you can hover at the conditions specified: weight, pressure altitude and air temperature, hover height, etc. They don't tell you what power will be required to hover. What's the problem with that you might ask? If you work out what weight you can hover at for the specified conditions, and it looks like you'll be up against some other limit besides a transmission torque limit, you'll get to your destination expecting to be close to, if not at, that limit. But, if you have an above-specification engine, you won't be close to that limit, and you'll lose respect for the performance charts. In fact, my quick surveys of most helicopter pilots show many don't use the performance charts at all. Think about that for a moment. Compare this to the commercial airline world, where takeoff distance is calculated for every flight. Then consider how many helicopter accidents are of the type "power required exceeded power available." To save you the trouble of trolling the United States National Transportation Safety Board database, I can tell you that it's still far too many. Consider one example where an adventurous pilot attempted to land from an OGE hover at very high altitude in hot weather when a quick check of the charts would have shown him it was not possible to even hover IGE at that altitude. The price paid for not paying attention and not being aware is high. What does all this mean? Simply this: the authorities don't approve all the performance data needed to operate helicopters safely. And, the performance information that is provided is often sadly lacking. In the next in our series on understanding airworthiness requirements, we look at reasons why range and enduranswce information is not "approved," and share a helpful way to keep yourself from running out of fuel.

# CHAPTER 4 *Civil Certification Part IV*v

**Vertical** April /May 2010

Comment: All commercial pilots should be intimately familiar with the operating regulations that govern the way they operate. The regulations that govern how helicopters are designed and tested for airworthiness are less well known, but have an equally large impact on day-to-day life. The impact may not be immediately obvious, however.

I'm on safe grounds in saying the airworthiness regulations are not well understood – I was a pretty experienced test pilot when I started working at Transport Canada – and it still took at least one year's on-the-job training to start to understand the basics of civil certification. When I left after 5 years, I thought I was pretty well versed in all the more subtle aspects, but I'm still running into interesting complexities.

## *Scratching The Surface*

And this series is only going to scratch the surface of the subject, so don't take anything written here as the complete gospel truth. This series isn't intended to make civil certification test pilots out of both of you readers, but it should give you an insight into how limitations in the flight manual are derived, what is required from a technical standpoint (and what isn't!) and areas where there are holes in certification you should be aware of.

First of all – why do we have airworthiness certification? Well, it took a while, but I finally realized that despite what marketing folks (and occasionally pilot evaluation reports in magazines like this) might say – there is no perfect design.

There's also no perfect operator, no perfect maintenance organization, and no perfect certification or regulatory authority. Think about it for just a second – if any of these were perfect – they'd be the only ones. If aircraft were perfectly designed and manufactured, would they need airworthiness approval or maintenance? But, as we are stuck on this plane of existence, we have attempted to develop a series of steps that keep us safe. Good design is the first step – meeting the requirements laid out in regulations is the next step. But what's the legal basis for airworthiness rules?

## *ICAO- A United Nations Success Story*

In a legal sense, airworthiness rules come from one of the few parts of the United Nations that actually does something useful – the International Civil Aviation Organization. ICAO was set up shortly after WWII to allow air transport to operate internationally. A set of broad rules covering personnel licensing and airworthiness (and others) were established and countries sign up to abide by those rules. There are a host of these rules, and the adventurous reader is encouraged to look up items of interest at the ICAO web site. The end result of these rules permits aircraft and crews to operate internationally. The airworthiness annex basically says that each country will set up a set of airworthiness requirements. Naturally, for many years each country did set up their own regulations, with little in common. For many years, this made it difficult for manufacturers to get their equipment approved outside the country of manufacture. A series of bilateral agreements between countries (Elbonia and Nefarious for example) would allow an aircraft certified in Elbonia to be approved without repeating the expensive process in Nefarious.

Over the years, the differences have been minimized thanks to a lot of work by harmonization groups, and now airworthiness approvals between different countries is much less expensive and time consuming. However, different countries still have the option to apply their own differences – Canada for example, has a thing about flight in snow for helicopters. I can't imagine why...

So each country will set up their own rules for certification, and most model theirs on the US system. For helicopters, the parts of Title 14 of the Code of Federal Regulations (14 CFR) that are of interest are Part 21 (general), Part 27 ('Normal' Category, up to 7,000 lbs maximum internal weight, Part 29 (Transport Category – anything above 7,000 lbs of 9 seats). A host of other Parts govern engines and maintenance.

## *27 or 29- What's The Difference?*

Why the difference between Part 27 and Part 29? In simple terms, if you're operating a small, single engine helicopter carrying only a few passengers, it would be unreasonable to expect the same level of safety as if you were carrying 20 passengers on an airline style operation. The dividing line for helicopters is more than 9 passengers – this puts the body count up to a point where front page headlines would follow a crash. Less than 9 passengers, not so much. While this may seem pretty brutal, if we were to apply the higher level of safety to small helicopters, they'd never get off the ground, and a lot of benefits would be lost.

An interesting aside here – the FAA's mandate is to write the minimum legislation necessary for safety. Fascinating approach- which begs the question - how do you know it's the minimum? After some reflection (in several glasses of single malt Scotch) it became clear (the question, not the Scotch) – you'll only know it's the minimum because you go below it every now and again. And as long as the accident rate isn't too high, and the nation as a whole is benefiting, things are OK. When the accident rate gets too high, or the political pressure starts getting too high, then a change in the rules might be contemplated.

Both Part 27 and Part 29 have the same structure – performance requirements are in nearly the same paragraph numbers.

Perhaps the difference in the level of safety is best illustrated by comparing the same paragraph in the two different regulations.

## *Same Paragraph Number - Different Rule*

Paragraph xx.1309 is one we'll spend more time on later, but as a comparison, look at the wording difference between the two Parts:

Part 27 Part 28 Remarks

| *Part 27* | *Part 28* | *Remarks* |
|---|---|---|
| (c) The equipment, systems, and installations of single-engine rotorcraft must be designed to *minimize* hazards to the rotorcraft *in the event of a probable* malfunction or failure. | (b) The rotorcraft systems and associated components, considered separately and in relation to other systems, must be designed so that —<br>(1) For Category B rotorcraft, the equipment, systems, and installations must be designed to *prevent* hazards to the rotorcraft *if they malfunction or fail.* | Part 27 assumes that a system *may* fail (probable failure), while Part 29 assumes the system *will* fail at some point in time. Notice also how Part 27 only requires hazards to be minimized, but Part 29 requires preventing hazards. |

And believe me, it takes quite a while to digest the importance of these subtle differences in wording. There is a very large Advisory Circular for fixed wing transport airplanes (Part 25) that deals only with paragraph 1309, and that is used for guidance in certifying Part 29 helicopters. We'll deal with Advisory Circulars in a later column.

Of more immediate interest, these differences mean that Part 29 (transport category) helicopters operate to a higher standard of safety. For example the HV curve for Part 29 helicopters with more than 9 passengers is a limitation, not a performance curve. More on that later.

## *Part of Safety Net*

While our safety record can always stand improvement, it's pretty safe to state that flying helicopters is no longer as dangerous as it once was. One reason for the improved safety is improved requirements. They are amended frequently, which provides a small problem for those who making new additional equipment.

Obviously it's not feasible to do a complete recertification of a helicopter just because you want to attach some new piece of equipment to the airframe. So the process of a Supplemental Type Certificate was evolved. If you wish to add a new air conditioner system to an airframe, you only need to show compliance with the appropriate part of the requirements, not all of them. So an STC amends the original certification, and the Flight Manual Supplement amends the original Flight Manual. And you need to know the changes well, as they may change limitations and procedures for your helicopter.

## *What if the Requirements Have Changed?*

But what if the 'appropriate' requirements have changed since the helicopter was originally certified?

The Bell 206 series has been around since just slightly after the dawn of time, yet new things are still being added to them. Should the developer of the new thing have to design to the latest set of rules? It would seem reasonable, until you realize that the basic airframe may not be capable of meeting the new rules. Seats are a good example – the latest seat crashworthiness requirements are a welcome improvement. So if you want to put new seats in an old Bell 206, it would seem reasonable to build them to the latest standards. Unfortunately, the underlying structure of the airframe may not be able to handle the forces the new seats would place on them in a crash – because the original structure was made to earlier, less stringent standards.

## *TSO'd Equipment*

Which leads nicely to another point that is not well understood – TSO (Technical Standard Order) approved equipment. Receiving a TSO approval means that the equipment has passed a series of tests that shows that it is safe to install in an aircraft. The tests are typically for altitude and temperature, vibration and electrical safety (known as 'shake and bake' tests). It does not mean that you can simply plug it in to the instrument panel. The installation of the equipment may be a complicating factor – for example, installing a TSO'd GPS that interfaces with the existing Horizontal Situation Indicator (HSI) navigation display requires that the switches and relays work properly – often a very complex a job. In simple terms a TSO'd piece of equipment means that it is capable of being installed, not that the installation will be satisfactory. It's never as simple as just plugging the box into the dash.

Just as operational rules play a part in the overall safety net, so do the certification requirements. It could be argued that they are written in blood – landing gear strength requirements to be able to pass dropping from a certain height came about because some airframe somewhere didn't survive a heavy landing. Same with things like fuel tank strength and survivable seats. You may not immediately see the results of the airworthiness requirements, and there is no need for you to be intimately familiar with the rules, but you will be affected by these rules.

# CHAPTER 5 *Civil Helicopter Performance Charts*

**Vertical** February / March 2010

*Comment: It's a cool day, down in the valley, and you're waiting for your passengers to show up.*

The Turbohopper has enough fuel to get you there and back plus the obligatory reserves, but not much more because you know how things can turn out. More baggage than planned, possibly even more than the two people you were told about. Sometime the passengers are just slightly heavier than the 'standard' weight.

You've even checked the 'hover capability' chart for the takeoff and landing elevations, and it appears you shouldn't run into any engine or transmission limits. Weight might be an issue.

The passengers arrive, and while they look at little more substantial than average, you don't think there's going to be a problem. They get briefed, get in, you start up, and away you go. Hovering at 95% torque at 2' AGL, (the chart height for IGE performance) down here in the valley, with the N1 and TOT pretty close to their limits, you figure that your approach to the mountain LZ will have to be planned to a bit more fineness than regular, but you've done that before.

And sure enough, the landing zone up in the mountains is approached with the power applied early, the rotor loaded up and getting very close to the engine N1 limit, so you think you're going to be OK.

But not today. The wind shifts just enough that you need that extra smidgen of power, and when you raise the collective, the rotor starts to droop and you hit the ground rather harder than you or the passengers like. In fact, you hit hard enough to do substantial damage to the airframe. No problem, the boss says, that's what insurance is for.

Fast forward several months, and the boss is livid. So livid, you're fired. The insurance company has refused to pay for the damage. The helicopter was overweight they claim, which invalidates your certificate of airworthiness and your insurance at the same time. Not only that, but the engine wasn't producing the power it should have, so you're caught on two counts. The Federales also want to talk to you now.

Holy rotor blades - how could this happen?

## *Power Available Charts / Topping Power*

We'll deal with the engine first. The civil manual for turbine machines has a topping chart, or power available chart in the beginning of the performance section. Since all the rest of the performance data depends on the engine being at least up to this specification, it's important to know if your engine meets this minimum. This is required in the airworthiness section of the certification regulations, and there is probably a statement to that effect in the flight manual, you remember. Determining if the engine passes the power check is normally in the performance section of the flight manual. But you had better know if the engine meets that minimum. If it doesn't you have a problem.

## *Piston Engine Power Available Chart - through the Back Door*

Piston powered machines have no such 'minimum specification engine' chart, so you need to know it's working well. Aside from weighing everybody and everything, how can you be sure you're within weight limits?

If you try this with the charts normally provided in the civil flight manual, you could be very surprised. Most helicopters are physically capable of exceeding maximum weight and having enough performance at low density altitudes to hover. That doesn't mean it's legal, merely that they have the capability.

In Figure 5-1 on page 29 the angled lines represent engine power available lines. If you're below the temperature, the engine has more than enough power to hover at the specified height above ground

(Example A). If you're above the temperature line for that pressure altitude, the engine doesn't have enough power to hover the helicopter at the specified height above ground in those conditions (Example B). It doesn't take a rocket scientist to see that in temperatures below standard day, you can easily exceed the maximum weight and still have enough power to hover.

In one accident, it was determined that the helicopter was at least 15% over maximum weight, and the crew (who didn't do a weight and CG calculation) didn't know it, because the helicopter could still hover. See Figure 5-2 on page 30

## *Turbine Engine Charts*

While this chart is for a piston engine helicopter, the same principles apply to turbine engines, with the added proviso that if your engine is better than specification, you might be even worse off if you're above maximum weight. Why worse off? Because your engine won't be at the limiting condition as determined by the temperature line when the chart says it would be, and you'll think you're better off, but you'll still be overweight.

Military style performance charts show power required to hover. This chart can be used to 'weigh' the machine. Calculate the power required to hover at maximum weight at some convenient height above the ground for the ambient conditions of wind, pressure altitude and air temperature. When you lift to the hover, if it takes more power than calculated, then you are overweight. Pretty simple. (if engine power available is an issue, there is another chart to calculate that). See Figure 2.

Try the same thing in the civil charts, and you'll end up not knowing much and assumes you already know the weight accurately. If you don't know the weight accurately, you certainly can't work backwards (like the military charts) to see if you're overweight.

## *How to Invalidate the Certificate of Airworthiness*

How does being overweight invalidate the Certificate of Airworthiness? A bit convoluted, but stick with me. The C of A will say that the aircraft is airworthy when operated and maintained in accordance with the Type Certificate Data Sheet (TCDS). This is part of the certification basis of the helicopter. The TCDS contains the same limitations as the limitation section of the flight manual, plus it references maintenance procedures. Exceeding those limitations, such as weight, means you are no longer in compliance with the TCDS, and your C of A is invalid.

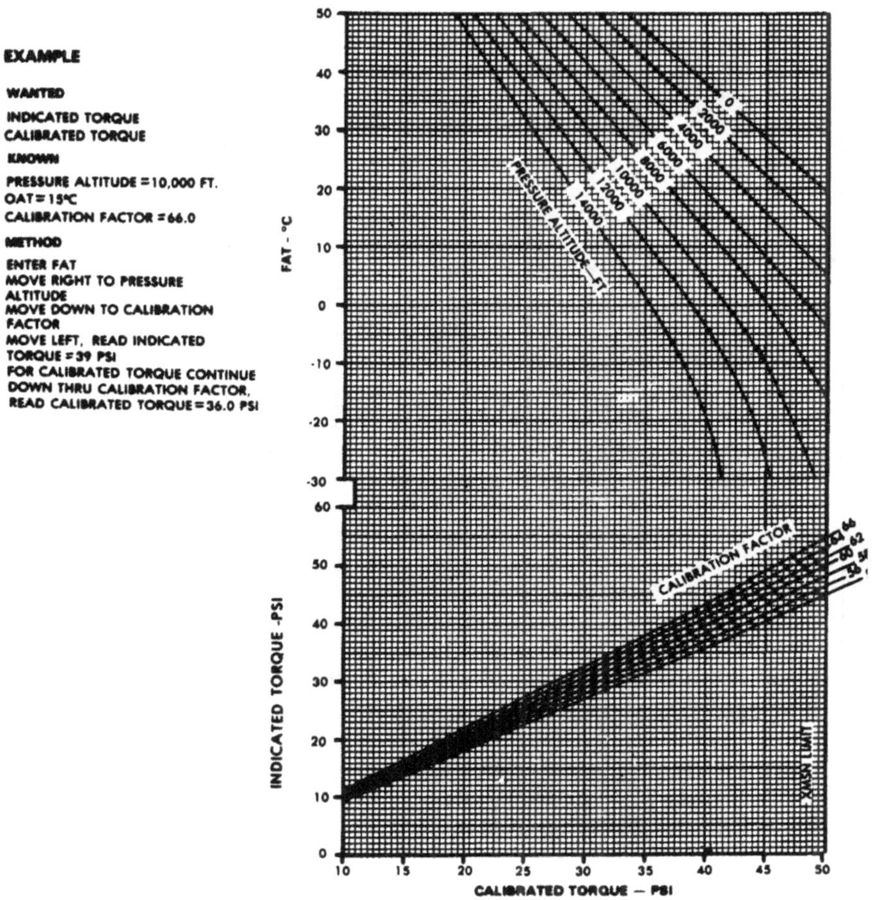


**Figure 5-1** Typical Engine Topping or Power Available Chart

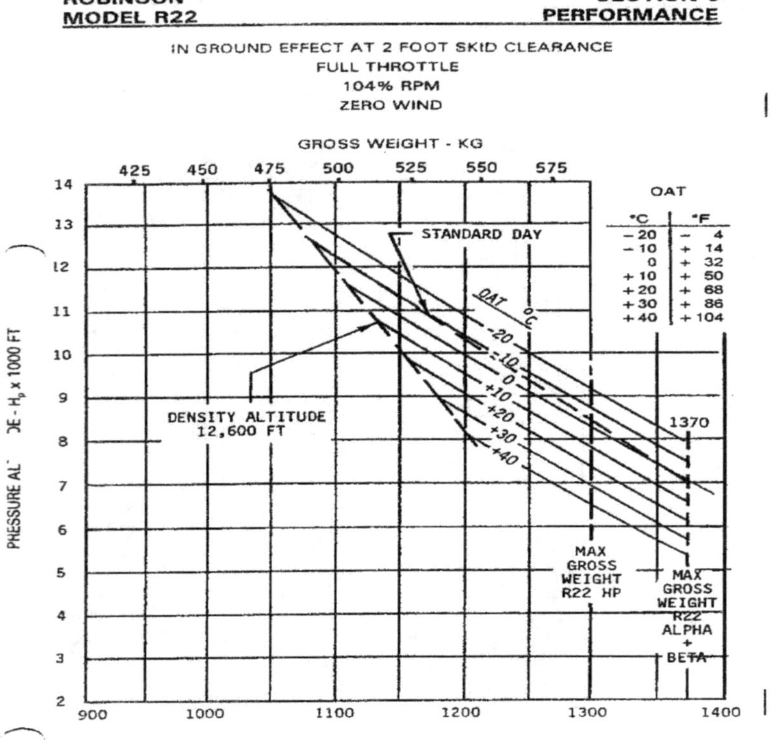


**R22 HP, ALPHA, & BETA**
O-320-B2C ENGINE

**IGE HOVER CEILING VS. GROSS WEIGHT**

**Figure 5-2 Typical In-Ground-Effect Hover Performance**

# CHAPTER 6 *Only One Height IGE Performance*

**Vertical** February / March 2010

*Comment: For those of you who bother to read the Flight Manual and the performance charts (and I think I know who both of you are), you may have noticed that there is only one hover height specified in the In Ground Effect (IGE) performance charts.*

Since helicopters are all about flexibility, and since we have to operate in a wide variety of conditions – why only one hover height?

For those of you who have really spent time reading not only the basic flight manual, but also the supplements (and I know that one person by name....), you will have noticed that for a low skid gear equipped helicopter, the hover height is different than for the high skid equipped version of the same machine. What gives???

For those of you who haven't noticed this, either refer to your flight manual or the diagram below.

To keep things simple, we'll only discuss 'normal' category helicopters, those covered by Chapter 14, Code of Federal Regulation (14 CFR) Part 27. These weigh less than 7,000lbs and have 9 or less passenger seats. Larger helicopters have slightly different requirements, but generally follow the same logic.

But before we start quoting regulations, let's look at the basics. At the same weight and density altitude and below the point where ground effect ceases, it takes more power to hover a helicopter the higher we are above ground. Every inch above the ground takes slightly more power. Your aerodynamic texts should have shown you this when you were getting your license. This is shown in Figure 1.

So if you want to use the minimum amount of power to get 'airborne' in the legal sense, you would hover mere inches above the surface.

Looking at this another way, if you are limited in power (as you will be somewhere in any helicopter) the amount of power you have will determine how much weight you can lift. The weight will consist of the empty weight of the helicopter plus the payload.

Payload is what pays the bills. The more you can lift on a trip, the more money you can earn. So, if you are the helicopter manufacturer, you want to have the maximum possible weight available to lift into the air and show this to potential customers.

Can you start to see the problem?

A great payload that you can lift one micron off the ground is not realistic – but how to make sure everyone plays by the same rules?

Fortunately, the regulations that govern helicopter certification and the flight manual have tried to make sure everyone plays by the same rules.

A helicopter that can only hover would not be of much use – sometime or other it has to get into forward flight. One of the characteristics of transitioning from the hover to forward flight is passing through translational lift. This point is where we seem to magically get a lot more lift from the rotor for the same collective (power) setting. It's generally a pretty busy time in most helicopter pilot's lives – altitude changes, pitch attitude changes, heading changes and of course, your airspeed is changing. What may have escaped un-noticed is that just prior to that magic point, if you are a low height above the ground, the helicopter may take a dirty dart towards the ground. (if you're transitioning to forward flight from an out-of-ground effect hover, you won't see this, for reasons which will be explained below).

A hovering helicopter is always producing downwash. When close to the ground, the downwash spreads out away from the helicopter, and the shape of the downwash pattern will be affected by the wind. If there is no wind, the downwash will eventually die away somewhere. If the re is wind opposing the outward flow of the downwash it will create a small wall where the two winds meet. If you are ever hovering in dust or snow, you can see this very well.

Where the downwash ends, a small set of vortices will build up. Normally these are not an issue, but if the helicopter is low to the ground, part of that vortex may adversely affect the rotor. The vortex will have a downward flowing section, and if that happens to meet the edge of the rotor system, it will reduce the lift produced by the rotor. Not a lot, but enough to be noticed. The effect will vary with the height of the rotor above the ground and the height of the vortex. If the rotor is well above the downward flowing part of the vortex, you'll never notice it. But if the rotor happens to be just below the top of the downward flowing part, the effect will be significant.

So, what to do about this and how does it affect the flight manual performance chart. If you start out mere inches above the ground, and happen to encounter the downward flowing part of the vortex, and you are at takeoff power, you will not have enough excess power to overcome the effect of the vortex. In flight testing, for performance, it is not permitted to use transient power levels, as these are reserved for the real world to make sure you can stay out of trouble. Not enough power means you won't be able to stop the rate of descent, and you'll hit the ground with some forward speed. Not a good thing, especially if the ground happens to be uneven (as is most of the world).

Remember that every inch above the ground requires more power to hover, and means less payload.

So the regulations are written in such a way that the effect of the downward flowing part of the vortex is considered. Section 27.73 is titled 'Performance at minimum operating speed' and is written in the very dry, technical manner as follows:

For helicopters--

The hovering ceiling must be determined over the ranges of weight, altitude, and temperature for which certification is requested, with--

- Takeoff power;
- The landing gear extended; and
- The helicopter in ground effect at a height consistent with normal takeoff procedures; and

Notice the wording 'normal takeoff procedures'. This is not ever, as far as I know, officially defined by the FAA, and is left up to the helicopter manufacturer to define. Most use either a 'fixed collective takeoff' or a 'hover power plus' method.

The fixed collective takeoff requires that the helicopter be established in the hover and without moving the collective from that position, transitioning the helicopter into forward flight. A series of runs are conducted, and when a height is found where the helicopter descends but does not touch the ground when the vortex is encountered, that is used as the hover height for the performance manual. After the little dipsy-doodle prior to translational lift is encountered, the rest of the takeoff path has to remain clear of the HV curve. (this should be noted by those who favor 'altitude over airspeed' takeoff profiles – not recommended).

The other technique requires that the within the confines (I hesitate to use the word limits as it has the wrong connotation) of the performance charts that there is always some power margin available from that required to hover and the limitations of the helicopter. For this technique, the pilot will start the transition by rotating the nose forward and adding some power (typically it might be 5% above hover power). This ensures a quick acceleration and prevent s the helicopter from descending when (and if) the vortex is encountered.

Both techniques have to achievable by mere mortals as opposed to only golden armed test pilots. Allowances for being able to judge the height and reasonable differences in technique have to be considered.

So to go back to our problem. Why does a helicopter on low skid gear has one hover height for performance, and the same helicopter with high skid gear has a different (and higher) hover height? The reason may be that with the high skid gear, the effect of the vortex may be more pronounced at the low skid gear hover height and in order to not hit the ground, a higher hover height was used.

The real question to me is why this is not required as a practical test standard maneuver? Requiring pilots to do a skidding takeoff teaches the wrong lesson (idea for another column!). And the practical test standard lists as a common mistake is not stopping the helicopter from descending when translational list is encountered – when this is exactly what should happen and be expected.

So now you know why there is only one hover height shown in the flight manual – it has not much to do with hover performance, and everything to do with takeoff technique and performance. Proving once again, that in helicopters, everything is connected, sometimes in a strange way.

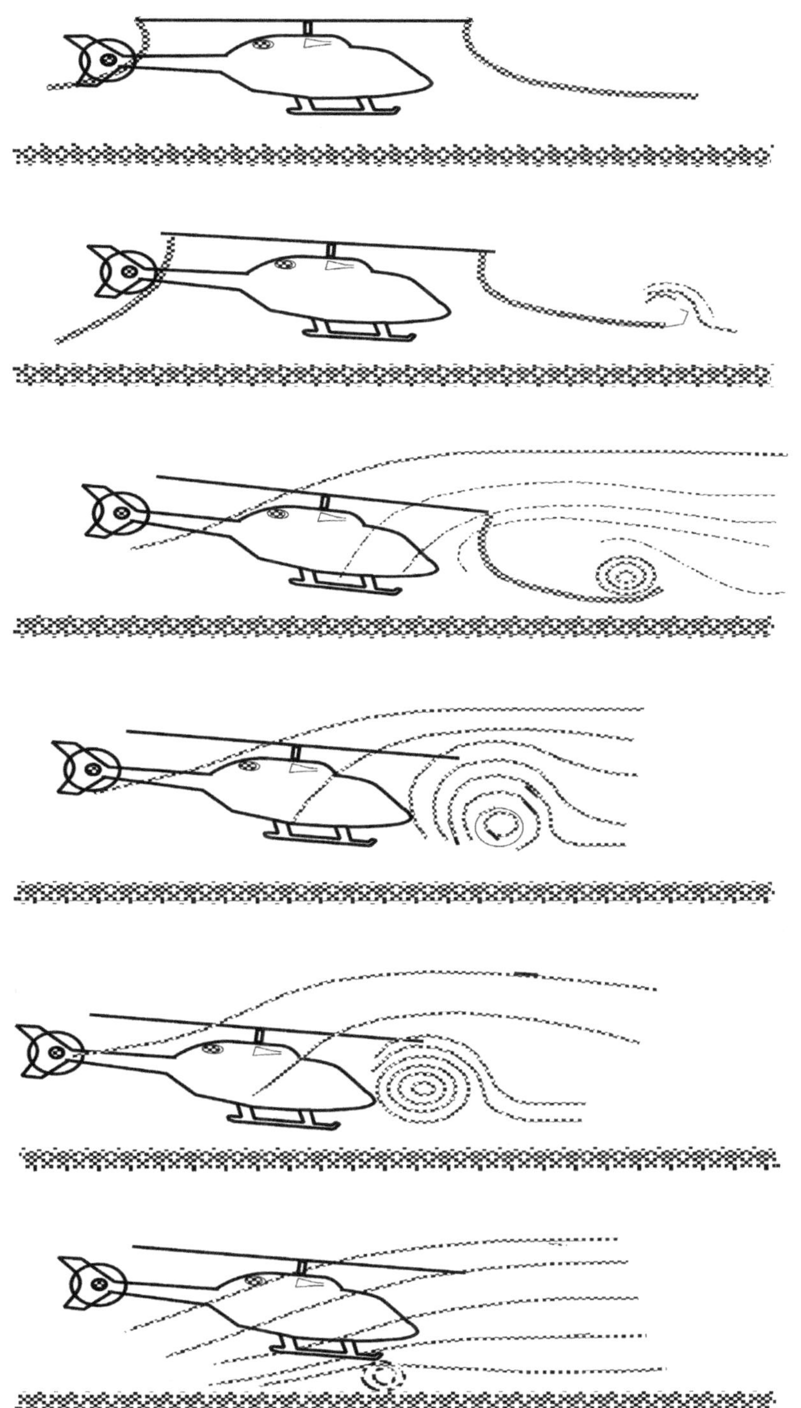

**Figure 6-1 Typical Sequence of ground Vortex roll up as Helicopter Accelerates from Low IGE hove**

Only One Height IGE Performance

# CHAPTER 7 *Maximum Performance Takeoff Myth*

**Vertical** February/ March 2007

*Comment: There is a persistent myth in the helicopter world about maximum performance takeoff. It shows up in FAA test standards, it's taught in nearly every flight school and the correct technique is argued about incessantly. I'm here to say that this is all hogwash, and that there is no such thing as a maximum performance takeoff.*

I feel confident stating this because there is no completely agreed upon definition of what this maneuver is in any manual or regulation I've ever seen (and I've seen quite a few). Even worse than that, there's no performance charts to back up what is to be done. Have you ever seen a "maximum performance" takeoff chart in any helicopter flight manual? Stop and think about this for a moment, would the fixed-wing world ever sit still for a maneuver that had to be demonstrated, but for which there is no agreed upon definition or chart to support it? Hardly. Yet, us helicopter folks are perpetuating something that means different things to different people and has no definitive procedure or chart to back it up.

## Origin Of The Problem

Helicopters are often limited in power, and may not be able to climb vertically out of ground effect. If we had the luxury of being able to climb vertically out of ground effect all the time, this whole argument would dry up and blow away like dust. We might have an issue with climbing through the height velocity diagram, but we'll leave that discussion for later.

Adding to the problem is that we often have to get the helicopter out of an area surrounded by high obstacles. When the two issues of "not enough power to climb vertically out of ground effect" and "surrounded by high obstacles" combine, we are left to figure out a way around the problem. It is from this dilemma that the maximum performance takeoff concept evolved. What we are really looking at here is a maximum angle of climb issue: we have an obstacle and we want to climb over it in the most expeditious way. Fixed-wing aircraft have a maximum angle of climb airspeed listed in their flight manuals, but helicopters don't. The airspeed is known as $V_x$.

Why don't helicopters have a Vx listed in the flight manual? To begin with, if you can climb vertically from out of ground effect, your maximum angle of climb airspeed is obviously zero, and you have a 90-degree angle of climb. What if you can't climb vertically to pass the obstacle? Well, many years ago, the United States Army recognized the problem and set about testing for the optimum technique to get the maximum angle of climb if insufficient power existed to climb vertically from out of ground effect. They did a series of tests where they accelerated the helicopter from a low hover to pre- determined airspeeds and then rotated the ship to climb at those airspeeds. They measured the height change and distance covered, then determined the optimum technique for that helicopter (a UH-1B). For this helicopter, the technique was: from a low hover, nose forward, apply collective to the first takeoff power limitation that occurred, and when the appropriate airspeed was reached, apply aft cyclic to rotate to maintain that target airspeed. The target airspeed was 28 knots of indicated airspeed (KIAS).

## Questions Without Answers

Now come the real world problems. How do you know if the angle of climb which results from this technique would guarantee clearance of the obstacle in the necessary distance? If you climb 125 feet in 850 feet of ground distance, but your obstacle was 130 feet high at 825 feet, you might not be too amused. If this technique worked at 4,000 feet pressure altitude (PA) and 75 F, would it work at 3,000 feet PA and 95 F? And, of course, you always carry around a distance measuring and height finding kit to accurately determine the confined area you want to get out of... don't you?

For those of us who don't fly the UH-1B (a great majority), what are we to do? Does 25 knots work better than 30 knots? Do we have some thing that might help us?

Is there a way to accurately measure the best angle of climb speed if you can't climb vertically out of ground effect? The fixed-wing world does it, so it can be done. Unfortunately, it involves a lot of testing, would result in a very complicated graph, and, at the end, you wouldn't be left with anything worthwhile anyway.

The way to obtain this number is to measure the rate of climb you can obtain at different airspeeds at different power levels. This would be shown as indicated in the chart—but it's only valid for one weight and one situation of excess power. (We've left off the actual rate of climb that might happen, as that's not important.)

Unfortunately, the first problem that comes up is also the one that dooms the whole process from the beginning. We can't measure airspeed accurately below 40 KIAS (see the shaded area of the chart). There simply isn't enough difference between the dynamic pressure and the static pressure to show anything sensible, or, more importantly, anything repeatable. At speeds below 40 KIAS, there is also the problem that small errors in sideslip or climb angle can result in large errors between indicated airspeed and real airspeed. You might think we can fly the slip ball to make sure we have a repeatable, accurate airspeed, but the slip ball does a lousy job of ensuring we have no (or even repeatable) sideslip. So, to get accurate results, we'd have to use a special airspeed system, and probably even a sideslip meter to ensure whatever indicated airspeeds we use are repeatable and reasonably accurate using the "normal" airspeed system.

Once we sort out the airspeed issue, then we have to work on the different power levels we're going to test. The amount of power used over the power required for level flight (the excess power, if you like) will obviously directly affect the rate of climb. We need to test a number of different excess power levels because we have a wide variety of power differences between power required for level flight and power available for climbing.

This brings us to the next obstacle: how do we know what power is required? This will change depending on the weight, the density altitude and the air- speed. If we're trying to come to one airspeed to use for Vx, this might not be a big issue, but we are trying to end up with a whole range of airspeeds (if we have a perfect airspeed system). Even if we were able to determine the power required, how on earth are we going to present this information to the pilot?

All that said, if we can actually get the information about power required, we have half the data we need. The next item of interest is power available. To determine the power available, we need another chart in the flight manual (or from an electronic flight bag). Once we have the power available, we can determine the climb rate and airspeed to use, and the angle of climb possible. As just one example, look at the line from the origin to the rate of climb curve: notice how it is parallel to the rate of climb for a large airspeed range? What this means is we'd have difficulty determining exactly what airspeed to fly to get the maximum angle of climb.

So, we've just made life for our helicopter pilot pretty complicated—check power available, and then use the weight (we do know the weight accurately don't we?) and density altitude to determine the airspeed to fly for maximum angle of climb. Next, determine the distance to the obstacle and the height of the obstacle. From that, work out the angle of climb that will let us clear it. (We'll ignore any effect that wind may have on this whole process, or we'll be here forever.)

## *What It All Means*

Remember, when all this started, we were talking about the maximum performance takeoff. What are we teaching if we don't teach something like this? We're teaching pilots that performance doesn't really matter. We are teaching pilots that they can ignore performance and charts with impunity.

Since we're here, let's talk about what else we're teaching pilots with this. Any maximum performance takeoff I've ever heard described will put the helicopter in the HV curve for quite a long period of time. Does anyone ever consider what the effect of this is? (Mind you, climbing vertically will do the same thing, but hopefully that is done with some premeditation.) For any helicopter with 10 seats, climbing through the HV curve violates a limitation. If you're ever asked to do this maneuver in such a helicopter, you can ask the check pilot if they really want you to violate a limitation.

The real issue is that the airspeed needed to obtain maximum angle of climb is probably well below where the airspeed indicator works accurately or repeatedly. How can we ask someone to try and hold an airspeed of say 18 knots, when the airspeed indicator won't even indicate that measure repeatedly? The actual airspeed that may happen with 18 knots today, with one acceleration method, may be a lot different tomorrow with a less aggressive acceleration method. The sideslip could also be different because you're crabbing slightly differently.

It's all a lot of words, and lot of technical stuff to say that we're not making things clear enough or straightforward enough for helicopter pilots if we stress the maximum performance takeoff.

# CHAPTER 8 *Real Maximum Performance Takeoff*

**Vertical** October / November 2008

*Comment: Those of you who have read my columns over the years (yes, both of you!) will know the low regard I have for the 'Maximum Performance Takeoff' as currently understood.*

To briefly sum up this maneuver has no definition, no performance charts and is interpreted in a great many different ways. The fixed wing community would never sit still for this sort of thing, but then again, they are older than we are, and live in a much more structured world.

That's not to say that there haven't been attempts at improving methods and techniques, and like a lot of things, the answer appeared quite some time ago, and we missed it!

## *EUREKA!*

In one of my spurts at simplifying my life and getting rid of the impedimenta of stuff that I've hauled around for years, I was scanning old papers and articles. What popped up was a paper from the US Army in the mid 1970's entitled - 'Optimizing Takeoffs in Heavily Loaded Helicopters'. I dimly remember reading it a long time ago, but something made me spend time looking at it again. Like many technical papers, this one had a lot of data, and it took some effort to put it all together. The folks spent quite a bit of time trying different takeoff profiles in a UH-1B in order to try to get the best climb gradient for getting out of semi-confined areas.

The fixed wing world would call this best climb gradient (or angle of climb) airspeed VX, but we don't have this number in the helicopter world. It would range from 0 to some number just below VY (best rate of climb airspeed), and would have so many variables that it would be difficult to put on a graph, let alone work out quickly in the field.

## *TWO METHODS TESTED*

So far, nothing too much out of the ordinary. The two methods tested by the Army were the coordinated climb / acceleration, and level acceleration and rotation at different airspeeds. The level acceleration and rotation at a slow airspeed gave the steepest climb gradient overall. But then something else crept in to the process. They started to look at the effect of hover height. And found a much simpler way to sort out the whole process.

One of the issues with whatever method is used, is that it has to be easy to use, and shouldn't require the pilot to try to use a chart - especially in the cockpit. After all, we're talking about a situation where you're already in the helicopter and airborne. Asking the solo pilot to suddenly have to refer to a chart or graph somewhere with a number of variables he may not be able to measure in any case is not ever going to work. It shouldn't involve airspeed, as that is notoriously inaccurate in the low speed environment.

Fortunately, the solution is extremely easy to use and remember. It involves seeing how high you can actually hover, and works even with a wind. It doesn't require much in the way of charts or special instrumentation.

## *DISCLAIMER ABOUT HV CURVE*

Before we get to the interesting bits - a disclaimer about the HV curve. Using the techniques discussed below will put you into the HV curve. But so will all the other techniques used for a 'maximum performance takeoff'. Be aware of this when you try any of the methods.

The method also assumes that you are using takeoff power and cannot hover higher above ground than the chart shows. You can practice this by just going to the height and not moving the collective.

## *How to Squeeze the Most Out of Your Helicopter*

To begin, if you can climb vertically out of a confined area, that should be the method you use, and you don't have to worry about forward airspeed to get the payload out of the confined area. But we'll assume that you can't quite make it over the top of the trees, and now need something to help you.

The method involves the following graph. Note the three hover heights shown, and this is for simplicity. Interpolation between points is easy.

If you can only get to 3' above the ground, then hold the collective fixed and accelerate until you get to 30 knots and climb and maintain 30 knots. Ah yes 30 knots. The problem is that the airspeed indicator doesn't work real well at this speed (there is a lot of lag as well as errors due to crosswinds, etc.). And then there's the problem of any wind existing at the time when you started hovering at 3'. How strong was the wind (and don't believe the wind from air traffic control, unless you know you're very close to their anemometer both horizontally and vertically)? So, the Mark 1 Modification 0 eyeball is going to be necessary to judge the speed at which to rotate and use for the climb.

If you can hover at 15' AGL, for example, then accelerate to an estimated 15 knots of forward speed and climb at that speed.

Now, the numbers given, and the graphs are really only totally valid for the UH-1B, but the general nature of helicopter performance in terms of power required vs. hover height above the ground and the change in power required vs. airspeed below 40 Knots, means that these numbers should be pretty close for any helicopter.

## *Trying It Out - It Worked!*

A brief experiment with this technique was tried with some impressive results. In the piston engine helicopter we were flying (on a perfectly calm evening), we could hover at 3' using 23" of manifold pressure. 15' required 25". We started from a marked position on the runway and tried various techniques and hover heights. From 15', we fixed the collective, noted that we had 25" of MAP and accelerated to what appeared to be 15 knots of speed and climbed at that speed. Passing a sign a couple of hundred yards away, we noted the altitude. The next run was from a 3' hover and as soon as we started to move forward, the power was increased to 25" but we continued to accelerate until we had an estimated 30 knots of speed when the helicopter was rotated and that same speed maintained. The height gain passing the same marker was nowhere as much.

Several runs were made and the results were consistent. It was necessary to use estimated ground speeds for the rotation and climb speeds because (as with most helicopters), the airspeed indications were, to be blunt, crap. This aircraft's airspeed always indicated 10 knots until we were passing at least 40 knots....

Is the method perfect? No, but its way better than anything I've ever seen before. It's easy to use, requires little reference to flight manual charts and graphs and appears to provide the best climb gradient for the capabilities of the helicopter.

Notice one other thing - there is an optimum airspeed for rotation that changes with the maximum attainable hover height. It has some margin for error - a few knots either side of optimum isn't going to make a lot of difference to the distance to clear the obstacle. But pay attention to what happens if you get too slow - you'll just not climb - this is shown by the distance to clear the obstacle rapidly increasing (on the left hand side of the curve). If you're going to add a cushion - go faster. Notice how the distance to clear a 50' obstacle from a maximum attainable hover height of 15' only changes from 250' to 375' if you rotate at 40 KIAS instead of 15 KIAS. On the other hand if you try it at 8 knots, you'll just not ever make it

Unfortunately, this method still won't tell you if you'll clear those obstacles that enclose you, but that's a whole different problem that we still haven't solved.

And always remember, that this method will take you into the middle of HV curve. Be prepared for the engine to quit at any point! To paraphrase an old piston engine airline pilot - I'm always slightly surprised when we get to cruise flight and an engine hasn't failed!

Now if only we could get the manufacturers to provide this chart in the flight manual. Or better yet, provide us with a good low airspeed system

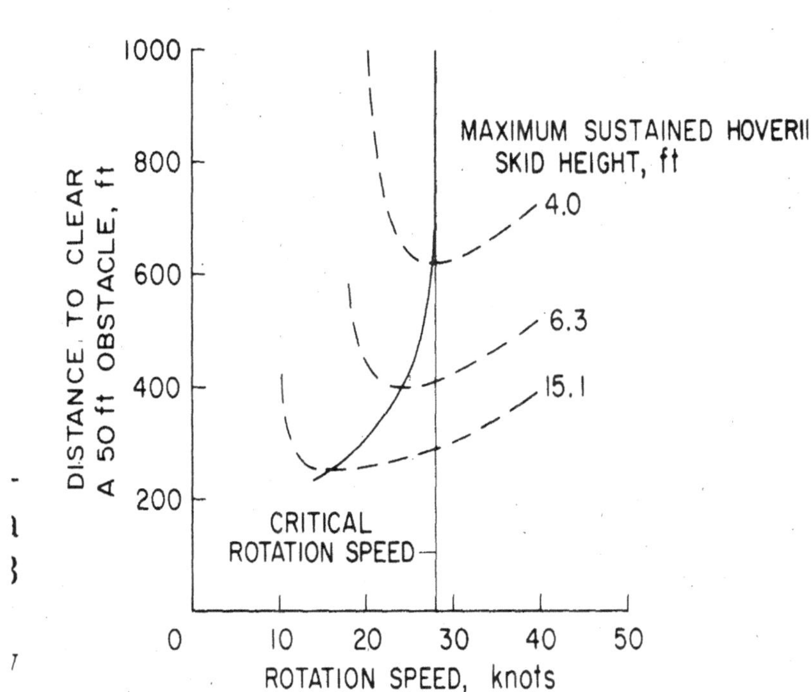


**Figure 8-1 Maximum Hover Heights. Climb-out Speed for Best Angle of Climb**

# CHAPTER 9 *Range and Endurance*

**Vertical** February / March 2014

*Comment: This series on certification and understanding airworthiness requirements has covered a lot of ground, and I hope it has kept all three of my readers awake (I discovered the third reader by accident in a on-line blog).*

Previously, we covered the more important charts for helicopters - including hover performance charts - and discussed why these civil charts are what they are. This final column will deal with the 'other' performance issues: rate of climb and range and endurance.

## *Rate of Climb*

Rate of climb is one of the 'approved' flight manual charts, although you may be wondering why this is so. After all, rate of climb is not something we normally worry about in helicopters. The operative word, though, is 'normally,' because for some helicopters in some situations it does become a critical feature. Of course, for most of us, rate of climb is not something we toss and turn at night worrying about. This brings us back to the question: why do we have rate of climb as an issue? The simple answer is that it's a holdover from the fixed-wing world.

The fixed-wing world worries about rate of climb because, in many instances, it's a real problem. If you're trying to meet a specific climb gradient (so many feet in so many miles), then you need to know your rate of climb. Instrument procedures are predicated on angles of climb, and if you look at some instrument charts, they'll state as much. For example, when climbing out of some mountainous regions in a heavily loaded jet, it's nice to know that your one-engine-inoperative rate of climb will keep you clear of the granite. On the other hand, if the rate of climb won't keep you clear of the hard stuff, you need to work out an alternative before you start your flight.

Okay, so we know why the fixed-wing world worries about it, but why do we rotorheads need to worry?

In the early days, the climb performance of piston-engine helicopters was, to be charitable, marginal. They could barely hover in hot temperatures at high altitude, and there are lots of stories of them struggling to get airborne at all. So, back then, it appeared that climb performance was something people might want to worry about.

Time, fortunately, has marched on, and we seldom hear about helicopters which are that marginal in performance. History has now taught us: any helicopter that can hover without exceeding power or engine limits will have a pretty respectable rate of climb at minimum-power speed.

## *IFR Climb Gradient*

The rate of climb in helicopters is not only pretty reasonable (I've not heard of anyone having less than 500 feet a minute if they can hover in ground effect), but at the airspeed for minimum-power speed (somewhere between 50 and 75 knots for most light helicopters) the climb gradient is much steeper than it is for any fixed-wing craft. So, if you were in instrument conditions in a helicopter, you'd have no trouble meeting obstacle clearance requirements.

I remember one incident in England, when I was flying a Royal Air Force Gazelle out of Upper Heyford (which served as a United States Air Force F-111 base). There was a large sign in the operations room that said all aircraft had to climb to a certain height (which I recall as being about 1,500 feet above ground level) before proceeding on course. This was obviously for noise abatement reasons. I dutifully climbed to this height, and was not yet over the end of the runway when I started to turn toward home - much to the tower controller's concern. He couldn't believe I was turning so early and had that angle-of-climb capability...

## *Angle vs. Rate of Climb*

Okay, so rate of climb is not an issue if you have the same amount of power to climb as you had to hover. But what if you're in a multi-engine helicopter, have lost an engine just after departing the hover, and are above safe single-engine speed (called takeoff safety speed or VTOSS)?

In this situation, there are two speeds that you need to be worried about: best angle of climb and best rate of climb. Again, our fixed-wing brethren have these two airspeeds clearly labeled - one is VX for best angle of climb, and the other, which is more familiar to us, is VY, best rate of climb.

Why don't us helicopter folk have a labeled best-angle-of-climb speed as well? For fixed-wing aircraft, the best-angle-of-climb speed is only one speed. For us unrestricted aviators, there is no single airspeed that works in all conditions. If there were more than enough power to hover out of ground effect, the best-angle-of-climb airspeed would, of course, be zero. If you're in another situation with respect to power, it will be a different number (but always less than best-rate-of-climb airspeed). There is no single right airspeed for all situations.

To make matters worse, even if there was a single right VX, you probably couldn't fly that airspeed anyway, as the pitot-static system wouldn't be able to show it accurately. (Remember, airspeed indicators don't work well below 40 knots, regardless of what the flight manual or instrument itself might show.)

For Category A helicopters, there is an airspeed that corresponds roughly to best-angle-of-climb airspeed, and that is the aforementioned VTOSS. VTOSS is an airspeed that is repeatable (i.e., will work the same way all the time) and gives a better angle of climb than the angle provided by the VY (best-rate-of-climb airspeed). And, for the multi-engine helicopter that has had an engine failure right after departure, the main concern is to get away from the ground as expeditiously as possible. Once clear of the ground, the main concern then becomes rate of climb, and the helicopter should accelerate to the best-rate-of-climb speed and maintain that for the remainder of the climb.

## *Range and Endurance Airspeed*

If you look closely at the charts in your flight manual that show range and endurance (you do know where they are, don't you?), you may be surprised to note there is no 'approved' stamp on the chart. Why are range and endurance charts not approved? Simply stated, the authorities don't have any interest in how far your machine can go: it's not a safety issue (until you run out of gas).

It would also be impractical to require range to be an approved chart, because of the difficulty and expense of re-calculating the data for every bump and bulge that is added to the outside. Think about it for a second: the difference in drag caused by searchlights, FLIR turrets, pop-out floats and the like would quickly drive anyone nuts! Doors off would be different than doors on. Heater on would be different than heater off. So, if the authorities did require range calculations to be part of the approved data, the number of confusing charts would be huge. (Endurance is less affected by things hanging outside the airframe - the effect of drag is much lower at the slower airspeeds associated with maximum endurance. So, we'll just ignore that subject.)

Couple the difficulty of getting accurate range charts with there being no requirement for the fuel quantity indicator to be accurate at any stage except empty (yes, you did read that right), and you can see a bad situation developing. We are caught between a rock and a hard place in trying to determine what our true range might be. And woe betide anyone who runs out of fuel before getting to their destination!

If you want to make your own range and endurance chart, be careful: the only correct way is to measure fuel flow at different airspeeds at the same weight. Use the chart on p.xx as your guide, and please note that you can't use power for the vertical axis - it must be fuel flow, especially for turbine-engine helicopters. Draw a line from the origin to the curve to get the maximum-range airspeed. If there is a wind, and you know it, draw the line from the wind speed: go faster into a headwind to minimize the time exposed to a headwind, and go slower with a tailwind to maximize the effect of the tailwind. The curve changes with altitude, so beware!

Fortunately for us, most helicopters are not long-range aircraft. Aside from offshore work and the occasional long-range transit, helicopters stick pretty much close to home. So, we don't often come across situations where range is an issue. But for those situations where it is, the solution seems to be to add a fuel flow measuring system to the helicopter and couple it with a GPS. The U.S. Coast Guard HH-65 that I flew for a short while, over 20 years ago, actually calculated the best airspeed for maximum range for the wind and atmospheric conditions - a very nice feature, and one that was needed for the mission.

Hopefully this series has shed some light on a few of the airworthiness certification issues that hang around the helicopter world. If you have any specific questions, please feel free to email me at shawn@verticalmag.com.

.

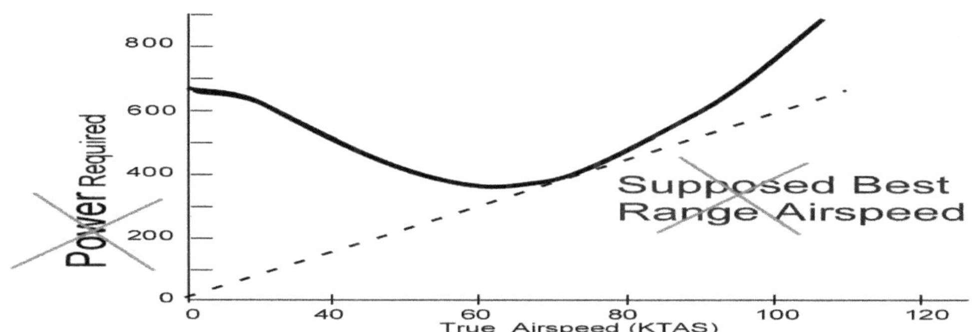


**Figure 9-1 you Can't Use Power vs Airspeed in a Turbine Helicopter**

.

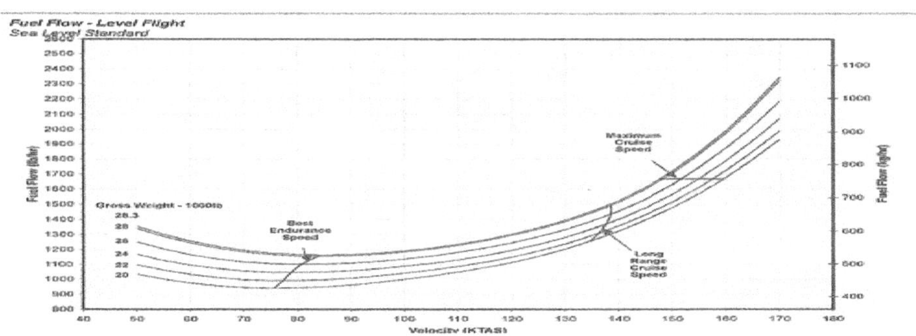


**Figure 9-2 Fuel vs TAS for several Weights, one altitude**

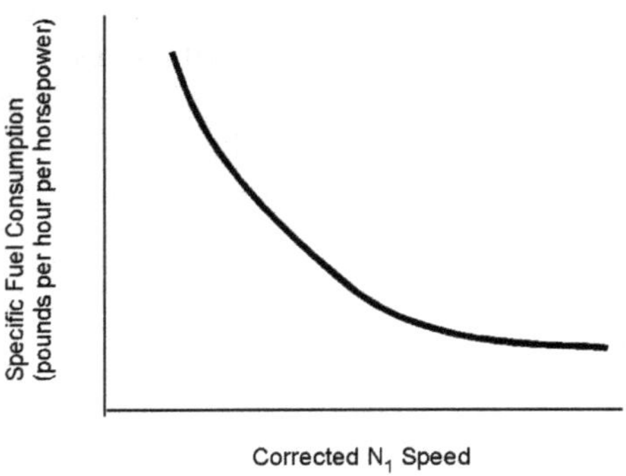


**Figure 9-3 Turbine Engines are More Efficient at Higher Power (less fuel per Horsepower)**

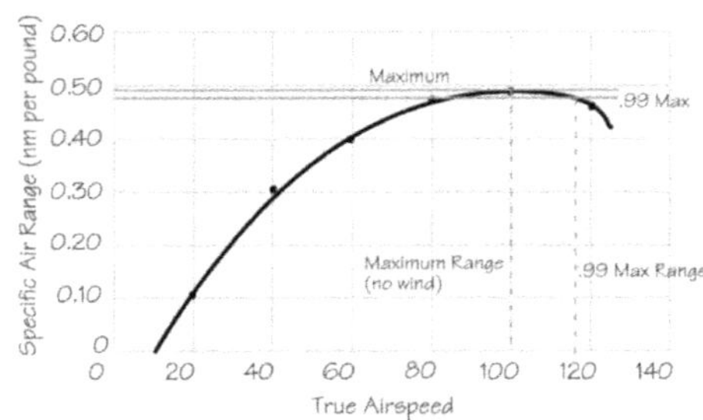


**Figure 9-4 Specific Air Range (SAR) and 99%giving Cruise Speed**

# CHAPTER 10 *Even More Range and Endurance*

**Vertical** April / May 2013

*Comment: Two of the topics I've been pondering recently are maximum range and endurance, and whether most helicopter pilots are properly versed in how to squeeze the most miles/time from each gallon/pound of fuel. After all, I've seen far too many misleading charts about how to get the best range — even from university professors who should know better!*

So, this issue's column will concentrate on achieving the best range, both with and without power, and will touch on how to determine the best speed for achieving maximum endurance.

## *Points of Clarity*

One of the first things to note is that range and endurance charts are not part of the "approved" data in the civil flight manual, and there are two reasons for that. The first is that from an airworthiness regulation point of view, there is no "safety" concern with range or endurance, especially when compared to hover performance or rate-of-climb performance. This is not just a helicopter thing either, our fixed-wing brethren have the same philosophy — takeoff and landing distances, and rate of climb are their main safety concerns. (Somehow, the airworthiness folks haven't heard that not having enough fuel can be a safety concern. Of course, just try running out of fuel on a long trip and see how lenient the operations folks are! But, that disconnect is another story.)

The second, and more practical reason for not "approving" range and endurance information is that every time a new bump or bulge is added to the outside of the aircraft, the range and endurance data would have to be re-determined through new test flights, and new charts would have to be added to the flight manual. If this were mandatory, we'd still be working on Bell 47 flight manuals.

One of the most-common errors when it comes to range is thinking that the ideal airspeed for maximum range will occur at the point where a tangent drawn from the origin on a power-required-vs.-airspeed graph — as shown in Figure 1 — meets the power-required curve. This approach does work with a piston engine, where the fuel flow has a linear relationship to engine power (in other words, when the fuel-flow-vs.-power graph is a straight line, as shown in Figure 2).

Unfortunately, this method does not work for turbine engines, because a turbine engine is more efficient at higher power settings. As such, the way to determine maximum range in a turbine-engined helicopter is to use a graph of fuel flow vs. airspeed, as shown in Figure 3. How we get the information to complete that graph, though, is the hard part!

## *Getting What's Needed*

I was reminded of the difficulty of getting good information to measure range while on a recent aircraft evaluation. Initially, it appeared we could obtain fuel flow information from the manufacturer's data part of the flight manual — until the manufacturer's representative pointed out that this information was estimated, and somewhat conservatively so at that. A bit more questioning revealed that the engine data shown on the multi-function display contained fuel-flow information, which appeared to solve the problem... until it was pointed out that this was predicted fuel flow as opposed to actual.

To get accurate fuel-flow data for this helicopter, it was necessary to record the fuel quantity every six minutes (since we only needed the data for one airspeed at cruise, and we were going to be at cruise airspeed for at least an hour, this was sufficiently accurate for the evaluation).

So, remember, if you're going to obtain fuel-flow-vs.- airspeed information, you'll need an actual fuel-flow reading, not a predicted one! The observant among you will have noticed that the airspeed data is true airspeed (TAS). For most helicopter operations at low density altitudes, and speeds below 120 knots, this is normally very close to indicated airspeed. But if you fly at higher density altitudes (above 10,000 feet/3,048 meters, for example), or faster than 120 knots, it's necessary to do the conversion to true airspeed.

Unfortunately, there are complications even after we get actual fuel-flow data. The main problem is that this information is only valid for one weight and density altitude. Thankfully, flying a series of tests at different weights and density altitudes can easily solve this problem; I'd suggest maximum and medium weights at low, mid-range and high altitudes. A secondary problem is that the airspeed you determine to be maximum range airspeed ($V_{max\ range}$) assumes no wind.

Yet, it seems that no matter which direction I'm traveling in, it's always into a headwind (especially when I have to get somewhere in a hurry)! As such, I've learned how to minimize the effect of headwinds — by flying faster!

This simple theory has to do with minimizing the amount of time you are exposed to the headwind. Conversely, you'll want to reduce your speed to maximize the amount of time you're being helped by a tailwind. This simple theory naturally assumes you're not limited by the maximum-allowable-indicated airspeed/never-exceed speed ($V_{NE}$). Obviously if you are limited by $V_{NE}$, that must be obeyed. Further, remember that the $V_{NE}$ on most helicopters decreases with higher density altitudes. Very simply, the easiest way to determine the best speed for maximum range with a headwind (or tailwind) is to draw a tangent from the wind speed-corrected origin to meet the curve on the fuel flow-vs.-TAS graph.

A couple of iterations of this will provide a general guideline that may be something like: increase TAS by one-half of the wind speed for headwinds and reduce TAS by one-quarter of the wind speed for tailwinds. Interestingly, the stronger the tailwind, the closer you come to the best airspeed for maximum endurance, which is always lower than the best airspeed for maximum range when there is no wind. The best airspeed for maximum endurance is found by determining the lowest point of the curve on the fuel-flow-vs.-TAS graph. The best airspeed for maximum endurance is not affected by wind, but is affected by density altitude, going up as density altitude rises. (Endurance is of course what pilots flying multiple short missions will want to concentrate on, so long as trip time/speed on each quick turn/mission leg is not crucial.)

Going back to the issue of the best speed for maximum range in a headwind or tailwind, we still have the outstanding question: what if you're limited by $V_{NE}$? To deal with that, you need to know the wind specifics not just at your current altitude, but also above you. If there's no wind or there is a slight tailwind above you — and other weather conditions such as clouds and icing allow for it — then it's best to climb using excess power (up to continuous power).

I'd recommend using a "cruise climb" airspeed (slightly slower than $V_{max\ range}$), instead of $V_y$ (maximum rate-of-climb airspeed) so you get a good combination of forward motion and climb rate. It makes little sense to stay at, say, 500 feet above ground level, when a higher altitude would provide a better fuel burn. Of course, there's another good reason for climbing — it gives you more choice of landing areas if you finally do run out of fuel!

## *Getting Your Auto On*

And if choice of landing areas weren't enough to consider, there's also the choice of airspeeds to use for an autorotation. How many of you have flown an autorotation to squeeze the last foot of range from the height you're at? That brings us to "$V_{max\ range\ autorotation}$." If you were absolutely desperate for range, and knew you would probably be running out of fuel in the not-too-distant future, it would make sense to be prepared to make the best use of all you had left. What's the best way to do that? Change your autorotation entry speed and rotor r.p.m. I'm actually quite surprised at the number of helicopter pilots who've only ever done an autorotation at the "recommended" airspeed for autorotation (typically somewhere around 60-65 knots) and only at "normal" rotor r.p.m. The same principle of attaining a "higher airspeed" when flying into a headwind in cruise flight also applies when entering an autorotation. The only difference is that instead of plotting fuel flow against TAS, rate of descent in autorotation is used on the Y-axis (see Figure 10-4 on page 50.

With a bit of work drawing tangents from different headwinds and tailwinds, a general guideline for the effect of these winds can likewise be found. When I show pilots how much farther the helicopter can go at a higher-than-normal airspeed and reduced rotor r.p.m., every one of them is pleasantly surprised, and wonders why they've never been shown this before. Adding to their surprise is the incredibly long distance that can be covered in the flare (due to the high airspeed/groundspeed at the start of the flare).

So, with a bit of homework, you, too, can squeeze more range or endurance from the fuel you burn. At today's fuel prices, that can add up to some tidy change — and perhaps either get you where you need to go when your fuel quantity is really tight, or get you that last turn (e.g., a last drop on a fire) before you have to refuel.

.

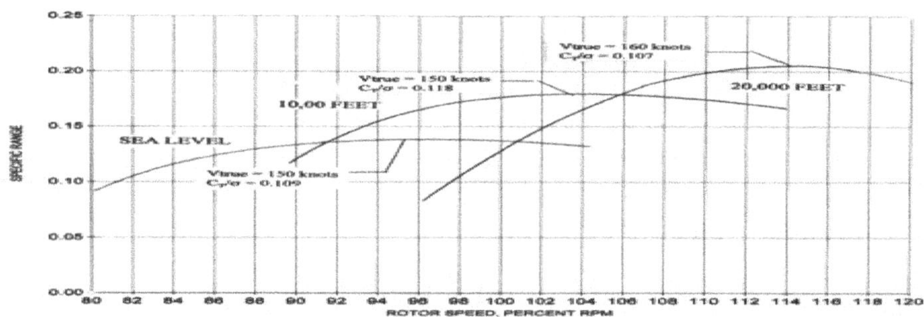


Figure 10-1 **Specif Air Range For Several Altitudes**

.

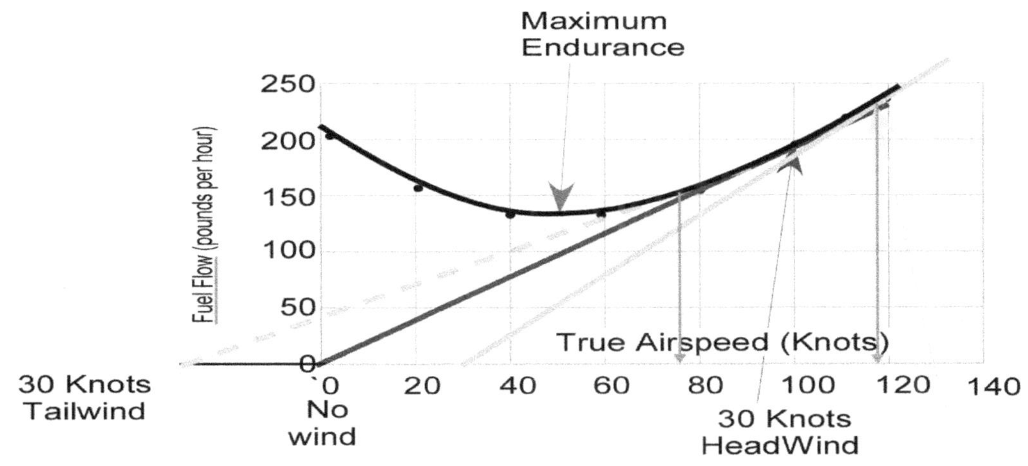


Figure 10-2 **Range with Various Headwinds and Tailwinds**

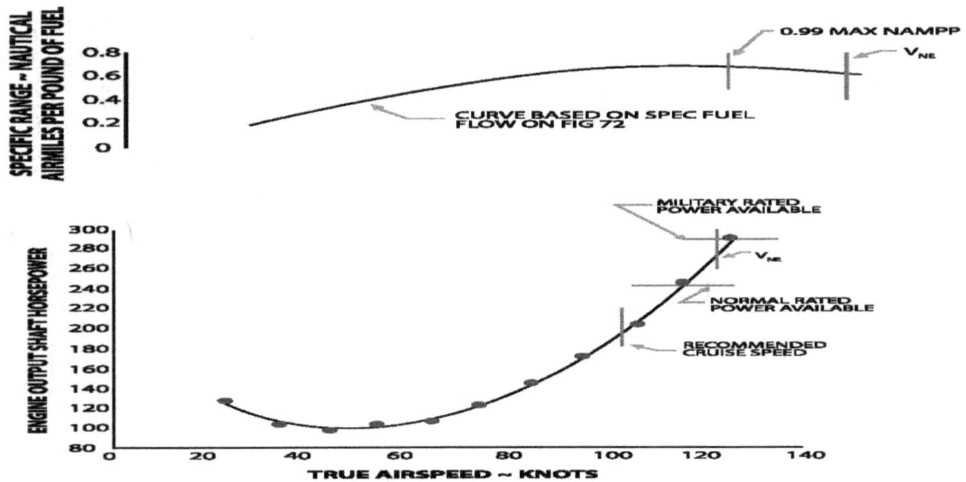


**Figure 10-3** **Specific Air Range From Fuel Flow vs TAS**

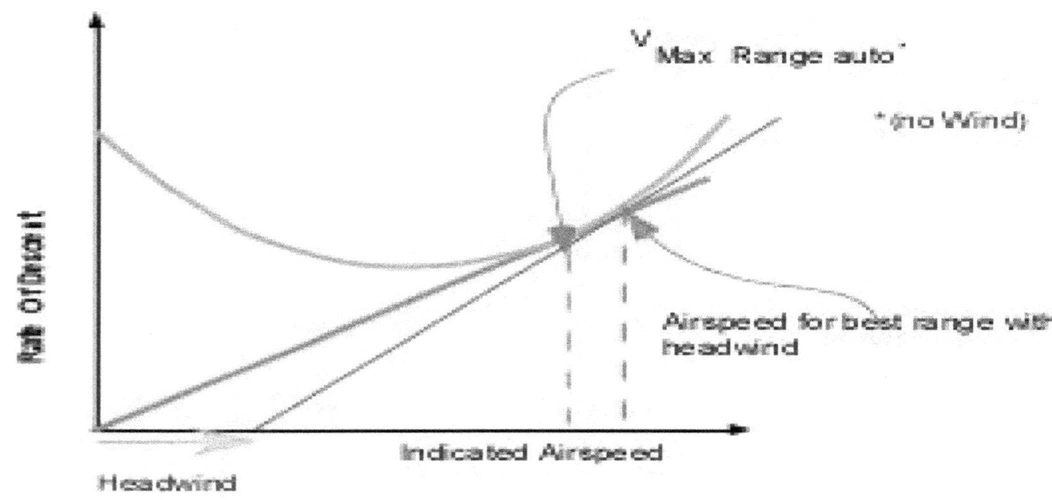


**Figure 10-4** **Range As it Applies to Autorotations**

# CHAPTER 11 *Transient Limitations*

Vertical December 2009 / January 2010

*Comment: When I first put forward the idea of talking about transients, the editor quipped that bums and drifters didn't fly helicopters... normally.*

Of course, when I further explained I wanted to discuss those numbers that exist beyond normal limitations, he quickly came around to the idea.

The first question to be asked is: why do we have transient limits? This is followed closely by: what can we do with them?

## Getting the Answers

The answer to why we have transient limits is that manufacturers recognize we don't live in a slow-moving or perfect world. Also, equipment cannot be designed to operate at its ultimate capability all the time - only at some reduced capability for extended periods of time. The exact 'size/quantity' of the reduced capability is where the tradeoffs start to occur. Let's look at a turbine engine as one example.

A turbine engine has areas that will cause concern for designers. One of these is the turbine wheels, which get blasted by burning gases while spinning at pretty high speeds. High temperatures destroy metal, literally trying to melt it. Couple this with rapid rotation of that highly heated metal, and the problem becomes multiplied. The metal pieces are not only being stretched by the heat, they're subjected to the high forces of rotation.

There is, though, a rotation speed and heat level that the metal can stand for long, long periods of time without a problem. Higher temperatures than that level will become a problem after a short time, as the stretched metal can expand to the point of rubbing against the engine surfaces, which is definitely not a good thing. Even higher temperatures than that can only be tolerated for extremely brief periods... but how brief?

This is where transient limitations come in to play. If the higher-than-normal temperature was very brief, it may mean no problems, as the engine was designed to handle that. The transient limits are there because the engine can withstand a very short period of higher temperature on the turbine wheel without causing damage. This is true if the duration of the excessive temperature is short and the amount of excessive temperature is known.

The quick amongst you will have spotted the problem: exactly how hot did it get, and how long did the high temperature last? If you're like me, and only have two eyes that were probably busy on some other important task when the over-temperature occurred, you might not be able to answer the necessary question with the necessary precision. If the over-temperature allows 30 degrees C for 10 seconds, but our 'event' was 20 C for 15 seconds, what do we do?

In the bad old days, this meant a call to the engine manufacturer, who would probably say that, to be safe, the engine should be removed and returned for inspection. Expensive.

Even now, though, if the over-temperature is too high and for too long (say 40 C for 15 seconds), it means the continued safe operation of the engine may be severely compromised and the engine should be removed and overhauled.

## Exceeded or Not Exceeded?

Other systems on the helicopter also have transient limits with different issues - one of the more popular is torque. Overtorquing a transmission is not something I'm going to promote or condone, but it is worth considering what the torquemeter is measuring and what the torque limit is trying to protect.

Torque is drag on the rotor blades. This drag is caused when the blades produce lift. Increasing the blade pitch increases the drag, and, in a steady state condition, torque is a good value of how much stress and strain is being placed on driveshafts, gear teeth and the like. This is not so in a rapidly changing situation, though, which is where the problem starts.

If we are at sea level on a standard day, let's say a steady collective position six inches up from the bottom of travel in a hover produces a torque value of 98 percent, with a takeoff power limit of 100 percent. If all we ever did was maintain a steady hover with the collective in this position, and didn't move the pedals, the torque would always be 98 percent.

However, life is seldom that kind, and one day we find we have to make a rapid collective increase to exactly this six-inch position (let's say we've got a mechanical stop in the collective that prevents us from exceeding that position). For reasons we'd rather not explain to the boss, we've had to make this increase very rapidly. The sudden increase in blade pitch will generate a very large change in the drag on the blades - much larger than we would have if we slowly increased to the same steady position. This is due to a rapid change in the angle of attack, which introduces a dynamic effect. So, we end up with an overtorque of say 105 percent. Since we only moved the collective to exactly six inches, we know that in the steady condition we aren't exceeding any limitations. Was it really an overtorque? What do we do? (This situation assumes we have a perfect electronic torquemeter [don't get me started on the significant issues with oil pressure torque meters!] See figure 1 for more details.)

The problem is we don't know exactly what causes the limitation in the drive system. Is it something in the engine, gears in the transmission, twisting of the driveshaft or something completely different? If it was an engine limit, and we can show the engine didn't exceed any other limits in the steady state, we ***might*** be able to argue that we didn't exceed a limit. If the reason is stress on the gears in the transmission, then it's more difficult to argue that no harm was done... and so on.

Manufacturers aren't required to explain the reason for a limitation, they must only state what the limitation is and what any available transient limits might be. So, when faced with one of our transient limit examples, we have to assume we may have done some damage to something. Let's hope we were able to accurately note and record the amount and duration of the over-limit!

One of my adventures outside the normal realms of flight occurred on a dark night when we exceeded the limitations of the transmission significantly. I was not amused to find out there was available a substantial margin above the value we used before any major inspection would be required.

## *Measuring the Overage*

This takes us back to our problem of not noticing the problem quickly enough, or, perhaps more importantly, accurately enough. Since we know all mechanical devices have limitations, and that some exceedance of those limitations may not be a problem, doesn't it make sense to install something that will accurately tell us by how much we've exceeded a limitation and for how long it was above the limit?

It used to be that such devices were primitive, very simple and prone to failure. A light would come on to say you'd exceeded a limit, and maintenance would have to reset the light. Often the light would come on for unexplained reasons and the pilot would have to argue that they had done nothing wrong. Now, with sensor and storage problems sorted, devices for monitoring are relatively cheap, easy to install and even easier to use. And with more than one source for data, it's easy to figure out if it really was a problem or not. When engineers know exactly how much the exceedance is, in time and size, they can make much better decisions. Buy recording devices and use them! Good pilots will not be afraid of the results.

Perhaps one of the areas where transients show up more noticeably than other places is in twin-engine helicopters, and, in particular, in twin-engine helicopters with hydro-mechanical fuel controls. The purpose of the fuel control is to keep the power turbine speed at a constant value. When one engine fails in a twin-engine helicopter, the remaining engine will do it's best to keep the rotor at the right speed. With a hydro-mechanical fuel control, there is no easy way to prevent over-temperatures, so the temperature limits for single-engine operations were quite low and had generous transients. When electronic fuel controls came along, which could limit temperatures, the temperature limitations were increased, but the transient limits were made less generous.

This brings us to the final question, when and how should we use transient limitations? The answer is that you should never ***plan*** to use them, as they're only for emergencies or unusual situations. Certainly, they aren't used in performance planning - no performance charts use transient limits. Transients are there to account for momentary requirements for extra power, but shouldn't ever be counted on to let you get away with being cavalier all the time.

So, the final answer is that transients are accounted for in testing and development, and can be used when you really, really need them. Just expect to pay a penalty if you really bust 'em!

# CHAPTER 12 *Know Your Limitations*

**Vertical** Not sure when published

*Comment: It was a wonderful, crisp, clear, calm morning at the lodge. Sam could count days like this as being part of the rewards for being a helicopter pilot. He could hear his heart beating in the stillness, and looking up at the ridgelines where he was going to be dropping off the skiers, he couldn't detect a breath of wind.*

The sky was so clear, the ridge lines looked sharp enough to cut his eyes, even though he was 8 thousand feet below them and several miles distant.

The light dusting of snow from the brief shower last night was getting cleared off the helicopter, the covers and plugs being removed as he walked over to the machine, feet crunching on the crisp snow. Reliable old beast this, he thought. Two engines, enough space for 11 good skiing friends and their gear. And here they come, he could hear their voices as they emerged from the lodge in eager anticipation of the days outing.

With the planned runs today, he'd be busy- if we apply the normal lapse rate from the temperature here at the lodge all the way to the top of the mountain, we'll be able to carry enough fuel for the morning's trips without returning and still be within the Weight Altitude Temperature limitations in the flight manual.

Shortly after, the machine loaded and all the necessary checks done, Sam decided that because of the light dusting of snow, he'd do a towering takeoff – lots of power at this height and temperature, and it would give the skiers a bit of something different. Throttles full open, everything ready, and off they went, climbing vertically to about 100 feet above the ground and then nosing over to shouts he could here even with his noise canceling headset.

The climb up the mountain was textbook- no wind, no turbulence and a aside from a small misting up of the windshield as they passed through the standard inversion caused by the lodge being in a small valley, it was just great. Arriving at the landing site, Sam noticed that the dusting of snow was a bit heavier here and so decided to bring the machine to an out-of-ground effect hover and let the snow get blown away- he had excellent visual references and aside from not as much power margin as he had anticipated from the pre-flight planning, things went OK. The skiers were quickly out of the machine and he was off to the pickup point.

This was a short trip down to the bowl several thousand feet below, and again, there was no wind this early in the day. Sam knew that by the time the skiers got down here though, the daytime heating would have generated some downflow which would give him a tailwind on departure. No worries, the performance planning showed plenty of power, even with a full load of skiers.

Sam landed by the poles, putting the main one at the right front of the helicopter, just by the pilot's door, facing into the expected wind and did the shut down. After some squinting into the sun he settled down to read the latest edition of the trade magazines. By the time the skiers had all assembled by the helicopter several hours later, Sam was just a bit concerned – the down-flowing wind was a bit stronger than he 'd anticipated. Still, no worries, he'd done this several times before. At least the landing had cleared away most of the snow and the heating had compacted what was left.

Skiers aboard, and quieter now after a good long run, Sam fired up the machine and got ready for the takeoff. Lifting off to a very low hover, as the power was right on the limits, he kept his gaze on the pole out his side window, and turned slowly around the pole to face downwind. The snow was a little more level than before- not much downslope to help him get speed and climb clear. A gentle push forward and the helicopter started to move forward, the small snow cloud staying persistently with him. He wasn't gaining much height above the ground and then suddenly the helicopter started to settle. A small tug up on the collective made no change in the descent, so he pulled up a bit more and was greeted by a reduction in the rotor RPM. Just as the guide in the left seat was about to say something, the world seemed to explode into a giant white cloud of soft snow, and he remembered little except the automatic shutting off of the fuel and electrics, and waiting in the cold and wind for the rescue chopper...

How many limitations did Sam break - even before the accident????

Answer next issue...

# CHAPTER 13 *Testing for Certification Part 1*

**Vertical** April / May 2014

*Comment: There was a time when test pilots were defined by a black and white British comedy, where the dashing test pilot, with girls on each arm, casually said to the assembled masses after the first flight in the sexy looking airplane, "Tell the designer chappie he did a good job." Things have changed quite a bit since then.*

## TEST PILOT DEFINED

The first thing to make clear is that in the helicopter world the term 'test pilot' is often misunderstood, thanks largely to the U.S. Army's maintenance pilot course. Graduates of this course are confusingly called test pilots, when a more correct title might be Post Maintenance Check Pilots (that's what the U.S. Navy calls them). This definition is guaranteed to generate a ton of letters — but, to be perfectly correct, a test pilot is one who is involved in research and development, experimental flying, or doing things that haven't been done before. I don't want to sound elitist, but words do have meaning.

So why do we need test pilots? Where do we find them? And what sort of background and training do they get? Let's imagine for a moment that a brand new helicopter has just been trucked into your hangar. It's never been ground run before, let alone flown. Who is going to fly it? Where do they start? I was involved many, many years ago with a company with more ambition than technical talent. They'd produced a helicopter... sort of. It used a car engine, and the designer, while well intentioned, had absolutely no design experience in aviation matters, let alone something as complex as helicopter rotor heads. Many aspects of the construction were admirable, but some were less than salubrious, and I was there to act as a technical consultant.

## A VERY SHORT FIRST FLIGHT

The team asked if I'd like to see a video of the first flight. Before they ran the video, I asked who had done the flying, and was told that it was a local commercial pilot with lots of hours, but no flight testing background. Reluctantly, I watched in quiet horror for the brief 10 seconds or so that the machine "flew." It was certainly not under control, and there was no buildup visible. The aircraft was started up, and the pilot immediately tried to fly. I think the machine reached something like 40° nose up and down, and 30° of bank in those brief, heart-stopping seconds. Only the over-designed composite fuselage saved the day as it slammed heavily to earth. Needless to say, the project no longer exists.

## ANOTHER FLIGHT OF FANCY

Another project with which I was briefly involved aimed to hover and cruise at near 400 knots. It was a neat idea, but it had some serious shortcomings in the landing gear (think of a flying saucer with struts and pads, and no wheels) and the advanced flight control system was driven by a joystick that appeared to owe more to computer games than good ergonomics. My suggestion of making a large scale model was rejected immediately, as well as the suggestion that we would need to spend quite a bit of time getting the physical aspects of flight control and control laws sorted out in a simulator. This project also fizzled out shortly afterwards.

## FINDING A TEST PILOT

So, who do you want to have as a test pilot? Not someone who dreams of doing the impossible, or someone who takes lots of risks. In fact, properly conducted, flight testing should be boring — there should be no surprises. If you're surprised, the flight has been planned or executed improperly. Do you need to be an engineer? Not necessarily, but a good technical background and a high curiosity level are very helpful. Most, but not all, test pilots are graduates of test pilot schools — an expensive course in learning the various test techniques and theory behind the way helicopters actually fly, and the closest thing to a post-graduate course in piloting that exists. Those who don't have the opportunity to attend such a course typically undergo a lengthy in-house, on-the-job training program with their employer. No-one leaps fully grown into the flight test business without some careful vetting — at least no-one who lasts a long time. It takes a lot of time, money and effort to get a helicopter design right, and even more time to check out all the things necessary for the flying public (pilots and passengers) to operate it safely. Remember in the beginning that there are no checklists, no flight manuals, no written limitations. Someone has to develop all of these.

All we have to go on is the assistance of the design team of engineers, and a set of requirements in the Federal Aviation Regulations (FAR). If it's a small helicopter, it will be covered by FAR 27. Fortunately, someone has written a book to decipher the relatively tersely-worded regulation, and it's called Advisory Circular 27-1B. I would not recommend it for bed-time reading. (The plot is so-so, and the character development not much better...) In actual fact, the test pilot's involvement starts a long time before the first flight. He or she will be assisting the design team in a large number of decisions about instruments and cockpit layout, and to make good decisions in this area, a lot of experience of a wide variety of machines is needed.

## *Before You Cut Metal*

There being no perfect flying machine, it's useful to learn from the good and bad points of other designs, so some broad experience is a good thing. Let's start with looking at some basics. Can you get in and out of the machine easily? What about when dressed in cold weather clothing? If not, why not? Does it meet the requirements for door opening and closing? In high winds, too? How about the field of view? Does it have the necessary instruments with the appropriate markings?

This is all before any metal is cut or composite material laid out. Another concurrent activity before anything takes to the air is the planning of tests, and the assessment of risks and potential problems. Once the actual testing begins, one of the sterling requirements becomes clear — an ability to observe and report is essential. Certainly there will be lots of instrumentation looking at stresses and strains and the like, but an ability to keenly see what the machine did in response to control inputs, and when and where those responses happen, has often been the difference between the success and failure of a program.

It's also worth noting that sometimes the response to not moving the controls is equally as important. As helicopters have become increasingly complex, test pilots have had to develop what can best be described as a pathological interest in failures — what happens when this sensor, or that computer fails? How will that affect the rest of the helicopter's operation? The flight tests themselves often have an element of risk, so the test pilot has to know what his personal criteria are for going no further in a test.

Tests like the H-V curve have a great deal of qualitative criteria, as well as engineering limits, and the test pilot has to balance risk with safety for the end users of the equipment. The ability to justify why an end point was defined as an end point may require years of experience. Next issue – what sort of tests are needed?

# CHAPTER 14 *Testing for Certification Part 2*

Vertical June / July 2013

*Comment: The tests that a test pilot is required to safely accomplish vary with the type of testing.* While this sounds a bit trite, it's worthwhile noting that not all flight testing is the same. The pilot involved in the first flight of a helicopter is going to be looking for different things than the pilot who's asked to assess whether the helicopter is safe for civil use, or effective for military use (two different and distinct things!), which in turn will be different than the pilot who is looking at new concepts of displays and controls.

## *Getting a New Type Into the Air*

The pilot who is taking a completely new helicopter design for its first tentative escape from the grasp of Mother Earth may not be using any particularly new or interesting tests, but the task will require a lot of careful buildup. Just one example of care taken in these early stages is a test to ensure the engine fuel valve shuts off when it's supposed to. It may sound simple, but it's obvious that somewhere in the past, a fuel valve didn't shut off when it was supposed to, likely with some unpleasant consequences. Perhaps next will be a test of the throttle to ensure it shuts off fuel to the fuel nozzle. Again, the logical explanation for this test is that at some point in the past, the throttle linkage wasn't set up properly.

The first start of the engine may be without the rotor blades to ensure all the dynamic components are functioning properly. After the shutdown, you can bet that a small army of engineers and technicians swarm over the machine to see how things went. Once the rotors are installed, the helicopter is started and left to run at idle for some time, and this is again followed by a lengthy look at the equipment. Then, with the rotor at idle, the first tentative moves of the flight controls will be made — not just slow, smooth control movements with the collective fully down at idle, but very specific types of inputs — stick raps (fore/aft and lateral), small inputs of different speeds, and then inputs at different frequencies of control reversals. This is all then repeated at different collective settings.

Once idle rotor RPM is cleared, increasing rotor speeds are subjected to the same precise tests. The aim is to weed out any nasty surprises that may be in store with the rotor blades on — before the aircraft leaves the ground. Once the rotor RPM has been cleared, the test pilot will be ready to start thinking about getting airborne. At flight RPM, the collective pitch is increased slightly and the whole sequence of previous tests is repeated. Finally, the helicopter is ready for light on the skids — and once there, the pilot will try a small dance on the pedals just to see how they respond. Not only is the collective raised in small increments, it's also lowered quickly to simulate a need to get rid of power. At long last, daylight appears between the landing gear and the ground.

## *Some Rules of Flight Testing*

The aim of all this buildup is one of the first rules of flight testing, which I like to state as: NO SURPRISES! Why? Flight testing should be a cautious, methodical progression from the unknown to the known. Each step should clearly identify what the next step should look like, and if something unexpected happens, it means someone has taken too large a bite. The reason for testing the rapid reduction of power is to ensure you can meet the second rule of flight testing: Always Leave an Out Or, in other words, never go somewhere or do something from which you can't easily escape. For example, once you've accelerated to an airspeed and stabilized there during the first adventure into forward flight, you must make sure you can return back to the hover from that speed. The rest of the exploration of the flight envelope and handling characteristics must be handled with the same degree of caution — there may be dragons lurking in some nasty corners, and the developmental test pilot has to be aware of these.

Flight test development is a three part process: Predict, then Test to Verify. And though it may sound pretty simple, this method will ensure that the first law — No Surprises — is met consistently. "Predict," means that engineers and technicians have worked out what should happen — what the response to an input should look like, or what the stress and strain on a component should be. "Test," means we find a way to measure that, and can "Verify" that things are as expected. If not, the test is stopped until the reason for the mismatch between theory and reality is resolved. Sometimes this means that new test methods must be developed, and this will require some careful consideration by all concerned. This leads to the next major difference between operational flying and flight testing.

Lost in Translation?

Any development project for a new aircraft type is going to employ a large number of highly evolved specialists from a whole host of different disciplines. Design engineers of types you've probably never heard will be involved, and they don't all speak the same technical language. Electrical engineers (and I'm not trying to put them down just because I didn't understand

imaginary numbers) don't speak the same language as airframe structural engineers. The folks who seem to do the translation between all these disciplines are in flight test. An electrical system will have an influence on a whole host of other systems, such as hydraulics (for switching them on or off), or power plants (how much power does it take to produce all those amps?) and so on. So the test pilot has to know enough about each system to be able to translate between all these folks. Though it's not always easy, it is absolutely essential. In operational flying, it's relatively easy to see that nearly everyone involved (except perhaps the end customer) speaks the same language and knows what all the words mean.

## *More Tests*

Having got the machine to the point where it can be safely flown, and completed all the thousands of steps necessary for obtaining a civil certification or military approval to fly, the next steps are done by the "certification" pilots. These pilots are trained in the various test techniques commonly used for evaluation, plus they have enough operational experience to be able to extrapolate their findings to the real world. Another reason for having these types of pilots is so that you've got a sober second party looking at the helicopter and its foibles — because one of the traps that can snare a pilot in development is that sometimes test pilots know too much.

This is not to criticize the folks who do the development (and sometimes do the certification evaluation), but you wouldn't want to test something without knowing everything you can possibly know before you test it, would you? And you wouldn't want to have something happen without knowing exactly what you're going to do when it happens (or doesn't happen). An example might be the failure of an electronic fuel control. In development, the pilot will be briefed in depth about the system to be fitted and tested. In order to test it, the pilot will know what the failure symptoms are, and exactly what to do when that failure occurs (meeting the first rule of flight testing — No Surprises).

But the real world isn't like that. Not all normal (let alone emergency) procedures are interpreted correctly, nor followed exactly. So what the test pilot knows and sees in carefully controlled conditions is probably not what the operational pilot sees in less-controlled circumstances. Therein lies the role of the certification (or military evaluation) test pilots. These types of pilots are trained to consider all the operations of the helicopter and will put themselves into the shoes (flying boots?) of a junior pilot, flying operationally for long enough to perhaps need refresher training, on a rainy night at 3:30 a.m. with a load of unhappy passengers and lots of turbulence — and who is now faced with an emergency. These pilots can interpret the regulations and specifications and determine if the helicopter and equipment can meet those dry and dusty tomes and be safe — and operationally effective.

# CHAPTER 15 *Testing for Certification Part 3*

**Vertical** August / September 2013

*Comment: In the third and final part of our series on test pilots, we look at how the challenges of real-world operations are incorporated into flight testing.*

After having provided an overview of who test pilots are and what they do in the first parts of this series, I'm going to put a bit of a different slant on things in this issue. We're going to look at how flight test people attempt to inject the real world on a handling issue that is just too complicated to put in everyday terms. In fact, I'll summarize the issue as:

Measure with a micrometer; mark with a chalk line; cut with a chainsaw.

The first of these is in the low airspeed environment — as shown in the diagram below. The pitot system doesn't work well below 40 knots (despite what some may tell you), and it certainly doesn't work except when in forward flight. We have two inseparable but mutually-exclusive problems — we typically don't have any information in the real world to help pilots here, but it's the helicopter's very ability to perform slow and multi-directional flight (with respect to the wind) that is its reason for being. Only helicopters can maintain their position over the earth while enduring winds from any direction — no other machine can do this. So how can we make sure (with some confidence) that a helicopter is capable of handling winds from the side and rear?

Here's where the test pilots (and flight test engineers) come in — you need to go fly in winds from the side and rear, and measure that the helicopter has enough control authority. Which leads to a natural question: what's considered "enough" control authority? In roll, pitch and yaw? The U.S. military decided some time ago that 10 percent control power was needed — but without defining what they meant by "control power." What evolved in that case was that at least 10 percent control travel was needed at the worst condition — simply because defining "control power" proved nearly impossible.

The civil world looked at things a bit differently — perhaps because of the knowledge that there were too many variables in the real world (discussed later), and that the best that could be defined was "sufficient" control to generate a rate to counter any gusts at the worst condition. If you're confused by that, an explanation will be coming shortly. Controllability Defined The defining atmospheric condition for demonstrating controllability was determined to be 7,000 feet density altitude, and 20 mph (17 knots) of wind from any azimuth. Like most airworthiness requirements, this can be traced back to the days of the Bell 47 and Sikorsky R-4.

Part 27, paragraph 143 of the United States Federal Aviation Administration (FAA) Federal Aviation Regulations states:

> *A wind velocity of not less than 17 knots must be established in which the rotorcraft can be operated without loss of control on or near the ground in any maneuver appropriate to the type (such as crosswind takeoffs, sideward flight, and rearward flight), with -- (1) Critical weight; (2) Critical center of gravity; (3) Critical rotor r.p.m.; etc.*

A quick note here — sideward and rearward flight in this case don't mean translating sideways or backwards with respect to the ground. In my personal opinion, these are unfortunate choices of words when the terms side- and rear-wind would be more appropriate and more easily understandable. But how do you test this?

This is where it's necessary to have a universal and repeatable method of testing that allows an answer to be given, with the full knowledge that the answer may bear little relation to the real world. The real world for helicopter pilots is full of capricious winds that can suddenly change direction and speed, and are difficult (sometimes impossible) to measure with any accuracy. Just ask yourself — how many times have you had to operate somewhere with no air traffic control or any other way to know the wind direction, let alone the speed? So, now to the test method. In order to make the test repeatable, you need to start with very little actual wind, and generate the side and rear winds by moving the helicopter.

Normally a pace vehicle is used with a fifth wheel to get accurate speeds (many automobile speedometers aren't that accurate below 40 mph, apparently). The pace vehicle is driven at the required speed, the helicopter flies formation on it at a specific relative wind direction (measured from the nose), and the control positions versus the total control travel (in pitch, roll and yaw) are measured. Starting at 10 mph, the speed is increased in 5 mph increments until either a speed well above 20 mph is reached and an adequate control margin is reached, or the helicopter runs out of control in one axis (unlikely in any modern helicopter).

## *Different Azimuths of Wind*

The test is then repeated at the next increment of relative wind — if you start with the helicopter moving directly to the left, the relative wind is 090 degrees, so the next increment would be either 060 degrees or 120 degrees. This exercise requires a lot of formation flying! In nearly all cases, for North American direction-of-rotation main rotor blades, the worst condition is typically the yaw pedals at 090 degrees of relative wind at about 20 to 25 knots (23 to 29 mph) — after that, the power required to maintain height above the ground decreases dramatically, which affects the tail rotor requirements. The test is then repeated out of ground effect. A Limitation? So, we've measured the effect of winds on controlling the helicopter with great precision in a very repeatable manner, like good scientists and engineers.

## *Measure with a Micrometer, Mark with a Chalk Line, Cut with an Axe*

But the information is of very little real use to operators who have to contend with no useful way to observe what might be considered by some to be a limitation — so most flight manuals merely state (in the limitations section) that: "the helicopter has been demonstrated to side and rear winds of XX knots." This always generates the question: Is this a limitation or something else? And the answer is that no, it's not a limitation, because it doesn't say it's a limitation — it's merely an indication that the machine met the requirement. Sort of like the aeronautical equivalent of "Your mileage may vary..."

It's also worth remembering that the test is done in a hover (albeit at maximum weight). If you have excess power above that required to hover at maximum weight at whatever atmospheric conditions, and you then decide to climb vertically, there is no guarantee that you'll have adequate tail rotor authority to maintain a constant heading. There is no airworthiness certification requirement for this condition, so there is no guarantee that you'll have that much tail rotor authority — and it would be difficult to make a case that it's unsafe and needs a new certification requirement.

## *High Risk Tests*

From a safety perspective, these tests are very high in risk — recovering from a control or engine problem at five feet above ground level when moving sideways across the ground at 30 knots is something that requires immediate and instinctive reactions. Having a compressor stall due to hot exhaust gas re-ingestion at 20 knots of backward speed (as opposed to merely hovering with a 20 knot tailwind) also requires some very good preparation and planning. During my flight testing career, an interesting request came in for a new helicopter type that required a higher takeoff and landing clearance than that approved in the original certification. Further testing was needed. The helicopter was flown to a high ridge-line site where a fairly constant 20 knot wind was known to exist. The worst case weight and center of gravity condition was established with a large ballast box on the right skid, and only one pilot in the right-hand seat. All that was necessary was to hover at 30 degree intervals of heading and show that there was more than enough pedal (and other) control margin at each azimuth, which was easily and quickly done.

## *Height Velocity Curve*

A similar issue that confronts those conducting flight tests is determining the HV (height-velocity) curve. The variables for this are huge, and the intervention time used in the civil world might arguably be too short, but at least there is a uniform standard applied to the testing. Measuring with a micrometer — we know the winds-peed at the helicopter to within two knots or so — but the real world doesn't give us that degree of accuracy. Marking with a chalk line — we can publish something that says what the helicopter has been demonstrated to, but it's not really a limit (because weight, center of gravity, density altitude and so on make it impossible to show a single limit for all these variables). Cut with a chain saw — the situation faced by a pilot in the real world should be away from the test conditions by a safe margin. So, in summary, the testing of these conditions to make sure the helicopter has sufficient control authority in the low speed environment is very different than actually operating the helicopter – but over time, it's proven to be the only way to get a repeatable test.

## *Best Kept Secrets*

Last issue, I questioned why we don't often hear about this type of flying. Typically, it's because this type of flying is done by company test pilots on development and prototype aircraft. The company generally doesn't want to announce their developments too early, and certainly doesn't want to advertise their failures — and the nature of development is that there will be things that don't work!

Also, the issues of performance, stability, and control testing are difficult to explain to those who don't know the theory and practice behind these subjects. I've been teaching them at test pilot schools for a long time, and it takes several months to get to a point where students begin to understand the why and wherefore of these tests. So, you can imagine the difficulty of getting the basics across to pilots who, while they are very good at what they do, are not versed in the fundamentals of these arcane subjects.

Finally, other research flying may have some military security issues. If you saw the movies related to the Osama Bin Laden raid, for example, those stealth Black Hawks didn't just appear out of thin air. It's nice to see that they were kept secret for as long as they were.

# CHAPTER 16 *Getting to Know Autopilots Part1*

**Vertical** April / May 2011

*Comment: This series is going to try to show those of you who are fortunate enough to have an autopilot how it works.*

This isn't going to be a bunch of schematic and wiring diagrams, and hopefully will contain very little description of components. I'm going to try to show you what will happen in the cockpit as we step through the various layers of a typical autopilot.

## *THE OBVIOUS DISCLAIMER*

This is a general overview of a generic autopilot and it's underlying stability and control system. The terms used are not going to fit every system, and readers are asked to at least know their system well enough to be able to translate the terms used here to their equipment. And obviously, since a lot of the inputs needed to demonstrate the various ways the systems act have to be done in flight, a suitable observance of common sense and safety must be applied by the pilot. You'll be letting the helicopter have a mind of it's own for a few minutes in the hover, and you need to be aware of what's around you. Don't let curiosity take the place of safety.

We'll look at the cyclic controls first, and in a later article, cover the pedals.

And the aim is not to provide a perfect description of how any particular AFCS works, but to permit you as the pilot to better understand how their system works. Observe what happens, and you'll be better prepared to understand what any particular type of system does (or doesn't work).

## *TERMS USED*

I'm going to call anything that gets between the pilot and the swashplate and makes an input to the swashplate an Automatic Flight Control System (AFCS). The autopilot part is the part that will control the helicopter to some external reference, such as airspeed, altitude or navigational course. The following diagram shows the academic definitions we'll use through this series.

For most of the series, we'll only be talking about a three axis autopilot, as this is the most common type fitted. It will have two modes, SAS and ATT. SAS stands for Stability Augmentation System, which only removes the effects of gusts. ATT stands for Attitude Hold, which will attempt to retain an attitude.

## *THE FIRST THING IS STICK TRIM*

Before they get to a machine with an autopilot, most helicopter pilots learn to fly on helicopters with hydraulic boost and no stick feel. The stick is loose and requires very little force to move it around. While this is good for conditions where you have to be making small corrections all the time, it's not good for anything else, especially when an AFCS is concerned. A lot of the things we'll be looking at will require the stick trim to be turned on and off to demonstrate what effect this important part of the system has.

## *NEXT IS THE FORCE TRIM*

Likewise for the Force Trim (FT) – sometimes it will necessary to press the FT to show it's effect, but for most of the time, it will be necessary to leave it alone.

And how you hold the cyclic is important – I'm going to assume you can hold it with a light, two fingered grip, and not a death grip like you're trying squeeze the dye out of it.

### *INPUT TYPES*

While we are looking at how the AFCS works, we're going to use a special type of input – a pulse is the main one, which is a small short input in one direction followed by release of the force/ position to let the stick return to it's original position. Since the stick trim is on, the stick will return to it's original position and we'll get to watch what the AFCS does.

### *OFF WE GO!*

The first thing we're going to investigate is the behavior difference between SAS and ATT modes in the hover. Make sure you've set yourself in a clear location where you can let the helicopter move around on it's own for a few moments. You obviously don't want to lose control, but it's important to let the controls be still for a few seconds to see what things happen.

### *SAS ONLY MODE*

With only SAS mode engaged and the stick trim engaged, when in a safe hover and the FT left alone (i.e. up), just let the controls stay in one place. The helicopter may hold it's attitude for a few seconds, but after a few seconds (or minutes) depending on the wind, it will start let the attitude change. If you're lucky, and a wind gust comes along at the right time, you'll see the pitch or roll attitude change and then stop at a new attitude.

If you now apply a small, short pulse to the cyclic in pitch only you'll see the nose moves in the appropriate direction with the stick input, but doesn't return to the original position.

A small short pulse in roll only should result in the roll attitude changing and then more or less holding a new bank angle.

Next turn off the Stick Feel and hold the stick steady. You might notice some attempt by the AFCS to move the stick in your hand as the system tries to correct for the gusts. You'll also notice that the system can't hold any attitude in pitch or roll, and you have to put the necessary inputs.

If you turn the Stick Feel back on, and now maintain the hover with the FT pressed and held down, the effect will be the same as if the Stick Feel were off.

Next, re-establish the hover with the Stick Feel on, and the appropriate digit ready to press the FT at the right time. Apply a small, short input to cyclic in pitch and press and release the FT. Watch what happens. Re-establish the hover and press and release the FT. Now repeat the small, short input in roll and press and release the FT. Watch what happens. Re-establish the hover.

Once re-established in the hover, don't press the FT and move the helicopter to a new position a short distance to the front. Don't use the FT. Notice the stick movements needed and where the stick is at the end of the maneuver. Repeat for a reposition a short distance to the side, again only flying against the forces.

### *ATT (ATTITUDE HOLD) MODE*

The ATT mode exploration is going to be broadly similar to the SAS mode exploration, but the system should provide a much more pronounced response.

With ATT mode engaged and the stick trim engaged, when in a safe hover and the FT left alone (i.e. up), just let the controls stay in one place. The helicopter should hold it's attitude in both pitch and quite well, but will drift in position with any change in the wind. If you're lucky, and a wind gust comes along at the right time, you'll see the pitch or roll attitude change and then return to the original attitude.

If you now apply a small, short pulse to the cyclic in pitch only without pressing the FT you'll see the nose moves in the appropriate direction with the stick input, but this time it should return to the original attitude.

A small short pulse in roll only should result in the roll attitude changing and then more or less holding a new bank angle. The response here will depend a great deal on the architecture of the system –

some will return to the wings level position, others will hold the new bank angle. Pay attention to what yours does!

Next turn off the Stick Feel and hold the stick steady. The response should be the same as the SAS only response. The system really needs the Stick Feel to operate in ATT mode.

Turn the Stick Feel back on, and now maintain the hover with the FT pressed and held down, the response should be the same as if in SAS mode.

Next, re-establish the hover with the Stick Feel on, and the appropriate digit ready to press the FT at the right time. Apply a small, short input to cyclic in pitch and press and release the FT. Watch what happens. The system should acquire and hold the new pitch attitude that existed when the FT was released.

Re-establish the hover and press and release the FT. Now repeat the small, short input in roll and press and release the FT. Watch what happens. The system should acquire and hold the new roll attitude that existed when the FT was released. Re-establish the hover.

Once re-established in the hover, don't press the FT. Move the helicopter to a new position a short distance to the front. Don't use the FT. Notice the stick movements needed and where the stick is at the end of the maneuver. Repeat for a reposition a short distance to the side, again only flying against the forces. The control inputs will be different than those used in the SAS only mode.

And that's enough for one lesson. Next article – the same thing in forward flight.

# CHAPTER 17 *Getting to Know Autopilots Part II*

**Vertical** June / July 2011

*Comment: In the first article, we looked at the differences between SAS and ATT modes in the hover.*

You should have a pretty clear idea of how the two are different, and hopefully will have been convinced that ATT mode is a useful, and very flyable mode. You should also be convinced that the Force Trim is your friend, and be flying with it on all the time. (At least if I was Galaxy Commander, you'd be flying with it on all the time...)

In this article, we're going to look just at the SAS and ATT modes in forward flight, and follow the same progression as in the hover.

A couple of things to clear up any confusion from the first article. The types of inputs we'll be using are a 'pulse' input where the stick is moved and then returned to the original position (easy with the FT on – just let the force off). The other input is the 'step' input where the stick is moved and held in the new position for long enough for the helicopter to respond.

The last clarification is the word 'click' which means press and immediately release the FT button.

Since use of the FT button is different than how you may be used to using it, a bit of discipline may be useful. One of the best ways to be disciplined about using the FT button is to curl your thumb around the other side of the cyclic grip.

## *One Main Difference from Hover*

In the cruise, there's a bit more time to watch what's going on to the system. I'm assuming that there are Actuator Position Indicators (API) for pitch and roll. We can now afford the time to look at these as the system works.

SAS-Only Mode

We're going to investigate is the behavior difference between SAS and ATT modes in cruise. Make sure you're in a clear area where you can maneuver without too much interference from ATC and other aircraft. Now, you obviously don't want to lose control while doing this, but it's important to let the controls be still for a few seconds to see what happens.

With the AFCS in SAS mode and Force Trim (FT) engaged, once in a stable cruise and with the FT button left alone (i.e. up), just let the controls stay in one place. The helicopter may hold its attitude in pitch and roll for a few seconds (or minutes, depending on the wind), but then it will allow the attitude to change, probably in a slow divergence. Just like the hover, if you're lucky and a small lump of turbulence comes along at the right time, you'll see the pitch or roll attitude change and then stop at a new attitude. Watch the APIs dance as the turbulence passes by.

If you now apply a small, short pulse to the cyclic in pitch only, you'll see the nose moves in the appropriate direction with the stick input., but the aircraft doesn't return to its original position. You'll need to bring it back to the original correct position and click the FT button. If you can divide your attention, watch the pitch API as you move the stick.

A small, short lateral pulse only should result in the roll attitude changing and then more or less holding a new bank angle. Depending on your set up, only a bank angle may happen, or it may result in an actual change in heading

Next, turn off the FT and hold the stick steady. You might notice some attempt by the AFCS to move the stick in your hand as the system tries to correct for the gusts. You'll also notice that the system can't hold any attitude in pitch or roll, and you have to make the necessary inputs to herd the helicopter along.

Turn the FT back on, and now press and hold down the FT button, and the effect should be the same as if the force trim were off.

Next, re-establish the cruise with the FT on, and have the appropriate digit ready to press the FT at the right time. Apply a small, short, pitch step input (move and maintain the new position) to the cyclic and click the FT at the new stick position. Watch what happens. The helicopter should stabilize (more or less) at a new attitude. Re-establish the cruise without first pressing the FT and then click the FT.

Now, make a small, short step input in roll and click the FT at the new stick position. Watch what happens. Again, the helicopter should try to stabilize around the new attitude. Re-establish wings level in the cruise however you want.

Once re-established in the cruise, and with the FT up, reduce power slightly. The helicopter will attempt to maintain the original attitude, and you'll need to click the FT to help it establish the new attitude appropriate for the new airspeed.

### *ATT Mode*

The ATT mode exploration is going to be broadly similar to the SAS, but the system should provide a much more pronounced response and the stick may be moving slightly on it's own as it tries to maintain it's commanded attitudes.

With the AFCS in ATT mode, the FT on, in a stable cruise just let the controls stay in one place. The helicopter should hold its attitude in both pitch and roll quite well, but may change height with any updrafts or downdraft. If you're lucky and a wind gust comes along at the right time, you'll see the pitch or roll attitude change and then return to the original attitude. The system is trying to maintain the attitude it had when the FT was last released. You may feel the stick moving on it's own – let the FT do it's job.

If you now apply a small, short pulse to the cyclic in pitch only, without pressing the FT, you'll see the nose moves in the appropriate direction with the stick input, but unlike in SAS-only mode this time the aircraft should return to the original attitude when the stick is returned to its original position.

A small short pulse in roll only should result in the roll attitude changing and then more or less holding a new bank angle. The response here will depend a great deal on the architecture of the system and also how the yaw channel is set up — some will return to the wings-level position, others will hold the new bank angle. If it does go to a new bank angle, it may or may actually change heading. Pay attention to what yours does – but you should know already!

Next, turn FT off and hold the stick steady. The response should be the same as the SAS-only response. The system really needs FT to operate in ATT mode. Some systems may automatically switch to SAS mode when the force trim is turned off.

Now, turn the FT on again, and in a stable cruise again, maintain the cruise with the FT button held down. The response should be the same as if the AFCS was in SAS-only mode.

Next, re-establish the cruise with the FT on and the appropriate digit ready to click the FT at the right time. Apply a small, short step pitch input and click the FT. Watch what happens. The system should acquire and hold the new pitch attitude that exists when the FT is released.

Re-establish the cruise and click the FT. Now repeat with a small, short step roll input and click the FT. Watch what happens. The system should acquire and hold the new roll attitude that existed when the FT was released. Now, re-establish the cruise.

Once re-established in the cruise, don't press the FT while you reduce the power. Note the pitch attitude will remain the same, as should the roll attitude. You'll probably have to re-adjust the cyclic and click the FT to get the conditions you want in the descent. Once stabilized, add power to climb and see what the changes are. The control inputs you make for these moves will be different than those used in the SAS-only mode.

My experience is that it takes some practice and discipline to learn to use an AFCS to its greatest effect. Flying in ATT mode is not difficult when you understand how the system works. If you take the time to learn to trim the helicopter and fly using pressures on the controls, instead of constantly re-trimming, you'll make your life much easier. And, this also will prepare you for using the autopilot.

# CHAPTER 18 *Getting to Know Autopilots Part II*

**Vertical** August / September 2011

*Comment: In the first article, we looked at the differences between SAS and ATT modes in the hover.*

You should have a pretty clear idea of how the two are different, and hopefully will have been convinced that ATT mode is a useful, and very flyable mode. You should also be convinced that the Force Trim is your friend, and be flying with it on all the time. (At least if I was Galaxy Commander, you'd be flying with it on all the time…)

In this article, we're going to look just at the SAS and ATT modes in forward flight, and follow the same progression as in the hover.

A couple of things to clear up any confusion from the first article. The types of inputs we'll be using are a 'pulse' input where the stick is moved and then returned to the original position (easy with the FT on – just let the force off). The other input is the 'step' input where the stick is moved and held in the new position for long enough for the helicopter to respond.

The last clarification is the word 'click' which means press and immediately release the FT button.

Since use of the FT button is different than how you may be used to using it, a bit of discipline may be useful. One of the best ways to be disciplined about using the FT button is to curl your thumb around the other side of the cyclic grip.

## *One Main Difference from Hover*

In the cruise, there's a bit more time to watch what's going on to the system. I'm assuming that there are Actuator Position Indicators (API) for pitch and roll. We can now afford the time to look at these as the system works.

### SAS-Only Mode

We're going to investigate is the behavior difference between SAS and ATT modes in cruise. Make sure you're in a clear area where you can maneuver without too much interference from ATC and other aircraft. Now, you obviously don't want to lose control while doing this, but it's important to let the controls be still for a few seconds to see what happens.

With the AFCS in SAS mode and Force Trim (FT) engaged, once in a stable cruise and with the FT button left alone (i.e. up), just let the controls stay in one place. The helicopter may hold its attitude in pitch and roll for a few seconds (or minutes, depending on the wind), but then it will allow the attitude to change, probably in a slow divergence. Just like the hover, if you're lucky and a small lump of turbulence comes along at the right time, you'll see the pitch or roll attitude change and then stop at a new attitude. Watch the APIs dance as the turbulence passes by.

If you now apply a small, short pulse to the cyclic in pitch only, you'll see the nose moves in the appropriate direction with the stick input., but the aircraft doesn't return to its original position. You'll need to bring it back to the original correct position and click the FT button. If you can divide your attention, watch the pitch API as you move the stick.

A small, short lateral pulse only should result in the roll attitude changing and then more or less holding a new bank angle. Depending on your set up, only a bank angle may happen, or it may result in an actual change in heading

Next, turn off the FT and hold the stick steady. You might notice some attempt by the AFCS to move the stick in your hand as the system tries to correct for the gusts. You'll also notice that the system can't hold any attitude in pitch or roll, and you have to make the necessary inputs to herd the helicopter along.

Turn the FT back on, and now press and hold down the FT button, and the effect should be the same as if the force trim were off.

Next, re-establish the cruise with the FT on, and have the appropriate digit ready to press the FT at the right time. Apply a small, short, pitch step input (move and maintain the new position) to the cyclic and click the FT at the new stick position. Watch what happens. The helicopter should stabilize (more or less) at a new attitude. Re-establish the cruise without first pressing the FT and then click the FT.

Now, make a small, short step input in roll and click the FT at the new stick position. Watch what happens. Again, the helicopter should try to stabilize around the new attitude. Re-establish wings level in the cruise however you want.

Once re-established in the cruise, and with the FT up, reduce power slightly. The helicopter will attempt to maintain the original attitude, and you'll need to click the FT to help it establish the new attitude appropriate for the new airspeed.

### *ATT Mode*

The ATT mode exploration is going to be broadly similar to the SAS, but the system should provide a much more pronounced response and the stick may be moving slightly on it's own as it tries to maintain it's commanded attitudes.

With the AFCS in ATT mode, the FT on, in a stable cruise just let the controls stay in one place. The helicopter should hold its attitude in both pitch and roll quite well, but may change height with any updrafts or downdraft. If you're lucky and a wind gust comes along at the right time, you'll see the pitch or roll attitude change and then return to the original attitude. The system is trying to maintain the attitude it had when the FT was last released. You may feel the stick moving on it's own – let the FT do it's job.

If you now apply a small, short pulse to the cyclic in pitch only, without pressing the FT, you'll see the nose moves in the appropriate direction with the stick input, but unlike in SAS-only mode this time the aircraft should return to the original attitude when the stick is returned to its original position.

A small short pulse in roll only should result in the roll attitude changing and then more or less holding a new bank angle. The response here will depend a great deal on the architecture of the system and also how the yaw channel is set up — some will return to the wings-level position, others will hold the new bank angle. If it does go to a new bank angle, it may or may actually change heading. Pay attention to what yours does – but you should know already!

Next, turn FT off and hold the stick steady. The response should be the same as the SAS-only response. The system really needs FT to operate in ATT mode. Some systems may automatically switch to SAS mode when the force trim is turned off.

Now, turn the FT on again, and in a stable cruise again, maintain the cruise with the FT button held down. The response should be the same as if the AFCS was in SAS-only mode.

Next, re-establish the cruise with the FT on and the appropriate digit ready to click the FT at the right time. Apply a small, short step pitch input and click the FT. Watch what happens. The system should acquire and hold the new pitch attitude that exists when the FT is released.

Re-establish the cruise and click the FT. Now repeat with a small, short step roll input and click the FT. Watch what happens. The system should acquire and hold the new roll attitude that existed when the FT was released. Now, re-establish the cruise.

Once re-established in the cruise, don't press the FT while you reduce the power. Note the pitch attitude will remain the same, as should the roll attitude. You'll probably have to re-adjust the cyclic and click the FT to get the conditions you want in the descent. Once stabilized, add power to climb and see what the changes are. The control inputs you make for these moves will be different than those used in the SAS-only mode.

My experience is that it takes some practice and discipline to learn to use an AFCS to its greatest effect. Flying in ATT mode is not difficult when you understand how the system works. If you take the time to learn to trim the helicopter and fly using pressures on the controls, instead of constantly re-trimming, you'll make your life much easier. And, this also will prepare you for using the autopilot.

# CHAPTER 19 *Getting to Know Autopilots Part 4*

**Vertical** October / November 2011

*Comment:* In the final installment of our series on automatic flight control systems (AFCS), we look at the autopilot portion of the AFCS and its control of yaw and heading.

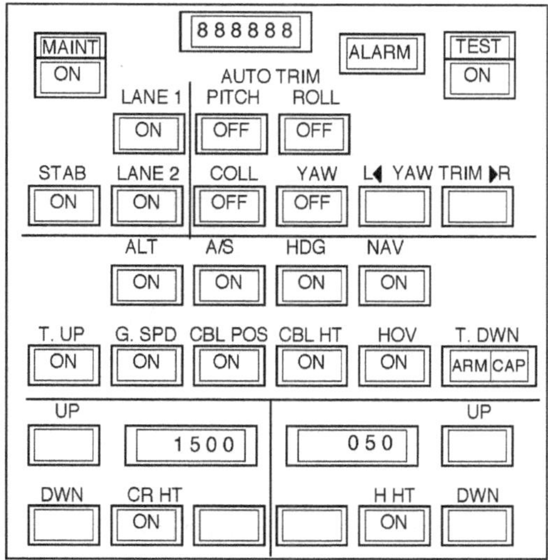


**Figure 19-1 Complex 4 axis AFCS Control Panel**

For a three-axis autopilot, control of pitch and roll only occurs above 60 knots in most helicopters. The stabilization aspects of the encompassing automatic flight control system, of course, work all the time; this makes the machine a fairly docile beast and reduces pilot workload.

The yaw axis of the AFCS, however, is a different kind of animal. In forward flight, anything that happens in the yaw channel will affect the roll channel, but in the low-airspeed area (anything below 40 knots, including side and rear winds), the yaw channel can act almost independently.

Unfortunately, to understand the yaw axis we have to get a bit more technical than in the past. The pain is necessary to really see how it works. I beg your indulgence. We'll start by examining in detail the hover and low-speed environments, followed by a simplified look at the forward-speed environment, and then briefly touch on that rather gray area that happens as we move between those two states.

### In the Low-Speed Area

Below 40 knots, the helicopter is in its own unique territory: it can hover and it can also maintain position with respect to the ground when it encounters wind. Winds can assault a helicopter from every direction, and the pilot's job of maintaining position is made much more difficult by the requirement to maintain a heading.

This is where the stabilization part of the yaw channel and the autopilot part merge and become pretty much indistinguishable. The reason things become muddy is that, as with pitch and roll, the stability augmentation system part of the yaw axis is designed to damp out unwanted excursions, and the heading hold is designed to maintain a yaw attitude. What's a yaw attitude? Why, heading, of course — it's got a number assigned to it. In the hover, we seldom want to turn to a specific heading, merely maintain the one we have or turn to point at something.

How does the yaw channel work? Much in the same way as the pitch and roll channel. The rate gyro senses movement and makes a correction to the yaw actuator and takes out the rate. With only a simple SAS operating in yaw, a gust will move you to a new heading by the time it takes out the rate. You then have to return to the desired heading. Now, how does the yaw channel know whether it's you or the wind that's causing the helicopter to yaw? There are two broad ways to let the system know you are the one initiating this: the force trim release (which for some reason is mounted on the cyclic — where it will also disable stabilization in the pitch and roll channel — why not a second release just for yaw on the collective?) or by some method that will confirm if the pilot is moving the pedals. This second method has two possibilities: a position sensor internal to the flight control system, or pedal-mounted microswitches.

The chief problem with a position sensor internal to the AFCS is that the same pedal position might be used for a lot of different relative wind directions and speeds. Think about how you would make a correction for heading without the AFCS. In a lot of cases, you apply a bit of pedal, and then, by the time everything settles down and the heading is back to where you want it, the pedals are back in the same position.

To get around this problem, a sensor internal to the AFCS could be a force sensor, which senses a greater than specified force applied to the pedal. This was used on the Sea King, the military version of the Sikorsky S-61, and took a bit of getting used to.

The other type of internal sensor could be described as similar to the damper on a screen door. The pilot moves the pedals, and this is sensed by the system, which allows the control input to change the heading. At the same time the pilot moves the pedals, a second sensor also opens, but it moves more slowly than the pilot's command. It follows/tracks the change being made, and, when the pilot stops moving the pedals, like the damper on the screen door, it eventually catches up and basically says to the AFCS: "The pilot has stopped moving the controls, damp out /hold this heading."

This brings us to a pet peeve of mine: the use of microswitches on the face of the yaw pedals as the way to tell the AFCS that the pilot wants to hold a heading. For most people, feet are very poor force sensors — mine regularly have to carry nearly 90 pounds each when standing still and alternate between zero and a minimum of 180 pounds when walking. Expecting them to sense a small force, especially when wearing potentially heavy pilot footwear, is very impractical, yet some helicopters have a sensor on the face of the pedals that is depressed with the application of a very small force. These switches have no detectable mechanical detent, and unless your feet were removed completely from the pedals, you were never sure if the switch was up or down. For this reason, I detested all such switches quite vocally for a long time. Then, I came across a set of pedal microswitches that took about 15 pounds to close, and had a definite click to them, that even I could feel through flying boots. These were quite nice to use, and I had to refine my objections more closely!

If these ways of sensing when the pilot wanted to hold (or not hold) heading were all that it needed, things would be pretty simple. Unfortunately, an additional signal is needed — one based on how fast the helicopter is yawing when the previously mentioned sensor combination has said, "Hold this heading." Let's say the helicopter is yawing to the left, and the pilot's feet were removed from the pedals, closing the heading hold microswitch when the heading is 325 degrees – this becomes the "hold this heading" value. If the helicopter is yawing at more than a few degrees per second when the "hold 325 degrees" command is made, then the AFCS will attempt to not just stop the yaw rate, but return to 325 degrees with an input of right pedal. Unfortunately, the size of the input has to be large enough to not only stop the yaw rate to the left, but return the helicopter to 325 degrees. The input will generate a yaw rate to the right, and the helicopter will blow right past 325 degrees, this time yawing right. Naturally, the system will try to stop that yaw rate with a left pedal input, and things become quite entertaining.

The original Sikorsky UH-60A Black Hawk had a problem in this area, and at least one helicopter crashed while demonstrating the issue. It wasn't a problem in normal operations, as the pilots (unknowingly) compensated by keeping their feet on the pedals. In the Black Hawk, the pilot had to manually fly to and stabilize at the desired heading and then remove their feet from the pedals to allow the heading hold to operate. This seems to me to defeat the purpose of an AFCS (which is to assist the pilot). Since most pilots don't want to remove their feet from the pedals, especially in the hover, the whole system was never used to its best effect.

An additional signal that says, "Don't try to hold a heading unless the yaw rate is very small (about 2 degrees per second)" is fitted to most helicopters with a yaw channel in the AFCS.

**In Forward Flight**

Once we're up and away, the yaw channel is normally used only to keep the slip ball positioned, and is only ever active in turns (i.e., for turn coordination). Normally the changeover from heading hold to turn coordination is controlled by an airspeed sensor. The problem is that if the slip ball is not in the right position, the cyclic-mounted trim release has to be used to allow the pilot to position the slip ball, which disrupts the pitch and roll channel stabilization, as well (but that's a minor problem).

How does the AFCS know that you're turning, and to not try to hold heading? A sensor for lateral cyclic position will tell the AFCS that the pilot wants to turn, and when established in the turn, a bank angle sensor (typically 5-6 degrees of roll) will do the trick: lateral cyclic to start the turn, and then bank angle when in the turn. Lateral cyclic alone won't work, however, because in most helicopters with an AFCS (but not all!) the lateral cyclic will be back in the middle when in a turn. Lateral cyclic only controls roll rate (and not bank angle) in most helicopters.

**Between Hover and Forward Flight**

The biggest problem with the yaw channel comes when transitioning between forward flight and the hover. At some point, the yaw channel changes from keeping the slip ball in the middle, to holding heading. If you are in a turn when this happens, then the yaw channel is going to try to keep you pointed at the heading that happened when the changeover occurred. You may not like that! More than one pilot who got below this airspeed in instrument-flight-rules flight was quite surprised by the effect. (But you should never let your airspeed get that low in IFR anyway, should you?)

So, to avoid getting caught in this situation in this transition area, make sure you're not in a turn when decelerating through the changeover airspeed and you'll be okay.

Transitioning from the hover to forward flight doesn't typically show up a problem since the pilot would see that heading hold was trying to maintain a heading as the helicopter accelerates.

As we've said throughout the series, it takes some practice and discipline to learn to use an AFCS and its various elements/functions to their greatest effect. Used properly, automatic flight control systems can be a great boon and reduce your workload; used improperly, they can be anywhere from a nuisance to a distinct flight hazard. So, get familiar with your system as soon as you can: learn how it works in each potential situation, how it might differ from previous systems you've used, and how it can be of benefit in each flight regime.

# CHAPTER 20 *More Training, not New Equipment*

**Vertical911** ALEA Spring 2009

*Comment: The National Transportation Safety Board (NTSB) recently convened a multi-day meeting to discuss the state of the helicopter emergency medical services (HEMS) industry.*

At those hearings, it seemed everyone had their chance to vent and get their two cents worth heard. Obviously, some presentations made more sense than others. Some had good recommendations, while others tried to justify the current state of affairs.

## *Equipment or Training?*

My favorite among all the presentations was the list of proposals presented by the Professional Helicopter Pilots Association (PHPA) - although, there were other lists that were variations on PHPA's theme. The relevant issues PHPA identified concerned two key categories: equipment and training.

Under the equipment list, there was:

- 'Night vision goggles or night vision imaging systems;
- 'Helicopter Terrain Awareness and Warning Systems (HTAWS);
- 'Wire-strike protection systems;
- 'Color moving-map GPS;
- 'Flight data recorders and health and usage monitoring systems;
- 'Multi-engine aircraft; and
- 'Instrument flight rules (IFR) certified aircraft/two-pilot crews.

Under training, there were two things: initial HEMS qualifications, and recurrent simulator training.

What's most interesting about this is that a lot of the suggested improvements are related to new equipment. While I completely support putting the right equipment in helicopters, the real issue is that there is a very large training bill associated with new equipment - there is hardly any point in putting new technology in a helicopter if the crew doesn't know how to use it.

## *Inherent Concerns*

The whole safety and new technology discussion brings up the issue of how much training is needed. A one-size-fits-all approach simply does not work. The amount of technical knowledge required to safely operate a single-engine, visual-flight-rules-only, steam-gauge helicopter is significantly different than that required to safely operate a twin-engine, autopilot-equipped, glass-cockpit, IFR-capable ship - yet the official requirements for this more technically complex ship are based on the single-engine VFR machine!

Hidden in the list under the IFR-certified aircraft/two-pilot crews category is the requirement for autopilots, a pet peeve of mine. Nearly every light helicopter I've ever flown was unstable, requiring constant and continuing attention to stop a diverging oscillation from running away with the whole situation. This means you can't divert your attention away from physical intervention on the controls for more than five to seven seconds at a time. When the weather is nice, and there's little else to do but drive the bus, this is a mere annoyance. Add in night, or no horizon, or both, and this instability becomes a major obstacle to continued safe flight.

Compounding this problem is that all these light helicopters have no artificial feel (a.k.a. force trim) to the flight controls. In other words, you can move the flight controls with little or no force. Again, this is not an issue if you're in good weather and have little else to do, since your hand position on your leg becomes that pseudo-artificial feel/force trim. But, whenever there is no discernible horizon, even a small movement of the hand in any direction will start a rate of movement that is not immediately noticeable. If there were an artificial-feel/force trim system installed and turned on, then you can't move the flight controls without knowing it (i.e., it takes some effort and a somewhat conscious decision).

There's a good reason why the certification requirements call for a centering or trim system to be installed on IFR helicopters. So, why isn't it mandatory for all helicopters?

I can think of three or four types that have full-time trim systems, where the pilots get used to flying with the system all the time, without howls of complaint. In fact, those who have been brought up on such systems complain about the absence of control forces in other helicopters. But, perhaps that's best left to another column.

## *The Training Conundrum*

The real issue is of course training. On my way to a helicopter conference, I happened upon a Gulfstream pilot for a fractional carrier. Always curious about how the other side sees things, I asked how many hours of simulator training did he get per year? Thirty-two,' he replied promptly16 hours every six months.' Trying not to show my surprise, I then asked about ground school: he gets one week every six months. I stopped asking questions at that point, in order not to embarrass the helicopter community in general.

At the conference, I asked how much simulator time the helicopter folks there got - and this is for large, complex helicopters engaged in offshore passenger carrying. The maximum number I heard was about 15 hours per year. Some responses revealed simulator-training time as low as 10 hours per year. These helicopters were at least, if not more, complex than that Gulfstream; and these pilots' missions were significantly wider in scope, had much less support from air traffic control, and had so many more variables than the Gulfstream pilot's mission that the situations defied comparison.

We should look at the training time given to the crews flying HEMS. Unfortunately, the situation here is not much more encouraging.

The minimum required by the regulators for HEMS crews doesn't come close to what may be needed to fully understand the complexities of an all-glass cockpit with an autopilot and digital fuel controls. Tell any airline operation about the annual recurrent training time provided to a HEMS crew, and they're likely to start offering up prayers for the salvation of your body and soul.

A recent legal case I was involved with had mature' pilot with relatively low flying time and not much recent flying time. He had been given less than six hours of flight time and less than 20 hours of ground school time to transition to perhaps the most complex, but very capable, light helicopter on the market. And this did not consider that the mission was perhaps the most multi-variable one for helicopters. There wasn't even a simulator for the model, and it had been in service for nearly 10 years. There also didn't appear to be any attempt to determine a level of proficiency or competency for anything beyond the absolute basics of flying the helicopter during training.

In comparison, a corporate helicopter of about the same complexity required 56 hours of ground school and 20 hours of simulator time.

And, this is just for the baseline equipment, start adding on wonderful (and necessary) equipment like TAWS, or some sort of enhanced vision systems, and the initial and recurrent training requirements go up. What constitutes proficiency at using an all-glass cockpit? I've just heard that it takes perhaps 400 hours of use to become proficiency at using a steam-gauge cockpit, and up to 1,200 hours to become familiar with a glass cockpit. And that's if you're a young, flexibly minded person - old age robs us of our ability to adapt, unless you've had a lifetime of changing aircraft types.

## *Single vs. Twin*

The normal questions that come up when it comes to helicopter safety, especially on the HEMS side of things, are do we want single- or twin-engine helicopters; or single- or dual-crew? If we look at these two issues separately, we see the same issue of training becomes the 800-pound gorilla in the cockpit.

Just as twin-engine, fixed-wing airplanes are different than single-engine airplanes, twin-engine helicopters require a different approach to flying to the extract maximum safety advantage. Unfortunately, the Federal Aviation Administration doesn't recognize this, and a lot of the industry in the United States considers a twin to be only slightly more complex than a single. Not a lot of training appears to be given to show the benefits and shortfalls of the twin. Yet, if the training were there, we'd see fewer incidents related to the use of twin-engine helicopters. Nearly all the new twin-engine helicopters fitted with the same type of engine have had a common problem of pilots not ensuring both engines were in flight mode, yet little appears to have been done to remedy the problem.

The dual-pilot vs. single-pilot debate is another area where training becomes a significant problem. How do you take someone who's been raised since the private-pilot stage to be a single pilot and meld them into a coherent team player in a multi-crew environment? The fixed-wing world has it relatively easy in this regard, as most of the time you start off as a junior co-pilot and know of no other way to operate. I only know of one helicopter operator who actually starts junior pilots off as co-pilots, and only lets them operate single pilot when they have demonstrated enough experience and maturity.

## *Knowing the Route*

It's also interesting to look at another aspect of training that is commonplace in our fixed-wing airline brethren - line training and route checks. If you're an airline pilot, you're not going to just get training on the technical aspects of the aircraft, you're also going to get training on the routes you'll fly; and get checked to see you know the route.

Now, consider the HEMS pilot in an area with a large number of hospitals. Is there training to ensure the procedures for each hospital are understood? It could be argued that it would be very expensive to fly the helicopter to each of those hospitals... but there doesn't even appear to be an attempt to provide simulation or other material to truly familiarize pilots with their area. How can you fit helicopter technical training and area familiarization into only eight of nine hours of training?

So, if anyone is still with me here, let me summarize: the issue isn't so much the type of equipment; or whether we have single or twin engines, one or two pilots, or TAWS or NVGs; the real issue is having the right amount of training to safely complete the mission every time.

# CHAPTER 21 *Weight and Center of Gravity*

**Vertical** Not Sure When!

*Comment: The issues of weight and balance can present not only physical limitations and issues in helicopter flight, but legal ones as well.*

Weight and balance is a subject in the helicopter world that is not as well understood as it should be. There are in fact two separate and distinct parts to the problem of weight and balance.

Weight is an obvious performance issue, even if we ignore the difficulty of getting the information we need from civil performance charts. For those helicopters that operate over a wide range of altitudes in a single mission, the effects of altitude and temperature are nearly impossible to take into account as far as weight goes.

## *Understanding the Issue of Weight*

To truly understand this issue, two separate charts are needed. One is a chart of power required to hover versus weight and density altitude, at a variety of heights above ground. There are lots of lines on a chart like this —military helicopters all have them. The other chart needed is engine power available versus pressure altitude and temperature.

In the civil turbine helicopter world, the engine power available chart exists (sort of – the engine power check chart), but the power required to hover chart does not (sadly). Pilots are not easily able to determine performance if they are going to try hovering at a location a lot higher or hotter than where they started from or at a height other than the single in-ground-effect height given in the flight manual.

Exactly how much do the helicopter, crew and equipment weigh? My memories of emergency medical service (EMS) flying include the med crew telling me, as they hoisted the lucky winner of the helicopter trip on board, that they estimated he weighed 240 pounds. As there was a legal requirement to calculate weight and center of gravity (CG) before taking off on the patient leg of the trip, it took an additional moment or two to make the calculation and record it on the flight log. (We must remain legal at all times!)

This brings up a good point. Do we use nominal weights or real weights? Nominal weights were developed for use by the airlines to save actually weighing all the passengers and their baggage. Now, an average weight may work out well for a load on a 747, but not for a helicopter hauling around firefighters and their equipment. Please use actual weights! The payloads of most helicopters are small enough that an error on the wrong side of weight can put you in trouble from a performance, as well as a legal, point of view.

## *Understanding the Issue of Balance*

Weight, of course, is only half the equation. We seldom have to pay the same degree of attention to balance as the fixed-wing world does, because we don't depend on the moment arm from the horizontal tail to balance all the moments and provide control. In a fixed-wing airplane control becomes quite entertaining with the center of gravity aft of the limits. With the CG too far aft in a helicopter, the problems can range from too much stress on some dynamic components to running out of forward cyclic. And the opposite for a CG that is too far forward.

CG has three positions — two that we worry about, and one that's nearly impossible to calculate and seldom affects things. The two CG positions we worry about are longitudinal (fore-aft) and lateral (side to side). The one we don't worry about is the vertical position (more on that later).

Every pilot should be able to calculate CG using any of the different methods but most importantly by using the one included in flight manual for the helicopter being flown. This includes manually calculating it manually with old fashioned adding, subtracting, multiplying and dividing. The CG should be calculated every flight, whether there is a legal requirement or not. And I mean both longitudinal and lateral CG, unless you're absolutely sure you have a laterally balanced load all the time. For instructors, have your students calculate the wt and CG every flight – even if you know it's not a problem – it builds good habits for later in life.

What is not often understood is that unless the helicopter has an extremely simple fuel system (one tank right under the CG), it may be possible to put the CG out of limits as fuel burns off. Check your flight manual!

## *Calculating Center of Gravity*

Anyone with any experience in spreadsheets can make up a thorough CG calculator that can even show the CG as the fuel burns. (See the diagrams on p.xx. If I can do it, so can you…)

Away from the office, though, calculating CG is a pain. We don't have the equipment to do it easily in the cockpit. Even the mechanical and electronic gizmos aren't easy to use with one hand. And, how do you not keep one hand on the cyclic when you're loading and unloading passengers with the rotors turning?

There are programs for most smart phones/PDAs to calculate CG, and they are worthwhile. Another trick is to pre-calculate the extremes of weight you'd accept. This ensures you stay within the CG envelope. Minimum and maximum fuel should be the starting points to calculating the maximum and minimum cargo/passenger loads. If you're doing fair ground rides, for example, this can keep you out of trouble.

## *Longitudinal and Lateral CG*

Why do we worry about longitudinal CG? Aside from control margins and stresses on dynamic components, the longitudinal CG position will affect the directional stability of the helicopter. With an aft CG, the moment arm from the vertical stabilizers and tail rotor is shorter and has less effect at keeping the pointy end forward. Sail boat people talk about the keel area ratio — the hull area ahead of the keel (CG in our case) must be less than the hull area behind the CG or the boat will want to point backwards…

We should worry about lateral CG because of the need to hover with winds from the side (i.e., you might run out of lateral cyclic.) We also should worry about lateral CG because of the effect it has on drag in forward flight.

How's that again, you ask? If you slavishly fly with the ball in the center all the time, a large offset in lateral CG will generate a lot of sideslip, which is not the most streamlined way to fly. While some helicopters have slip strings and can avoid this problem, if all you have is a slip ball, then you need to note the slip ball position in an into-wind hover and keep it there in forward flight.

Lateral CG isn't just an issue for a load that just sits there. It's also an issue for a live load, such as police officers jumping on or off the skids. Next time you stand on the bathroom scale, do a mild hop up and down and see what that does to the weight displayed. It's a pretty remarkable difference for even a small bounce. Now imagine that happening on the skids of the helicopter as two large officers jump on or off the skids at the same time. If you have the flight manual handy, calculate the effect that has on the CG, and you'll be very unpleasantly surprised. Although, not as surprised as the pilot who couldn't stop the helicopter from rolling onto its side was, though. The folks in the picture obviously got on symmetrically!

## *Vertical CG*

When thinking of vertical CG, consider carrying a load of gold on the floor versus an empty helicopter. The gold on the floor will obviously move the vertical location of the CG down significantly. Normally, there is little change in the CG's vertical position, but if you have a lot of surface area below the CG, such as fixed floats, a high CG (when the helicopter is empty) will have a different effect on the handling than when the CG is low. This is, if you like, a vertical keel area ratio. In other words, if the side area below the CG is greater than the side area above the CG, then any side wind will cause the helicopter to roll toward the wind. In forward flight, the side wind is sideslip, and the effect it has is called a dihedral effect. If there is a sideslip when there is too much surface area below the CG, the helicopter will roll into the sideslip — not a good thing.

Underslung loads move the CG down considerably, and can have an adverse effect on handling in forward flight. Moving the CG down also complicates normal control, as the rotors are being used to move something a long way from the normal CG.

Finally, there is one last point to consider about weight and center of gravity. If you exceed the limitations of the flight manual, the certificate of airworthiness (and probably the insurance coverage) becomes invalid. Always remember, there are legal implications as well as physical ones.

Weight and center of gravity are important for handling, and weight is very important for performance. Pay attention to both and you'll stay out of a lot of trouble!

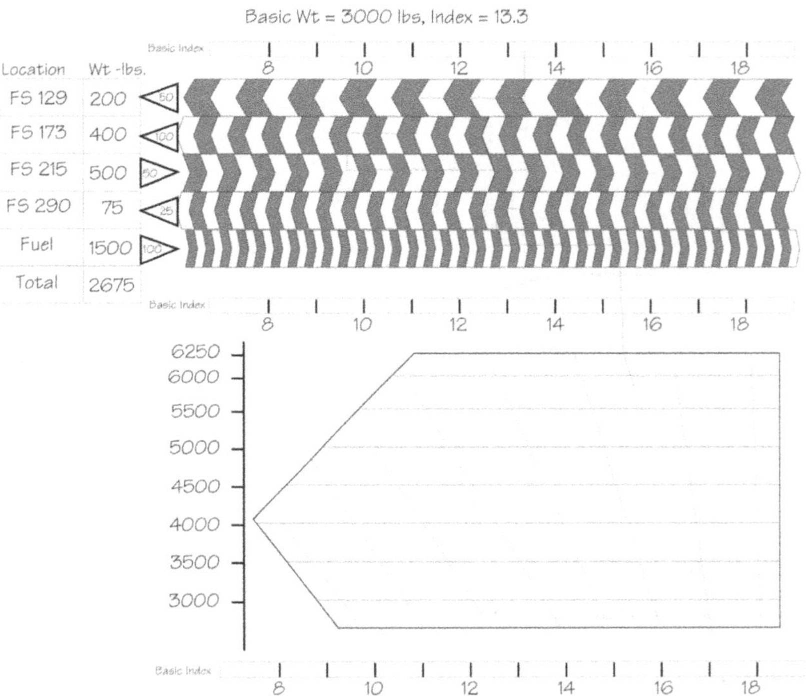


**Figure 21-1 Arrow- Type CG Chart**

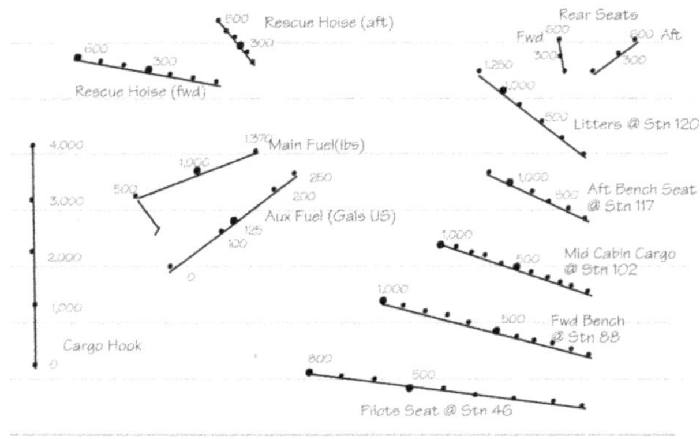


**Figure 21-2** **Sliding Part of cg-wt calculator**

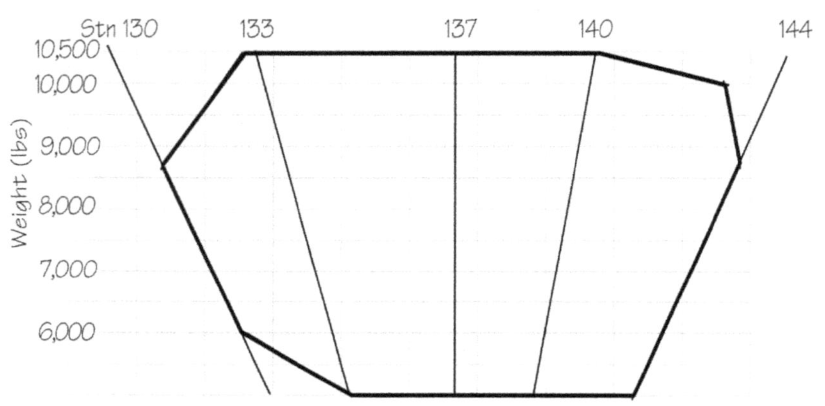


**Figure 21-3** fixed **part of cg -wt calculator**

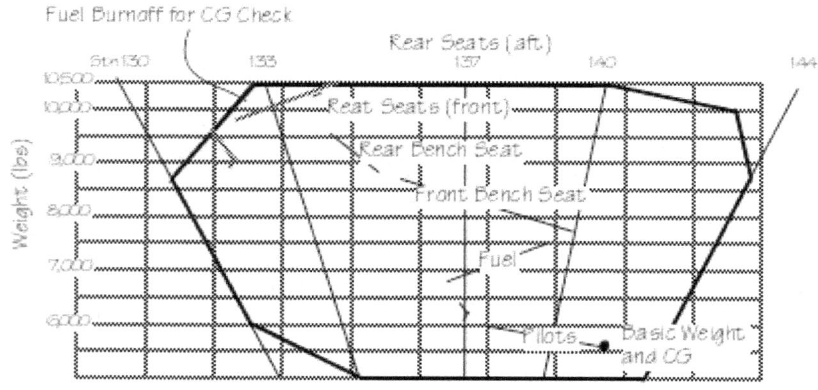


**Figure 21-4** **Combined Result**

# CHAPTER 22 *Cargo Hooks and Load Cells*

**Vertical** February / March 2012

*Comment: Although weight sensors and lift charts are standard fare on tower cranes, the aerial variety still sadly lacks these seemingly simple but very essential elements. .*

**Figure 22-1 Chinook with Two Hummvees**

If you've ever been around a downtown construction site with those marvelous self-erecting cranes, or any other place where things are lifted off the ground by mechanical means, you'll likely have been impressed by the ability of these devices, but probably missed an important part of their safety. Just looking at the booms on one of these cranes, however, it should be obvious that the amount of weight that can be lifted at the end of the crane's reach will be less than that close to the crane's tower. To make sure that these limits are respected, these cranes incorporate load cells on their cargo hooks, as well as complex tables of what can be lifted at what distance from the crane's tower. On the smaller end of the industrial lifting scale are the forklifts that busily buzz around warehouse floors. Even they have limits on what they can lift to what height.

## *What Has This Got to Do with Helicopters?*

Well, helicopters are often used as aerial cranes, lifting a wide variety of loads in locations that ground-based cranes can't get to, or operating in areas that are completely inaccessible to ground-based vehicles. Let's face it, if it could be lifted by a ground-based crane, it would be a lot cheaper than using a helicopter. Yet, even with the cost and value of the helicopter as an aerial crane, few, if any, helicopter operations are required to have load cells on their cargo hooks. In fact, I don't know of any regulation by any civil authority that requires a load cell to be included (and operational) when a helicopter is lifting underslung loads. (The presence of load cells that feed into the flight data recorder (FDR) on some Russian helicopters leads me to believe Russia may have a requirement in their rules somewhere, but that's another story.)

## *Understanding the Need*

Before getting into the reasons why we should have them fitted (and their information recorded into any FDR), it's worthwhile looking at why we've ignored the problem up to now. To do that, we have to reach way back into the mists of helicopter time, to the early machines — the piston-engine ones that could lift themselves and a relatively small payload into the air at low altitude on a cool day. The cargo hooks on these early ships were often connected directly to the transmission, but the performance of these helicopters was so limited that anything that might be hung underneath them was such a small fraction of the total weight that the external load couldn't do much structural damage to the airframe, even after lots of repetitions. Also, the ship's structure was pretty well always visible, so if it did sustain any damage, it would be readily noticed.

Things have moved a long way since then: turbine engines, advances in structural materials, and advances in rotor blade aerodynamics have given us helicopters capable of lifting much heavier loads, especially when considered as a percentage of the empty weight of the helicopter. Cargo hooks are now connected to the transmission via complex structural elements in the fuselage, and these are often hidden from direct view. However, other limitations in the airframe, such as torque or engine limits, do not always respect the load-lifting capability — in other words, the engine and transmission are often capable (at low density altitudes and air temperatures) of producing more lift than the structure can safely handle.

One example of this limitation vs. capability situation occurred with the Puma fleet of the Royal Air Force. These helicopters had only a collective pitch angle limitation in the hover (as opposed to using a torque meter, which the clever among you would say wouldn't have made any difference, and you'd be right. But that's another story...) — and no load cell on the cargo hook. When installing road barriers in Northern Ireland, the helicopters would load up skips containing wet cement in the harbor, where there was a stiff wind blowing, until they reached this collective pitch limit, and would then proceed inland to drop off the concrete. Two problems arose with this method — one immediate, and one long-term. The immediate problem was that there was often no wind at the drop-off point, and the helicopter couldn't hover with the same weight that was easily carried in the windy harbor. The second problem was that the weight picked up in the harbor exceeded the maximum structural weight limit of the airframe, and significant structural cracking of the transmission support was only found when heavy maintenance was conducted. leas from the pilots for load cells were met with deaf ears by those who did not understand the problem.

In a more pointed story, the same people who refused to listen to those requests for load cells also told the pilots, "All the loads you'll pick up have been reviewed and approved, so you don't need to worry." One of my friends related that one day they went to pick up an "approved" load of a Land Rover and trailer, and couldn't budge it from the ground. Mystified, they did some checking and discovered it was the mine disposal officer's Land Rover, which had a very thick steel plate welded to the bottom...

Other military helicopters used as aerial cranes can have different load concerns. The Boeing CH-47D Chinook, for example, is fitted with three cargo hooks, which is a useful innovation if you want to drop different loads at different locations but also has an unintended consequence: it's easy to put the center of gravity out of limits unless you can weigh the load on each hook.

The civil world has an additional complication for its load-lifting helicopters — none of the civil flight manual performance charts have enough information to permit the helicopter to be "weighed" using a power-required-to-hover chart, such as nearly all military helicopters have. These charts, which include the effect of wind and height above ground, allow the crew to determine the power required to hover at maximum weight for a given situation, and then if it takes more power than that to hover, the crew would know they were overweight.

Civil charts only have a "hover capability" chart, which does not have this information. Numerous examples exist from the helicopter logging industry of pilots who would regularly overload the cargo hook and ignore limitations on the engine and transmission. Those pilots didn't necessarily reap the long-term effects on the helicopter, but inevitably someone did — tail booms would fail, or some other dynamic or structural component would give up unexpectedly.

## *THE REAL-WORLD ISSUE*

A good example of the value of knowing and adhering to load limits was seen in the visits I made to the hangar of a company that did a lot of logging using two different models of helicopter. One ship was fitted with a cargo hook load cell as standard (and it fed data to the flight data recorder); the other wasn't fitted with any such device. There were obviously many other factors involved, as well, but the observation I made was that each winter, when logging operations were shut down, the helicopter with the cargo hook load cell simply sat in the hangar, while the ship without the scale had to be stripped to the bare bones and have lots of structural repairs made.

A recent accident in Canada even more tangibly showed the consequences of not having cargo hook load cells. A very experienced long-line pilot was attempting to lift a supposedly "standard" drill part to move it to a new location. Unfortunately the load was both too heavy for the structural capability of the airframe, and too heavy for the pressure altitude/air temperature that existed at the time. If a cargo hook load cell had been fitted (and appropriately displayed to the pilot), the load would have been rejected for two reasons — one for being just too heavy for the structure, and one for being too heavy for the performance capability that day.

From another point of view, fitting a cargo hook load cell would allow more accurate billing of customers for loads lifted — and customers may even want to insist on this to ensure they're not paying too much! It would also be nice to have better performance charts that would allow civil helicopters to be "weighed" using a torquemeter. Perhaps the proliferation of smart phones and tablets will help solve that problem, but until then we could still use cargo hook load cells (and suitable recording devices) to help keep us all honest. (I remember way back in my military flying days that we used to accept loads if we could hover at less than the takeoff torque limit — I was horrified to discover, when I finally understood performance charts, that we had probably overloaded the airframe by at least 10 percent, which helped explain the structural cracking of the main lift beams in our helicopters!)

Helicopters that don't use cargo hook load cells and get overloaded won't provide the same kind of dramatic evidence of a ground-based crane that fails or falls over, but the long-term results are just as ugly! Unless the helicopter industry (ranging from insurance companies to operators) agitates to have them fitted, when regulations do eventually come down (given the track record of rules created by regulators alone), there's a good chance we won't like the results

# CHAPTER 23 F = M x A

Vertical December 2011 / January 2012

*Comment:* Force equals mass times acceleration (F = m x a) is a fundamental equation from high school physics that has some surprising ramifications for helicopter flight.

I would hope that all of our readers can remember back to high school physics and the formula for Newton's second law of motion: F = m x a (force equals mass times acceleration). It's a relatively simple concept, but a very powerful one, and pretty relevant to all things helicopter.

Flying a helicopter is all about the balance of forces and moments. When they're all in balance, the helicopter will remain in a steady condition. Upset the balance, and you'll very shortly be in a new situation, and one that will continue to change until the new forces and moments balance each other again. This is normally the realm of a very esoteric subject called "flying qualities" or "stability and control." All our readers will be pleased to know we're not going to explore that complex subject in this article. And, I'm even more pleased that I don't have to explain it!

However, in regards to the force-equals-mass-times-acceleration equation specifically, there's a side to it that we should explore: a side that is not well understood, but is very important for flying helicopters. It has to do with, surprisingly enough, performance — and indirectly has also to do with handling qualities.

## Revisiting Lift and Drag

We get hung up in our day-to-day helicopter life with the things that are in front of us: rules, standard operating procedures, and, of course, limitations. Often, the limitation that most concerns us is torque.

But, what is torque, and why do we worry about it? How does a concept like torque (foot pounds, or a force applied at a distance from the center of rotation) really mean anything to us? The answer requires a return to first principles in mathematics and physics.

If we look at hovering a helicopter, it's natural to think in terms of weight, which is a force. To hold a helicopter in a steady hover requires that the rotor system generate a lift force equal to the weight of the helicopter. Regardless of where the helicopter is going to hover, a lift force equal to the weight of the helicopter needs to be generated.

Think of it this way: if we were to use a crane to lift the helicopter (Figure 1), the strain on the cable would be the same if the helicopter were one inch clear of the ground or 100 feet clear of the ground. Similarly, if the helicopter were at sea level or at top of Mount Everest, the strain or tension on the crane's cable would be identical (slight differences in force of gravity aside).

If this were the only way that things worked, of course, our life as helicopter pilots would be much, much simpler. So, until someone invents the anti-gravity device and makes it work on a helicopter, we have to put up with the other, more inconvenient laws of physics.

Specifically, even the most junior helicopter pilot knows there is a difference in the power required to hover a helicopter in ground effect (IGE) compared to out of ground effect (OGE), and at low-density altitude vs. high-density altitude. (To keep things simple, this discussion is only going to be about the power required to hover a helicopter, not the power available from the engine, especially the power available from a turbine engine. And, we will also not talk about why there is a difference between power required IGE compared to OGE — it will be assumed that regardless of which of the variety of explanations you accept as the cause, it takes more power to hover OGE than IGE.)

Did you notice how easily and quickly we switched from lift force required to power required? Pretty sneaky, eh? And, I'd wager a cup of coffee most of you didn't notice the change.

Why did we make that change? The reason is actually very straightforward, and understanding it will unlock many of the mysteries of helicopter performance.

F = M x A

So, let's start with the zero-airspeed hover, as it's the simplest case to consider. (I'm now concerned that introducing a formula into the article will drive away any our remaining readers. I can actually picture you throwing down the magazine and running screaming from the room. So, to Vertical's publishers and editors: if I've destroyed our readership and the advertisers desert us — please forgive me!)

Lift is produced by the passage of air over an airfoil, and the amount of lift generated is determined by the lift formula: $\text{Lift} = \frac{1}{2} \times A \times \rho \times C_L \times V^2$

When this formula is applied to helicopters, v stands for the velocity of the airflow, which is made up of the rotational speed of the blades and the airspeed; consequently, in a zero-airspeed hover v is a function of the rotational speed of the blades only, which is generally constant. The other parameter that can be considered constant is A, the blade surface area over which the air flows.

For the purposes of this article, the important elements of the lift equation that can be changed or that will vary are:

CL — the coefficient of lift, which is a value of how much lift the blade produces as its angle relative to the air changes; and

$\rho$ — Rho, the Greek letter that is shorthand for air density.

We turn rotor blades to produce airflow over the blades to generate lift. The amount of lift the blades produce depends on the angle the air makes with the chord of the blade (the angle of attack). The relationship between how much lift the blade produces compared to the angle of attack is shown in Figure 2 (no cranes here).

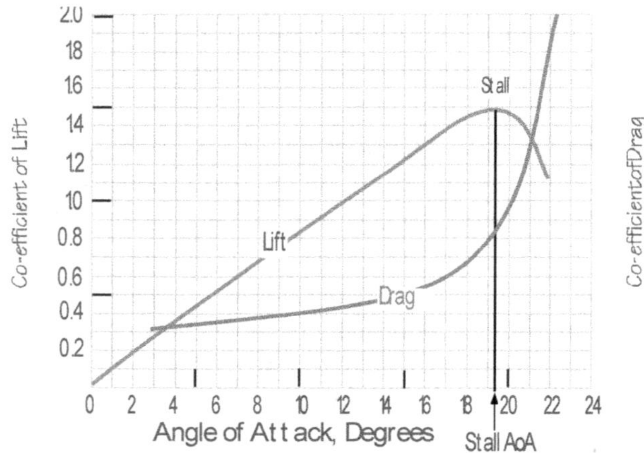


**Figure 23-1 Lift and Drag vs Angle of Attack**

Drag- Nothing is Free!

Since there is nothing free in this plane of existence, there is a price to pay for generating this lift. It takes power to overcome the drag of the blades as they pass through the air.

The amount of drag produced is governed by a formula that is identical to the lift formula — with only one change, the coefficient-of-lift parameter is replaced by the coefficient-of-drag parameter:

- $Drag = \frac{1}{2} \times \rho \times C_D \times A_B \times V^2$

Where

- $\rho$ = Air Density

- $A_B$ = Area of Blade (assumed to be 1 unit)
- $C_D$ = Co-effecient of Drag
- $V$ = Velocity of the Air

(There, now I've completely destroyed the magazine — all the readers are gone.)

The amount of drag generated relative to the angle of attack can be displayed as a curve that is broadly similar to the curve showing lift vs. angle of attack. This curve does, however, have at least one important difference: in the area where we helicopter pilots normally operate our rotor blades, the rate of change of drag in respect to the change in angle of attack is much more rapid than the respective rate of change of lift (see Figure 3).

## The Effect in Real Life

Why is all of this important?

The issue at hand comes from the change in air density. Higher density altitudes, at any elevation, mean lower air density than a standard day at sea level. If the same amount of lift needs to be produced in order to hover and the air density is lower, the coefficient of lift must be increased; this requires increasing the angle of attack, which can only be done by increasing blade pitch. Unfortunately, this is where Figure 3 is different than Figure 2: an increase in blade pitch to increase CL generates a larger increase in CD — and the force required to turn the blades increases, too.

Since we measure this force in terms of engine parameters, we experience this in the cockpit as an increase in the power (torque) required to hover at higher density altitudes (all other things being equal).

So, in a roundabout way, we now know how we come from a force to a power situation, and how understanding the concept of force helps us understand certain aspects of helicopter performance.

## An Interesting Aside

Of course, I also mentioned that understanding force can help us understand handling qualities, so let me elaborate on that as a fun additional thought.

If we sit in an OGE hover in a no-wind situation, the lift force is equal to the weight of the helicopter. That should be clearly understood.

Now, if a small reduction in collective position is made, the lift force being applied is reduced. According to the title formula: if the force is changed for the same mass, an acceleration will occur. For this collective reduction, this means that, in theory, the helicopter should be accelerating toward the ground. (The term "accelerating" means continuous increase in speed; whenever the rate of climb or descent is steady, there is no acceleration.) If we accelerate at one foot per second per second, after five seconds, theoretically, we should be moving toward the ground at five feet per second.

This doesn't happen in reality. Why not?

The answer lies in the aerodynamics of the rotor: when the rotor blades move down through the downwash, a small increase in the angle of attack occurs; this offsets the reduction in angle of attack brought about by the reduction in collective. (All of this is only valid for small changes in power/collective position, which is the way most of us operate in the hover, and is obviously only valid in a pure, OGE hover.)

In engineering terms, the collective reduction has an immediate acceleration, which is then nearly stopped by the aerodynamic offset. If this were not so, pilots would be working a lot harder to maintain a steady OGE hover, because the reaction of the helicopter to a change in blade pitch would be much less predictable.

At the bottom of all this lies the equation: F = m x a.

$F = M \times A$

# CHAPTER 24 *What are we training Helicopter Pilots to Do with Tail Rotor Failures?*

Not Previously Published

*Comment: As regular readers of my columns will know, I'm a bit different in my approach to things.*

One of the things I'm wondering about is our training procedures. I have several pet peeves which I'll try to work out here over the next few months.

The first one is tail rotor control failures – it seems that a lot of effort is placed on practicing these and getting proficient at flying these. The indications are confusing, and the issue is often that the student doesn't' seem to be able to determine whether it was a right or left pedal stuck forward nor what to do about it.

My approach is much simpler – why do we even bother to teach this at all? I've trolled through the accident databases and can't find any instances of these failures. Now perhaps that's because the helicopter landed safely following the incident, and no report was filed (a report should have been filed as it was a flight control malfunction). I realize this is similar to questioning our ability to fly, but really why do we teach beginning pilots a procedure for which there are no significant number of failures, which is confusing at best for even experienced pilots and which gives a false message about the way to cope with an emergency?

Most light helicopters have only mechanical push-pull rods or cables running between the pedals and the tail rotor. The only things that can happen are either a jam due to something being dropped in the pedals (shouldn't they have a cover over them when not being flown from that seat, or be designed so they can't be jammed?) or the control run can break.

The main reason it appears that we still do tail rotor control failures is because the UH-1 series had a tail rotor control system that could and would jam or fail in some way.

If we are going to insist on tail rotor control failures, why not broaden the scope to include main rotor control system failures as well? They should be just about as likely.

.

# CHAPTER 25 *Helicopter Specific Ratings*

Not Previously Published

*Comment: The fixed wing world has always been a good comparative basis to the rotary wing world. I have found that there is no point in re-inventing the wheel (or even re-calibrating the roundness), and when a problem rises up in the helicopter world, the fixed wing world often has already seen and solved the problem.*

They have about 50 years more experience than we do and a lot more of everything – numbers of aircraft and pilots, variety of missions, size and range of aircraft types, equipment to cope with nearly every eventuality (icing, for example, or Category IIIa approaches). 50 more years of experience that has often resulted in regulations and procedures that basically say "we need to do things this way for safety reasons". Don't get me wrong – I'm not advocating we blindly duplicate what the seized wing community has done. In fact we often need to fight against many of the things that have been foisted upon us, like many air traffic procedures. But that's another story.

It stands to reason that the fixed wing community has probably experienced nearly every problem we're encountering – obviously in slightly different manner. One of the problem areas that has become evident over the years was the qualifications and training of pilots. This problem was solved by introducing a large number of ratings or endorsements, requiring training and demonstration of ability for differences from a 'normal airplane' for such things as tailwheel configuration, complex piston engine, multi-engine, turbine, jet and so on. The tailwheel endorsement obviously wasn't needed when the 'normal' airplanes were all tailwheel, but as training aircraft became nose wheel / tricycle configured, it became necessary to make sure that pilots flying things that weren't the 'norm' were properly trained.

And what do we have in the helicopter world?

Aside from the few helicopters that are above 12,500 pounds that require a type rating, we have an large change from the 'normal' types of helicopters that are used for training to the kinds of machines used for commercial operations, but we don't have a corresponding set of ratings or endorsements to ensure that pilots are properly trained.

Anyone who thinks there is much similarity between a light piston (of any make) and a large turbine twin needs to have their head examined. And not just in weight and engine type – there are huge differences in the way the machines should be flown, how the systems operate, how you work with a co-pilot, and so on. Yet officially and legally, there isn't any recognition of these differences.

For example, Category A light twin helicopters have nearly as much redundancy (read that as lots of systems) as any business jet or small airliner. Category A procedures rival (and probably exceed) fixed wing balanced field length calculations in complexity and options. The turbine engines on helicopters are arguably more complex than any fixed wing jet engine. Try talking to a FW jockey about 30 second One Engine Inoperative ratings and the reasons for it and watch their eyes glaze over...

And that's the just the technical side. What are the effects of these differences on the philosophical side? Fixed wing pilots change types pretty regularly – which means learning new numbers, new procedures, new limitations, and probably obtaining a new rating. They have to learn to change mental gears quite frequently. They take training pretty religiously.

And us? No need for a new rating when you get a new helicopter. No need for structured training to pass a check ride on a new type (unless you're a Part 135 operator). Just jump in and go – they're all pretty much the same aren't they?

I've heard horror stories of no checkouts, of pilots who clearly didn't know the machine they were operating, of pilots who continue to fly twin turbine helicopters using the same profiles they used on a piston single – even after factory training. And so on.

Like everything else, there are at least two sides to this story.

On one hand a significant contributor to the healthy state of aviation in the USA is the mandate of the FAA to write only the minimum legislation necessary for safety. This eminently sensible rule keeps a lid on well-meaning officials and prevents them from writing new rules to solve problems that could and should be solved by enforcing existing rules. There are also those who say that this system has served us well, and that there really isn't any problem and why change something that isn't broken?

On the other hand, it's a different world now from when helicopters first came into commercial use (nearly 50 years ago now – they were underpowered, not too fast, and there wasn't much difference between them in terms of performance or handling).

Maybe something between the rest of the world's approach of type ratings for each model and what we have now would be sensible. The SFAR for the Robinson series is a model that has served to reduce the accident rate in those machines and may be worth considering as a starting point.

How about turbine and twin engine endorsements? Both would require demonstrating a degree of proficiency to someone designated by the FAA that you know and understand the operation and limitations and procedures appropriate. There is after all a world of difference between a Bell 47 and an S-76, yet according to the FAA, they are all the same type of helicopter. For those who were trained solely on turbine machines, stepping in to a piston engine machine is a real eye-opener, so perhaps a piston engine endorsement is also worth considering.

Insurance companies often require significant experience in turbine machines before providing cover – would a formal rating or endorsement ease improve things for low time pilots?

Now I don't want to get into a constitutional argument about using other countries laws as a basis for changing ours, but – nearly every other country in the world requires type ratings for different models of helicopters. This includes written exams and flight tests. There must be a reason for that. Adding something to the FAA license requirements might aid those who are going to work in other countries under other aviation authorities.

Between the rest of the helicopter world, and even the fixed wing world here in the USA, there are lots of reasons why we may want to think about changing things as far as helicopter ratings go. If the industry pushes for this before the Feds dictate something, it may be more to our liking...

# CHAPTER 26 *Low Cost Simulation*

**Vertical** August/ September 2007

*Comment: With the range of low-cost flight simulators growing as quickly as the computing power that fuels them, Vertical looks at what goes into making a sim.*

The use of simulators in training may have been slow to take root in the rotorcraft industry, but for many operators and manufacturers, simulation is now simply an accepted (and embraced) part of life in the industry.

But what makes a simulator work? How can you make a computer duplicate the actions of a complex machine with so many parts that are not only moving, but moving in the air subject to various aerodynamic forces?

Firstly, it's important to note that the cost of helicopter simulation is rapidly decreasing due to the explosion in computer power — and this is bringing a wealth of low-cost simulators to the market. The increase in computer capability affects both the modeling of the helicopter and the simulator's visual display of the world. Let's talk about the visual display first. In my view (no pun intended), this is the one area that seems to make the most difference between helicopter and fixed-wing simulation. Fixed-wing pilots don't use visual information as much, because they normally only really require detail when taking off or landing (or other tasks such as air-to-air refueling or shooting guns). Helicopter pilots are generally using visual cues throughout their flight with reference to the ground, and it's vertical cues we use most (except when long-lining).

Image 1 shows an example of how a simulator could be used to improve the vertical cues used in hovering that obviously could not be done in real life. The pilot can hover in amongst the poles (or above them) and use them to provide cues about the helicopter's movement. The poles can't be "hit" — they're just there for reference — but the improvement in the amount of information the pilot receives about pitch, roll and yaw is quite astounding. Other innovations in the use of the computing capabilities will yield more such training improvements.

## Crunching the Numbers

While improvements in computing power have clearly changed visual systems, they've also brought what used to take Cray supercomputers several days to accomplish into the world of real-time. Rotor blade element modeling is now affordable by all, it seems. Which leads nicely to discussing the two distinct and different ways to "model" a helicopter. Each has its advantages and shortcomings.

The first and easiest to set up is called the derivative model. We take the equations of how a helicopter flies (yes, they do exist, but not for the faint of heart — see Figure 1 below which is only a general equation of motion), and apply suitable values for each of the elements of the equation. For example, if we know how much yawing moment the tail rotor applies to the helicopter for each degree of blade pitch change in a certain flight condition, we just put that number in to the component of the equation. But since the motion in yaw is going to depend on a whole lot of items besides just the tail rotor's change of pitch, it's necessary to know what each of those effects will be. For example, the effect of airspeed on the amount of force generated by the vertical stabilizer will change with not just airspeed, but with the angle of the air hitting the vertical stabilizer (normally a function of sideslip angle). And it doesn't end there. It's easy to see how the equations become long and complicated — and we haven't even touched on how roll and yaw cannot be separated due to cross coupling effects. God help you if you're trying to model something like the Sikorsky H-60 series with the canted tail rotor where tail rotor movements affect not just yaw and roll, but also pitch — when all you have is some number to plug in to the equation of pitch due to tail rotor pitch change.

Taking the H-60 series as an example of how a derivative based model can quickly become difficult to make into a reasonable simulator, we'll now look at what could broadly be called "physics-based" modeling. In this type of modeling, the actual physics of the helicopter are used as the basis — a rotor blade is modeled based on drawings of the rotor blade, which is then split into many very small elements (think of them as slices along the blade of very thin width). The position of the element on the blade in terms of distance from the rotor hub is known, as is its pitch angle relative to the hub, and its radial position with respect to the tail boom. So is the airspeed at the element, as well as the angles of the air hitting it (angle of attack, rate of climb or descent and lateral angle of the air hitting the blade).

All of these go into the magic blender and the lift and drag forces at that element can be calculated. As if that's not quite enough math for one day, the lift and drag forces generated by the whole rotor blade can now be calculated for each position around the rotor disc, and those values then summed with the forces generated by all the blades. These forces are coming from the rotor hub (or tail rotor hub) and must act on the center of gravity (CG), along with all the other forces acting on the helicopter. If we stick to the earlier example of the S-60 tail rotor from the derivative model, for comparison of with the physics model — all we have to do is know the airspeed and various angles that the air is hitting our element of the tail rotor, the size and shape of the airfoil, and the airfoil characteristics.

Now we can calculate the lift and drag generated by each element, sum them up (making pounds of thrust) and apply that to the center of gravity a few feet away making a moment (foot pounds) of force. When summed with all the other forces and moments, it will tell how the helicopter will yaw about the center of gravity. Or it should, if we remember that the CG has not just a fore-aft and lateral position on the airframe, but also a vertical position with respect to something else. We normally understand the importance of fore-aft and lateral CG, but forget about the importance of the vertical CG. Normally it's not very important, but when you're trying to model the effects of changing the forces and moments acting on the CG, it's crucial to know where it is with respect to the landing gear, for example. Doing the arithmetic for these equations (whether derivative- or physics-based) is relatively simple for the computer, and doing them at blazing fast speeds means that the model developed can be made quite complex.

## *On the Other Hand...*

Now comes the downside to each of the methods. For the derivative model, how do you gather the data to show the effects of the tail rotor on yaw rate for all the conditions of weight, CG, density altitude, airspeed sideslip and so on? There is a limit to what could be found from scale models in a wind tunnel, so at some point actual flight-testing is going to be required. The matrix of test points is very large, and requires a specially instrumented airframe and some very specialized test techniques to ensure that only one variable is changed at a time. From the large mountain of data that's collected, someone has to do some very clever mathematics to obtain the number to go in front of the derivative for the tail rotor effect. And that's just for one item. Many minor effects can often be ignored, for example, the change in yaw rate due to a fixed horizontal stabilizer as airspeed changes. For the physics based model, it's a question of making sure you account for every component. That's why helicopter simulators are much more complicated than fixed-wing, and why low-cost commercially available "simulators" struggle to be truly accurate representations of helicopters. They're not bad, and some good training value can be made using them. But it's important to know the holes in them. Low-cost helicopter simulators are getting better, but it takes a very complex model to accurately duplicate all the things that happen on helicopters. Beware of what you see and learn!

# CHAPTER 27 *Low Cost Simulation*

**Vertical** December 2014 / Januart 2015cellbody3

*Comment: This year's Heli-Expo was certainly notable for the number of low-cost (i.e., less than $1 million US) flight training devices that were on display.*

Technology in computer processing has combined with much improved visual projection systems to finally provide a whole gamut of products aimed at the helicopter market. And, it's about time. These devices range from those using versions of Microsoft's Flight Simulator (not the latest version, though, it's too much of a processing hog for the visuals to run fast enough), to highly sophisticated systems with their own software. For simplicity, we will call all of these devices "simulators," even though they aren't all motion-based devices.

Low cost "simulators" range in approval level from an aviation training device (ATD) through to an advanced aviation training device (AATD) and finally to a Level 3 or 6 flight training device (FTD) on FAA approval levels, or a flight and navigation procedures trainer (FNPT) for those using the European JAA approval system. Some are generic models (not specific to a type), while others are type specific.

Don't be fooled by the cockpit layout as an indication of the approval basis, though, simulator certification is a complex business. Unless you spend a lot of time looking into the approval basis and the credits available for using a device, be prepared to be confused. Although, you can gain some insight with various manufacturers' web pages available to help guide you through the process. In the past, helicopter simulators were exclusive to big iron. These helicopters were so expensive to operate, it was worthwhile to have a simulator to train on. There were also other benefits to having a simulator, including: requiring less calendar time to train; having increased safety for emergency procedures; and being more realistic for many emergency procedures than anything one would want to do in the real helicopter. For the most part, these simulators were used for type specific training, but sometimes other training would be done in them as well. Most notable of these was recurrent IFR training, as it was cheaper than flying the real helicopter and a more effective use of everyone's time. So, should we be satisfied if these things trickle down to the new generation of helicopter simulators? Or, should we expect something more?

## *EMERGENCY PROCEDURES*

Emergency procedures in most light helicopters are confined to engine failures or systems emergencies. So, let's dissect these. Effective training requires that failures be reasonably realistic, regardless of the simulator's cost or complexity. But, how realistic? It depends on what you're trying to teach. My experience is that roughly 75 per cent of what you need to understand in an engine-off landing can be taught in nearly any simulator with a good visual system, and a rotor system and rate of descent vs. airspeed curve that is representative. But 75 per cent of what? And what 25 per cent is not emphasized? I would suggest that reacting to the engine failure promptly and correctly is a main point, and then adjusting the rotor's rpm and airspeed to try and arrive at a pre-determined spot is a secondary teaching point. Learning how to judge when and how much to flare requires reasonable visual cues close to the ground. That is also a worthwhile teaching point. As there is no absolutely right, by-the-numbers way to carry out these maneuvers, students should actually be correcting for their own mistakes. There is also another dimension that should be explored with engine failures. Obviously, it would be dangerous to give engine failures in the real helicopter, where there is a significant risk of damaging the ship due to unsuitable terrain or being inside the height-velocity curve.

Assuming again that the simulation is reasonable, giving the student engine failures in these conditions, and then showing them how to make the best of a very bad situation, is training that is truly useful and safe. What should not be emphasized? I would suggest the very final part of the landing involves so many real-world cues, missing from even the most complex simulator, that if the student gets the machine to a spot with nearly no airspeed and a very low rate of descent, this is all that matters. The last part is best learned in the real machine. Other systems failures can also be introduced to develop the pilot's ability to think. Subtle electrical failures can't be done at all in the real helicopter, let alone safely practiced. This is where thinking beyond how we've done things in the past is needed and opens the door for other aspects that can be taught in the simulator.

## *WHAT ELSE CAN BE TAUGHT?*

A senior test pilot for one of the manufacturers was once heard to say that the first 10 hours of flight time shouldn't be spent in the helicopter — he implied it should be in a simulator. This would enable key aspects, such as the concepts of effects of controls, attitude flying and reading instruments, to be covered thoroughly and completely in a much lower stress environment. The overall effect would be significantly reducing the steepness of the learning curve, and making students much more comfortable when it came to the real thing. Airborne time could be made much more productive in this way. Two other aspects, cross-country navigation and decision-making in bad weather, which are closely related, can also be examined in a simulator. How many of us were ever given the opportunity to make a decision about flying in less than ideal conditions while we were going through flight training? I'd wager not many. When I first encountered weather that made me land and sort things out, I wished I'd been given some guidance on judging these things while I was in training.

Cross-country flights can be easily and well represented in the simulator (assuming the visual database is a real-world one). Weather conditions, such as wind shifts, visibility and clouds, can be adjusted so students get a taste of the real thing in very safe and repeatable conditions — you can even pause the flight if things get out of hand. This is not something you can do in the real thing! The decision-making skills learned here would be very large!

One instructor has even said he wouldn't send his students to a strange airport unless they'd been there first in the simulator (he was rightly worried about his rating riding on the student's actions). He would position students just outside the control zone and then play ATC to make sure they knew the radio procedures and airfield layout, and had planned their actions. From this, they also learned to utilize whatever tools were available to prepare themselves for flight. Inadvertent IMC (instrument meteorological conditions) can be very safely trained in the simulator as well, but only pretended at in the real helicopter. Obviously, IMC is much more realistic in the simulator, as you can't see outside at all!

CHANGING HOW WE THINK

All of these are not the normal things done with simulators in the past, but we have an opportunity to change how we do things now that we have the technology at our disposal. We just need to think differently — and some of that thinking needs to come from the regulatory authorities. Sad to note, the regulatory authorities haven't seen fit to credit the use of simulators for much beyond IFR training. One even recently rescinded VFR credits for new devices! Others give a small number of hours. Yet, not all people feel this way. I overheard a representative of a major authority mutter to himself at a recent trade show: "We need more low-cost simulation for light helicopters." Amen.

Now, please follow through with appropriate credits! Credits aside, though, if simulators provide safer, cheaper and better training than being in the actual helicopter, why aren't more training schools using them? And, given that simulators can be used in any weather condition, are probably more reliable than the real thing, and have a higher profit margin than real ships, I'm even more surprised that they're not highly used. We are at a point where we have an opportunity to incorporate this new technology into our thought process. Now, we just need to take the steps to do it. To start us on this path, consider this mind bender: When training in the real helicopter, we can only simulate things in flight... but when training in the simulator, we can make them real.

The wing world has already served as a great point of comparison for the helicopter world. It has shown us how we unrestricted aviators, while enjoying more freedom of action, and being nicer folks in general, have not paid attention to what could be done to better our circumstances. This issue's column is going to concentrate on simulators and training in them as an example of where we could certainly do a lot better. By using this increasingly available technology, we could help ourselves in the same way the fixed-wing world already has.

## *Inherent Complexities*

If you didn't know it already, one of the major differences between rotary- and fixed-wing is that helicopters are much more complex than airplanes — which means it's a lot more difficult to get a good helicopter simulator. I can certainly confirm that notion. Having had some experience in teaching pilots how to flight test helicopters, I quickly saw that the complexities in comparison to seized-wing aircraft are significant. Trying to mathematically model those complexities correctly takes people who know all the upper and lower case Greek letters, and how to use them in various formula. But, it can be done, and with modern computing, it can be done at reasonable cost. Adding to the difficulty of modeling helicopters is the requirement to accurately model the visual cues we need and the atmosphere we fly in. These are problems, however, that can be overcome if there is sufficient will to make things happen.

Of course, the problem is not just one of technical complexity, it's financial as well. Boeing 747 pilots get their first real flight in the aircraft when it's in revenue service — they do not fly the real ship in training. They have been doing this since very early on in the model's program. Think about that for a moment. This means the performance and handing of the 747's simulator is so close to the real thing that all the flying, both normal and emergency procedures, can be taught in it, safe in the knowledge that the real aircraft is exactly the same. A $25-million simulator for a 747 is not difficult to justify when the real thing costs several times that amount, and the revenue lost when an airframe has to be used for training is substantial. But, when a helicopter costs $4 million, while the simulator costs $25 million, and the per hour cost of the sim is $2,000, while the real helicopter's direct operating costs are $800, the equations start to look — at first glance — somewhat backward.

The comparison of purchase and operating costs alone, though, leaves out several very important benefits of the simulator. These benefits include, but are not limited to, being able to:

- • Realistically train one's crew;
- • Do things you can't do in the real helicopter;
- • Do things you could do in the real helicopter, but if done in the real ship it wouldn't be done in a safe way;
- • Do things you could do in the real helicopter, but if done in the real ship it couldn't be done in an economical way.

There are lots more, but let's leave filling out this simulator-over-real-helicopter benefits list to a future column.

## *Development Differences*

What we need to concentrate on for this discussion is the differences between helicopters and fixed wing not just in the use of simulators, but in the acceptance of simulators. For most new fixed-wing ships, the delivery of the first aircraft coincides with the delivery of the first simulator. Simulator development parallels the real aircraft so that flight test and certification crews can actually be using the simulator as part of the certification effort. That means customers can begin training prior to delivery of the first aircraft. In the helicopter world, this is not the case — in fact, there are several complex, twin-engine, instrument-flight-rules-approved helicopters that have been on the market for more than 10 years that are only now just getting simulators approved. For some upcoming helicopters, the simulator will not be in service until well after the real machine enters service. Why are helicopter simulators not naturally introduced at the same time as the real machine?

Part of the problem is that getting the data to model a simulator is different than the data needed to obtain certification of the real helicopter. Getting data of any sort requires careful planning and takes time, which in turn costs money. Fixed-wing aircraft are relatively simple when it comes to gathering the data needed to model their aerodynamics and performance, but helicopters are much more complex. So, unless data was obtained during specific tests at the same time as certification, it's going to be awhile before the simulator gets developed. The amount of data required depends on the level of fidelity of the simulator. A generic simulator (one that flies like a single-engine turbine helicopter for example) doesn't need to fly exactly like any particular helicopter. But, you don't get a lot of training credit for this, and it would not be able to provide you with a type rating on the real machine (assuming these even existed for small helicopters in the Federal Aviation Administration [FAA] world, but that's another story).

For a simulator that's going to do all the training necessary for a type rating (with no flying in the real helicopter), it had better fly exactly like the real thing — and something like that takes a considerable amount of data to create.

Consider, for example, that there is no requirement during certification for the roll rate to be measured; but there is a requirement for this for the simulator to be able to duplicate the amount of roll rate you get for a given amount of lateral cyclic movement. Then, there's everything else that accompanies the lateral cyclic movement, such as changes in torque, adverse or proverse yaw, and change in pitch attitude, all of which must be correct to within very tight tolerances. How about if the real ship has an automatic flight control system? It would mean failures must be duplicated accurately. As complex as it can be, it has been done: the Sikorsky S-76 has several Level D simulators available. The real question is why hasn't it been done for all the helicopters that have sprung up since the S-76 simulator came into service?

## *Usage and Acceptance*

A recent presentation by a major fixed-wing airframe manufacturer highlighted the importance of simulation in that company's development process. For this company, every stage of development on its new aircraft was done first in a simulator of some description. A very realistic flight simulator was available very early on in the program and was used by the flight test and FAA crews to fly each test point before it was attempted in the real thing. (Obviously, it would only be "close" to the real aircraft at the beginning, but it would be continuously fine-tuned as the test program provided real-world data). I've never heard of this or anything close to this happening at any helicopter manufacturer, anywhere, in any model's development program.

So, what does this mean to us unrestricted aviators? It's likely going to be at least a year or two after the real aircraft hits the market before you'll get any training in a helicopter simulator. I'd be surprised if it occurred in a shorter amount of time, and very surprised if any new helicopter certified in the next five years has a simulator delivered at the same time. Now comes the real rub: how many pilots who fly a helicopter type that has a simulator will actually get to use the simulator for training? Compared to our fixed-wing brethren, it will be a paltry percentage.

Nearly all those who fly business jets spend at least two weeks per year at a major simulator training center. A Gulfstream pilot will typically get over 30 hours of simulator time per year, all as part of the cost of doing business. One of the reasons that this much training is done is because the insurance companies dictate it. If you don't do this much training, you face either not flying in the airplane or having an insurance premium that is sky high.

In the helicopter industry, where more than three hours of simulator "training" per year is a lot, it will be a long time before we budget for the travel, replacement crew and training costs to be an equal to the fixed-wing world. For too long, the regulatory authorities have allowed flight tests and checks to be done in the real helicopter because no suitable simulators existed. Given the small explosion of simulators in the Gulf of Mexico alone, we could see a lot more check rides being done in the simulator; partly because it's certainly easier to predictably schedule and control the check-ride cycle!

Just think of the changes that might happen if simulators were mandated by either the insurance companies or the regulatory authorities. We'd see more people getting better training on the systems and the operation of helicopters. Perhaps that 25 percent of pilots who don't use the autopilots that they have installed in their ships would be reduced to near zero. Perhaps helicopter pilots would really start to learn why they shouldn't fly in reduced visibility at night. Perhaps there are so many things we could discuss, this column would never end. In the meantime, let's hope and pray we get more helicopter simulators for smaller helicopters, as it can only help the health and safety of our community.

# CHAPTER 28 *Too Many Clocks*

**Vertical** August / September 2009

*Comment: I fear I'm starting to sound like the old curmudgeon my wife thinks I am... but* I'll say it again, there is a huge difference between the fixed-wing world and the helicopter world - one that is only now starting to become smaller. Let's hope that difference continues to diminish.

One of those key areas of difference is power monitoring. In helicopters, this is a complex situation of too many 'clocks' to watch.

Is there a link between the relative simplicity of monitoring power in the fixed-wing world, and their enviable safety record? Let's take a closer look so you can decide for yourself.

## Comparing Takeoffs

### Fixed Wing

When a turbine-powered airplane is about to take off, the pilot lines up with the centerline of the runway, notes the wind direction from the conveniently placed windsock, and decides his or her control strategy to deal with whatever crosswind may exist. He or she then applies the brakes and advances the throttle - perhaps to a physical stop, but most likely to a torque limit that is always the limiting factor. Either way, there is only one place for fixed-wing pilots to look to make sure they have not exceeded a limit. From there, after a quick check of the temperatures and pressures, to be sure each is okay, the pilot shifts his or her gaze out the window. The brakes are then released, and the pilot monitors airspeed as he or she controls the direction down the runway, which is mostly a matter of yaw, maybe a bit of roll, but certainly nothing to do with pitch (until at the right airspeed). At the appropriate time down the runway, back pressure is added and liftoff happens.

Liftoff in a fixed-wing aircraft happens at pretty much the same airspeed each time, regardless of weight and/or center of gravity. Varying centers of gravity create only minor differences in control strategy, and affect only the pitch control. The control inputs in roll and yaw are mostly linear as airspeed increases. Aside from perhaps a minor adjustment to the throttles to ensure the torque limits aren't exceeded as airspeed increases, no attention is paid to the engine instruments (except if the engine were to fail).

### Helicopter With The Same Turbine Engine

Let's put the same powerplant in a helicopter and compare what needs to take place to lift off to the hover.

The first thing to notice is that, in most places, a helicopter pilot isn't really sure of the wind's direction or speed close to the helicopter. There's no windsock. The pilot has to judge wind direction from natural sources like grass and trees, or, if they're available, through manufactured objects like flags.

Getting from the ground to the hover necessitates continuous monitoring of the helicopter's attitudes in pitch, roll and yaw - which requires the pilot's attention to be focused outside the helicopter. Once a movement is detected that requires correction, a judiciously appropriate manipulation of the controls is needed to stay in the desired position in the air. The placement of the controls, though, change significantly with different weights and centers of gravity, so no single set of control placements will always work. And, the control inputs change with the amount of power applied. All of this is a necessary part of flying helicopters, and wouldn't change no matter what we did with the engine.

When it comes to monitoring the engine, as power is applied - especially if the helicopter is loaded close to its weight limits - it is necessary to ensure that the revolutions a minute (r.p.m.) of the rotor is within limits, the engine torque is within limits, the compressor speed is within limits and the exhaust temperature is within limits. Tiny needles on clock faces show all these limits, and each one is changing at the same time. Depending on the pressure altitude and temperature, different limits may be reached first. On a cold day, for example, the torque may be the limiting factor. On a hot day, exhaust temperature may reach a limit before the torque does. In any case, four instruments need to be watched, at the same time as the pilot is supposed to be looking outside for visual references.

For many years, this was the situation in all helicopters: too many different clocks to watch when the pilot should be concentrating on flying the machine. Pilots adapted by developing a quick scan-of-the-gauges technique, and an extra sense for what the powerplant was doing. Experience also taught us 'today we should be TOT [turbine outlet temperature] limited, because of the air temperature' and other such out-in-the-field axioms. But, it was hardly progress. Electronic instruments barely improved the situation - for the most part because they were merely digital duplicates of mechanical displays.

## *A Different Approach*

One can argue that the 'too many clocks to watch' situation is no longer true in modern helicopters. The French were first to break the mold with the VEMD (vehicle and engine multifunction display): a single, large needle that shows what the first limit is and how close you are to it. With the unveiling of the model 429, Bell has joined these ranks with its 'power situation indicator' - creating a single place to look to find out what you need to know to use the engine's power.

Can't we take this a step further? Why do we have to look inside at all?

One of my fondest memories of flying the Sud/Aérospatiale Gazelle was its collective pitch-stop system. The system seemed to stem from the fact that the engine manufacturer was less-than-confident about the exhaust gas temperature (EGT) measuring system on its powerplant - as reflected by the miniature-sized TOT gauge with very few lines on it. (The best one could say about this system was that a gauge was installed.)

The makers of the Gazelle did, however, determine what the engine was capable of and could express it in terms of collective pitch. So, to provide some protection for the engine, a series of tactile stops were incorporated into the collective. Adjustable for outside air temperature (only a few marks for this were needed), the system provided the pilot with a very easy-to-use safety feature.

With this stop system, you could pull to the intermediate pitch stop (IPS), (where there was a spring that changed the collective force slightly), and know you were never going to exceed any continuous power limitations. In fact, you could pull as fast as you wanted to the IPS setting and never exceed any limits - I did it one day with next to no fuel on board and succeeded in generating 1.25 g (or 0.25 g above just sitting there), and the engine did not miss a beat. Evidently, the only way to exceed a limit was to go to some ludicrous altitude and simultaneously roll left and pull up to IPS.

A second stop was called maximum pitch stop (MPS). To get to that collective position, it was necessary to pull against the spring-force gradient. You couldn't exceed MPS with the engine running.

A further, ultimate stop was provided for use with the engine at idle or off for autorotations. But, I digress.

The beauty of the system was that the pilot could concentrate on looking outside and know that, as long as the collective was below IPS, no limits would be exceeded.

Another helicopter (not a Western one) had a system for limiting power at the takeoff rating. The pilot would know takeoff power was being used because the rotor r.p.m. drooped if the collective was raised any farther. There was no need to look inside while hovering: just make sure the rotor r.p.m. didn't start to slow down. (There was an override available in the event more power was needed to prevent something nasty from happening.) Again, the pilot could concentrate on the really important part of the operation - controlling the helicopter.

## *THINKING OUTSIDE THE BOX*

If we continue to explore the edges of old-fashioned thinking, we might ask why we need some of the instruments we still have.

For example, of what use is the torquemeter? The obvious answer is to make sure we don't put too much power through the transmission. But, why don't we just make transmissions that can take all the power an engine can give?

Russian helicopters don't have torquemeters. Their transmissions might be slightly heavier than ours, but, given our recent record of transmission-related accidents, perhaps the price for heavier transmissions is worth paying. The Russians also limit the power output of their engines without much concern.

Some recent helicopters have incorporated collective shakers when a limit is being exceeded, as a way to warn the pilot who may have missed the various red lines and other indications that something was not quite right. It's nice idea, but couldn't this be taken farther?

Why can't we have a system that provides the equivalent of the Gazelle's IPS, but is responsive to existing conditions? This system could predict when the first limiting condition, maybe continuous power, was going to happen and provide an appropriate tactile stop. Or, how about a system that could predict when the rate of collective movement might result in exceeding a limit within the next three to five seconds?

There's a lot more, but I think we can all begin to see the possibilities for the kinds of new, dynamic systems that can replace our antiquated ones. And, in the coming years, I'm sure improvements will be introduced that we haven't even considered. After all, 40 years ago, who could have imagined we'd be this far along?

Whatever happens technologically, our focus should be on reducing the number of clocks and needles we have to watch and monitor. Make it as simple as it is in the fixed-wing world and we'll undoubtedly improve yet another aspect of helicopter safety.

**Figure 28-1 Typical old style Instrument panel**

**Figure 28-2 VEMD One Place to Look for the First Limit**

## CHAPTER 29 *Tyranny of Mechanical Displays*

Not Sure

*Comment: Digital computation has provided huge advances in nearly every area of human endeavor. It's hard to think of anything that has not been touched by computers, especially aviation.*

Digital displays are now the norm instead of the exception, and while they often provide us with much more data, we're trapped by the constraints and limitations of the previous mechanical displays.

We're not making best use of the technology often because regulations dictate what the displays should look like. I know of one helicopter where the regulatory authority would not accept a new way of displaying engine performance for the most petty of reasons. The engine displays were an analog dial, with a numeric display as well. There was an arc with green, amber and red segments. The needle and numbers were green when the parameter was in the green, amber when in the amber region, and not just red, but flashing red if in the red region. The display was rejected because there was no small radial tic mark between the amber and red segments, as required by the regulation.

One display manufacturer recently told me of a display being rejected because the reviewing pilot thought that the red section wasn't red enough (there is no defined color wavelength or Pantone color in the regulations for any color).

I'm sure that display manufacturers could add more tales of regulatory personnel and their whims causing problems, but there is a larger issue.

Nearly every electronic display duplicates a mechanical instrument, with it's attendant limitations. Tape altimeters, for example, only show ±500 from the current altitude, and the numbers are scrolling all the time when climbing or descending. If there is an ATC assigned altitude and the aircraft is climbing at 2,000 feet per minute (not unreasonable in the early stages of most airplane climbs), the time from that assigned altitude coming into view to being broken is 15 seconds. Is there any wonder that altitude busts are common?

Course deviation bars are merely digital duplicates of the mechanical needles. While those needles served us well enough when that was all that could be done, why are we still using them? Whether electronic or mechanical, Course Deviation Indicators (CDIs) show the same amount of light whether you're on or off course, and the pilot has to interpret position.

But no-one seems to want to really explore what could be done with digital technology to give us information we can really use.

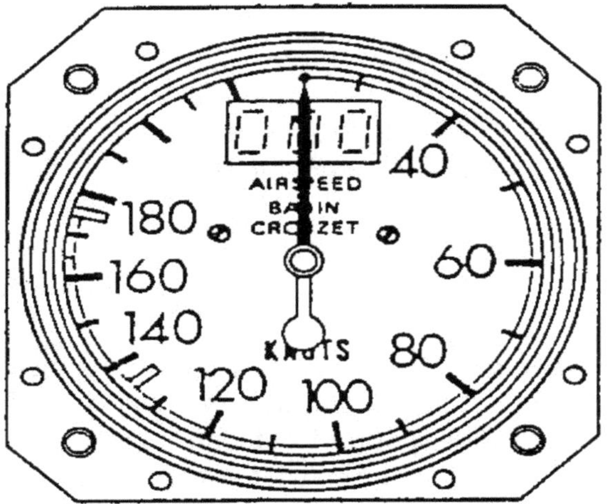


**Figure 29-1** **Mechanical Airspeed Indicator**

# CHAPTER 30 *Slip Balls Exposed*

**Vertical** January 2019

*Comment: Examining the lowly slip ball and the confusion that surrounds its use in the helicopter world. .*

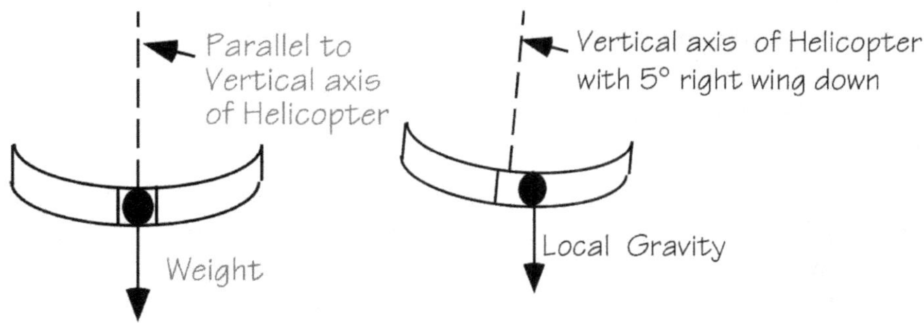


**Figure 30-1 Slip Ball Positions**

There are few instruments in the cockpit of (nearly) every helicopter that are as misunderstood as this lowly device. It has one moving part, no electricity and no other inputs to make it work. It's simple, easy to read - but very misunderstood. I am, of course, referring to the humble slip ball.

## *The Source of the Confusion*

So, what exactly does the slip ball do? Well, it is difficult to find any discussion of this device that says much beyond - "tells whether the aircraft is in balanced flight."

Unfortunately, in our fixed-wing dominated world, this definition is deemed sufficient. Yet, for us helicopter folk, who live in a world where offset lateral-center-of-gravity (CG) and very low forward speeds are the norm, this definition is far from complete.

Spending a moment or two in the fixed-wing mindset, though, will show us why this simple definition is prevalent. Fixed-wing airplanes spend the majority of their time in cruise flight, and seldom need to worry about the slip ball. In fact, they have so little concern that fixed-wing pilots are notorious for not using the rudder when they should - engine-failure training in multi-engine airplanes often reveals this lack of practice and understanding. About the only other times these pilots might be called upon to use their feet (to control the rudder) is when landing with a crosswind, or when flying an airplane that demonstrates adverse or proverse yaw when rolling.

In forward flight in a fixed-wing airplane, the slip ball is a pretty useless piece of equipment. It is always in the middle, and aside from moving slightly when rolling into and out of stable turns, it stays that way. In a stable turn, the slip ball is pretty nearly always centered because there are few fixed-wing airplanes that have significant offset lateral-CGs. So, the slip ball, being little used, could be pretty safely ignored by the large majority of the aviation world, and the common, everyday definition of "showing balanced flight" suffices.

What adds to the helicopter world's confusion is that we have a mistaken belief that the slip ball has some connection with sideslip (the name "slip" sort of hints at that). In the fixed-wing world there is a pretty strong correlation between sideslip and slip ball position - but that isn't true in the helicopter world.

## *Redefining the Concept*

It is easy to see why the slip ball needs a different definition in the helicopter world. To begin with, there is the issue of sideslip. Sideslip is the angle the relative wind makes with the nose of the helicopter, the side wind, if you will. A helicopter with a single main rotor will always have some inherent sideslip due to the tail rotor pushing the fuselage sideways. This is merely the translating tendency that we are (or should be) familiar with from basic helicopter aerodynamics, but put into forward flight ***(see p.xx for the diagram of inherent sideslip)***.

Even a helicopter with a lateral CG that is neutral (i.e., centered) will have inherent sideslip, although the slip ball will still be centered. I know of at least one helicopter model that has the slip ball and attitude indicator rigged so that on a level surface the slip ball is not centered, and the attitude indicator is not indicating level. See the photo if you don't believe me!

The reason is that when flown "wings" level and slip ball centered, the fuselage will be in the zero sideslip condition for minimum drag.

Now, when we throw in offset lateral-CG, the situation becomes much more complicated.

The first indication that the slip ball is measuring something unusual (in comparison to the fixed-wing view) is that in a hover, into wind, with an offset lateral-CG, the slip ball will not be centered. But, being taught slavishly to keep the slip ball centered, we force it into that position in forward flight. (Good luck centering it in the hover!)

Many years ago, I had occasion to have this demonstrated to me in a two-ship formation flight of Bell UH-1Ns. We were on a long-ish cross-country trip that required the use of internal auxiliary fuel tanks - mine was on the left-hand side, and the other helicopter's aux tank was on the right-hand side. We both had three passengers, who happened to be seated on the same side as our aux tank. I was leading, and partway through the trip, the Number 2 helicopter, flown by my boss, called up and asked if my slip ball was centered. "Naturally," I replied, slightly puzzled he would ask such a question.

His next question was even more puzzling: "What's your compass heading?" I told him, and then preempted the next likely question by radioing: "And the compass is aligned."

There was a short pause, and then he said, "Let me take the lead."

After he passed me, he told me to go into line-astern (directly behind the lead). It was then that I could see why he was puzzled: we were both tracking the same direction, but our ships were each pointing in different directions by about 10 degrees. It was years later that I realized the cause of the problem - the different offset lateral-CGs of our two ships had caused a very different inherent sideslip when we had the slip ball centered.

I also later learned that if we'd flown with the slip ball where it was in the hover, we'd have had minimal sideslip and minimal drag. I'd love to know from where this little-known piece of advice had originated.

See the diagram.

This story highlights the concept of the slip ball ***not*** measuring sideslip when it comes to helicopters.

I've also seen some helicopters that were in a wide variety of sideslip conditions in cruise flight, but the slip ball was still centered. This happened because those helicopter models each had a large "dead band" where they literally didn't care what the sideslip was. In technical terms, it meant the helicopter had weak directional stability around the trim point.

## *Answering the Question*

Of course, the question of "what exactly does the slip ball measure?" still hasn't been answered.

Simply stated, the slip ball measures the relationship to local gravity. That means it shows where the local gravity is - local gravity being the combination of the acceleration due to the Earth's gravitational field, combined with any centripetal acceleration caused by turning in flight.

In the hover, local gravity is straight down, and if you have an offset lateral-CG the slip ball will show that clearly: it will roll to the "low" side of the aircraft. At cruise speed, when in a properly co-ordinated turn, the slip ball will be centered, indicating that local gravity is acting through the middle of the helicopter and that the aircraft is therefore "in balanced flight." If the ball is displaced to one side or another, it means local gravity is acting at an angle to the helicopter's vertical axis. The reason that the ball does a good job in this condition is that the high speed of the helicopter applies a centrifugal force that generates a load factor.

However, when the helicopter is close to or below maximum endurance airspeed, the ability to generate a load factor degrades significantly. Think about it in terms of being able to generate any g's. At 40 knots, you can turn quite steeply and not feel the g-forces you would feel if you were at, say, 90 knots at the same angle of back. So, the ball can't work as effectively in these low airspeeds.

I've noticed this in flight-testing for performance - particularly when trying to get repeatable results at slow airspeeds, as anything below 60 knots requires a display of sideslip in order to obtain good data. A quick demonstration of this to budding test pilots and flight-test engineers involves making them fly different sideslip angles (using special flight-test booms or even a slip string) and note the slip-ball position (always centered).

With an underslung load that's misbehaving, the slip ball will react to the movement of the helicopter. One school of thought regarding the slip ball and underslung loads is that you should only react when the slip ball is moving, and then counteract that with the appropriate pedal. The proponents of this call it the Calibrated, Rapid Application of Pedal, or CRAP, method.

And, I have one more story to round out the discussion. Once, while visiting a Swiss operation, I was flying an Aérospatiale Alouette III, and we were attempting to climb to have coffee at a mountain hut. (What else is there to do in Switzerland in a helicopter?) My initial attempts to squeeze much climb rate out of the machine by keeping the slip ball centered led me to believe we were going to exhaust our fuel before we got halfway there. The Swiss pilot gently suggested that I center the slip string, and the rate of climb went from anemic to sparkling... and the coffee was good too!

Those who advocate only having a slip string, though, overlook the fact that it's not useable at night (unless lit), and not well placed for use in instrument meteorological conditions. While useful in many ways, inexpensive and easy to fix (and every helicopter should have one), a slip string is not the complete answer for dealing with sideslip.

So, the lowly slip ball, that holdover from the fixed-wing world, needs to be better defined and understood in order for us to use it wisely. Whoever thought that such a simple device could cause so much confusion?

**Figure 30-2 Offset Lateral CG (for certification Tests)**

# CHAPTER 31 *What's Wrong With This Picture?*

PROFESSIONAL PILOT February 2008

*Comment: Being a helicopter pilot for the best part of 30 years and having dabbled in the fixed-wing world from time to time means a bit of cross pollination has taken place. ..*

**Figure 31-1 Learn to fly one of left airplanes, and to fly one of right side ones, you need a rating**

**Figure 31-2 Learn to fly a R-22 and as far as the FAA is concerned, you can fly an S-76 with no additional training or rating**

It has also given me a perspective on the helicopter community not provided to those who never venture outside it. The helicopter community is a very youn8, poor and distant relative to the fixed-wing world las if we didn't know that).

In part, this is due to the relative age of the helicopter community-by the time helicopters came into their own as useful flying vehicles (mid-1950s by most counts), the fixed-wing world was quite mature and had at least 30 years more experience.

And this meant not just calendar years but the mass and variety of experience. Even now, the fixed-wing world has more variety of aircraft and missions, and an order of magnitude more machines than the helicopter world will ever have. However, an awful lot of lessons that were learned the hard way in the fixed-wing world have not been applied within the helicopter community, which seems in fact seem to have resisted them.

Helicopters and their operators seem to be treated like second-class citizens by most of the aviation community. This could be due to the relatively small proportion of helicopters, the relative mystery of how they operate, and the places where helicopters operate (mostly away from airports). However, in large part, I think it's also due to the helicopter community itself. So let's examine some of the important ways in which it differs from the rest of aviation.

## *Uneven Playing Fields*

If you learn to fly fixed-wing in a Piper PA28-140 Cherokee and want to fly a PA2BR-200 Cherokee Arrow, you need to have an endorsement for a com.plex aircraft. the difference in horsepower is a mere 60 hp (less than 50%), the engine type is the same-although the variable-speed prop is slightly different-and the wheels go up and down. And if you want to fly something more complex, like a twin or a jet, you'll need more ratings and endorsements.

If you learn to fly a helicopter in a Robinson R22 (single 1:t-hp piston engine, reversible flight controls, skid landing gear), you can, at least as far as FAA is concerned-, walk straight into a Sikorsky 576 (2 turbine engines, total approximate 1000 shp-nearly 10 times more power and weight, stabilization and autopilot, hydraulically boosted flight controls and retractable undercarriage) without passing a single additional written exam or flight check.

Those folks who think the current situation is just fine point out that the insurance companies would never let you do that.' Perhaps not, but let's consider some of the 6ther conseqr'n.'t of this lack of concern by FAA.

FAA's Rotorcraft Handbook was rewritten several years ago. It contains not a single word about range and endurance performance. And it has at least one significant error, saying, 'Autopilots contain automatic disconnect features in-turbulence.' I know of only one helicopter autopilot that did this, and it has fallen heavily out of favor-the other helicopter autopilots all 'hang in there' extremely well in turbulence. Discussions about systems and turbine engines are rudimentary at best as is anything to do with Category A operations. The end result is that US pilots don't know as much about helicopters as maybe they should.

It turns out that a lot of helicopter pilots don't use the autopilot. At a recent conference, the chief pilot of a very long-running single-pilot IFR EMS helicopter operation stated that 25% of his pilots didn't use the autopilot except during check rides. Stunned, I started checking and all my sources confirmed that this was about right

Reasons given included lack of understanding of the systems, outright fear of the systems, the arrogant assertion that the pilot could fly just as well as the autopilot, and dislike of the stick forces necessary for the autopilot to function. No significant commercial fixed-wing operation would permit its pilots to fly anything but the 'company way'. so why is it is any different in the helicopter world?

Failure to use the autopilot can be implicated in the crashes of at least 3 twin-engine IFR-equipped helicopters in the past 3 years.

## *Performance Charts*

Fixed-wing operations use detailed performance charts that are essential for them to operate safely. These are used regularly in commercial operations and contribute to the industry's safety record. However, most civil helicopter pilots never open the flight manual for the performance charts, since they don't tell them what they really need to know. At least 2 recent accidents have been caused by pilots attempting to land on mountaintops that were well outside the capabilities of their machines.

Civil turbine-engine helicopter performance charts provide 'hover capability' information based on a minimum-specification engine-yet nearly all machines have engines that are above specification. A pilot using the charts will find that he/she often has much better performance than predicted, conclude that the charts have nothing worthwhile to say and consequently ignore them.

For hover performance-the thing that matters most to helicopters-there are charts for hovering in ground effect (lGE) and out of ground effect (OGE). The IGE chart is for only one height above ground, and does not account for wind. The technique for transitioning from the hover to forward flight for this height is not a required maneuver for any license.

## *Myths and Oversights*

There is no agreed definition of what constitutes a 'maximum performance takeoff,' even among FAA inspectors. There are no charts in any helicopter flight manual that provide information relevant to the maneuver. Flying this profile in a helicopter with 10 or more seats violates a part of the limitations section of the flight manual-yet this is one of the practical test standard maneuvers. I doubt the fixed-wing world would allow this situation to continue in its midst.

Despite being one of the busiest helicopter operational areas in the world, the Gulf of Mexico lacks a reasonable IFR structure or even good FAA-based flight following. Numerous crashes happen here every year and, in most cases, an unreasonably long time passes before the flight is missed. What's going on?

## *DIRECT COMPARISON*

Recently, Cessna started training on its new Citation Mustang light jet-a process that involves at least 25 hours in Cessna's simulator, plus a significant amount of ground school and real aircraft training. Even after all this, a pilot might not be allowed to fly single-pilot IFR unless he/she demonstrates sufficient proficiency. This is all permitted by the rules in Part 61, by the way.

Contrast this with a pilot coming to fly one of the new light twin-engine helicopters (7000-lb or lower max weight). They have as many, if not more, systems than the Mustang and are operated in a much more unstructured environment (typically EMS with a crew). There are no simulators in the US for training on these machines (although some helicopters have been in operation for over 6 years). And, to top it off, a typical Part 135 EMS operation provides the minimum 5 hours of training on type (including mission training).

One transport-category helicopter with a complex airline-level flight management system (FMS) came with no ground school training on the FMS for over 2 years following its introduction. Contrast this to a biz-jet with an equivalent system that requires 7 days of ground school and simulator time solely on the FMS. Little wonder the accident rate for helicopters is higher than it is for fixed-wing.

## *ALTERNATIVES*

In most countries outside the US, each helicopter type requires a type rating-not just a check ride, but a written exam as well. While this may seem to be going a bit too far-after all, there is not much difference between the major groups (piston, turbine, twin)-there are often significant differences in systems like hydraulics and electrics.

More importantly than any piece of paper, this approach instills a technical appreciation for the machines operated.

Some FAA folks have said they don't want to write new rules about helicopters. This is fair enough-rules are difficult to write and get approved. However, if they are going to be consistent in leveling the playing field by insisting on one level of safety, then they should also remove all the various ratings and endorsements on the fixed-wing world.

Seriously.

I would recommend that the US helicopter industry insist on a minimum of 3 different ratings-piston, turbine and twin-with appropriate written and flight tests. This would have the effect of instilling greater appreciation of the technical differences. Better performance charts (military ones are a great example) might help pilots understand their available performance and use it better. And testing on the use of autopilots would ensure that pilots really knew how to use them.

The International Helicopter Safety Team has set a goal of reducing helicopter accidents by B0% by 2015. As the US is the largest user of helicopters, it would be a good thing if the industry and FAA worked together to fix some of these problems.

# CHAPTER 32 *Runways Vs. Helipad*

**Vertical** 2012

*Comment: The previous article dealt with the differences between airlines and helicopters regarding weather reporting. T*

his column ventures a bit farther and compares the runway and it's environment with what helicopters are faced with.

As a starting point –the only reason an airliner flies IFR is to get to a position to land on a runway. Not the normal way to look at IFR flying, but it sets the starting point for this discussion. We'll use a night approach to an oil rig helipad as a comparison.On breakout from IFR approach, airplane will have 'standard' environment:IFR techniques not often used, even in night conditions that should be classified as IFR.Insist on standard approach techniques, particularly at night or in marginal VFR conditions.

One of the things that becomes clear from this comparison is that for a helicopter approaching an oil rig at night, a consistent approach procedure would help to align us with the way things are done by airliners.

In this case, a short procedure might be in order. Use a GPS, and start at 3/4th of a mile from the rig, and more or less aligned with the wind (or other direction determining condition, such as only one approach path to the helipad). The start point has a short leg while the helicopter decelerates to arrive at about 1/3rd of a mile from the helipad, 200' above the helipad, at an airspeed between 40 and 60 knots. This makes for a consistent approach procedure. From this point, a 'standard' approach to the helipad can be made. And a 'standard' approach makes for consistency, and makes it easy to see if things are going wrong.

And the same approach should be used day or night, good weather or bad. Because you don't want to change the way you do things only when things are not going well.

We certainly have the technology to make a short but consistent approach to a rig.

Once we get the first part consistent, however, we're still only partway to a solution.

In good weather over land, there is an embarrassment of riches as far as cues are concerned for judging deceleration and rate of descent. Remember that the pitot system stops giving reliable information below about 40 knots, the very time we may need information on a dark night. We can install a

We currently have no way of getting any reliable information about rate of closure with the landing site, so someone clever could do a land office business if they could make a software and hardware add-on to GPS receivers that would give us a good indication of how the approach was proceeding.

Now, to be sure, there aren't a lot of accidents that appear to be caused by lack of information about position and speed with respect to the landing site. There are one or two I could perhaps point to, but I'll bet there are a lot of helicopter pilots who had misjudged an approach to a remote landing site at night or other less than ideal conditions. Since there's no requirement to report such events, and since they don't require a missed approach with the complexity of a fixed wing instrument missed approach, they are not in the annals of our incident database.

But every little of consistency helps, every little method we can use to reduce the variables when we don't need to use the flexibility, every little way we can ingrain a standardized way of doing things must help to reduce the possibility of something going wrong.

Runway and Landing Environment

| Airline Situation | Helicopter Situation | Possible Method to Improve |
|---|---|---|
| On breakout from IFR approach, airplane will have 'standard' environment: | IFR approach techniques not often used, even in night conditions that should be classified as IFR. | Insist on standard approach techniques, particularly at night or in marginal VFR conditions. |
| Directly in front of both pilots | For oil rigs, sometimes one pilot cannot see landing area when high drift angles necessary due to winds | Ensure multiplicity of approach paths possible so that both pilots can see landing area. |
| 'Standard' closure rate with lights at 'standard' rate due to approach airspeed. Gives good depth perception. | Different approach gradients and speeds used on approach result in every approach being different. Some approaches conducted downwind. No standard way of judging closure or descent rates visually or using flight instruments or navigation equipment. | Develop method of showing closure rates visually and using navigation systems. |
| 'Standard' approach gradient set at 3° (or very close) | No standard approach gradient | Determine suitable approach gradient for each type, and have glidepath angle remotely adjustable from cockpit for glidepath. |
| Instrument approach guidance consistent with runway environment | No instrument approach procedure | Develop VFR short range approach procedure for helipads and heliports to permit 'standard' approach paths to be flown. |
| Runway lights designed to provide good references. | Often poor lighting on helipad, and often no other lighting. | Develop better helipad lighting configurations |
| Relative distance from touchdown known (either DME, or from geometry of height above runway and known glidepath angle) | Relative distance unknown without prior calculation and monitoring of altitude / distance | |
| No other interfering lighting. | May have lots of other lights on the oil rig, making it difficult to see helipad. | Develop definitive lights to show helipad location clearly. |
| VASI / PAPI lights aligned with direction of landing | VASI / PAPI lights may not be used and probably not aligned with direction of landing | Get VASI / PAPI lights that can be adjustable for both azimuth and elevation for helipads and heliports. |
| Landing direction dictated by runway, crosswind accepted as part of landing task | Landings made into wind, crosswind not accepted / favored over landing into wind | Accept approach with crosswind in order to have good approach lighting. |
| Constant airspeed until landing flare | Variable airspeed depending on wind and approach angle | Develop 'programmed approach' speeds from GPS |

Quite a list!

# CHAPTER 33 *Escaping From Confined Areas*

**Vertical** 2011

*Comment:* Helicopters work where fixed-wing aircraft can't, and that often means confined areas.

But is there a sure-fire way for us to get out of these difficult spaces?

The world isn't flat (at least according to recent theory), nor is it all wide-open spaces.

Helicopters — which tend to be used only when airplanes can't be — have to work in those areas where fixed-wing aircraft can't go. Among the most commonly encountered places where fixed-wing ships can't go are areas that are hemmed in by obstacles. These are areas that confine our takeoff and landing techniques and call for considerable flexibility, which thankfully is something helicopter pilots are famous for.

Why do we worry about this so much? The simple answer is payload, and the inescapable fact that payload is called that because it's what pays the bills. Maximize the payload, and you can make enough (sometimes just enough) money to keep operating.

**Examining the Issue**

The problem faced is complex, and involves multiple, ever-changing variables, with largely incomplete/unsuitable available details. In particular, I've previously written in this column about how poorly the helicopter world is served by the performance charts found in civilian flight manuals, and confined areas throw these issues into sharper focus.

Hover out of ground effect might provide some of the answer to escaping from confined areas, but if you can easily climb from a hover out of ground effect, it means either you have too much power or you've left some payload behind. If you're limited by weight, and have a lot of power remaining, there's not much you can do about that (and you should be grateful for the excess power). But, it's much more likely that you've loaded the helicopter up to the maximum you can carry, and now are faced with getting it out of an area that has something restricting the way you can exit.

It would be nice if we could measure all the variables and have a performance package that would tell us the helicopter's exact capability and how to obtain that. But, given the current state of sensors and equipment, it's impractical to think this might soon be possible. We'd need to measure the height of the obstacle, let's say it's trees, and the distance available to clear those trees. The wind speed and direction at the top of the trees would be a great bonus, as a headwind would be very useful, and a tailwind not so useful. The maximum power the engine is capable of producing changes with the atmospheric conditions, so knowing this exact figure is also of value. Then, the whole thing needs to be put into some monstrous equation that would hopefully spit out the maximum load that could be lifted, as well as provide the exact maneuvers that would be needed to obtain that performance.

Maybe I've watched too many sci-fi movies, but somehow I imagine a blue sheet of laser beams (they're always blue, aren't they?) that scans the area around the helicopter and magically computes all these variables. It would then project the necessary information onto the pilot's three-dimensional, full-vision visor (by that time we'll all be wearing them — the iVisor?) and the pilot would just have to follow the necessary cues.

But, we're a day or two away from this kind of magical equipment. Currently, even if we could ask a pilot to measure the distance to the obstacle and the height of the trees (all pretty simple geometry and trigonometry), how are we going to get that into a meaningful chart? And would we want you to have to do that in-flight? Well, probably not. So, until the sci-fi version comes along, we're stuck with several approaches to extracting the maximum payload from the confined area.

**Methods to Potentially Avoid**

*****The Obvious Method:*****

The obvious method requires that the helicopter climbs vertically until it clears the top of the trees. Simple and possibly effective, but what if you don't clear the trees?

You're now in a high-power situation and have to get back down to the ground. Be cautious about lowering the collective, as any rate of descent you develop has to be stopped by what little excess power you have. Too rapid a rate of descent can start to nibble at vortex ring state. And dealing with any emergencies will put you in an unenviable position. The possibility of engine failure here, and what you will do if it occurs, needs to be thought out before you start.

***Charging the Barrier:*** Charging the barrier is what my instructors called the method where you back up as far as you can, close to the ground, and then start a co-ordinated climb and acceleration forward. It's not such a wise method: if you don't have enough power to clear the trees at whatever speed you can develop, you'll be in a world of hurt. You won't be able to stop the forward speed quickly enough; you'll also have been raising the nose so you can't see what you're trying to avoid... the list of sins this technique contains is very lengthy. There's a lot of good reasons to not use this technique if you can avoid it, and one of the better reasons is that an engine failure at any stage here is not something you want to contemplate, let alone try to deal with.

***The Pendulum Method:***

I call this technique the pendulum method because I don't know of any other name for it, and it actually describes it perfectly at any rate. It requires a large enough area to get some flying speed, but initially not enough to clear the obstacles. It also requires good judgment, which is always in short supply.

Basically, you start by charging the barrier, then slow down and not just stop, but allow yourself to move backwards. The height gained in the first part of charging the barrier is used to gain a bit more speed moving backwards than you had moving forward, and that speed is used to gain height as you accelerate rearward. The acceleration rearward is continued to an acceleration forward, which in turn gains even more height, and so on. Eventually, the height will clear the trees as you move forward, or the speed will be sufficient to let you zoom to clear the trees — or perhaps both will happen.

The problem with this method is that it takes a good deal of judgment and skill, and since every confined area will be different, a good deal of adaptability as well. If things go wrong at an inopportune moment, the result may not be pleasant.

**Back it Up: The Well-Thought Out Method**

I've been around the rotary wing world for quite a few years, and have done a lot of different things, but I can't count any real "bush flying" in that experience. As such, someone else probably has already talked about this next method for confined areas — but it certainly bears repeating. I found out about it over a glass of wine with an extremely experienced pilot, and it made more sense than anything I'd seen or heard about before.

Simply stated, with this method, you back away from the barrier while climbing. To begin, determine the wind direction at the top of the barrier. Next, note how far toward the downwind of the confined area you can safely go. Then, move uas close to the upwind side as possible, while in a low hover. Start backing up and climbing downwind using takeoff power. Continue backing up and climbing until you either clear the obstacle, stop climbing or reach the downwind "no further back" point. If you've cleared the trees, start to move forward and you're away.

If you haven't cleared the trees before reaching the downwind "no further back" point, or you've stopped climbing, you need to reduce the payload. This will require descending back to the start point at the upwind end of the confined area, which should of course be visible between your feet. But you won't be trying to simultaneously descend and back up downwind, which is never a comfortable situation. (Try that in a clear area to see how uncomfortable it becomes — climb to 30 or 40 feet into wind, and then try backing up while descending downwind. Ugh!)

This back-it-up technique has the added bonus that if the engine quits, you know exactly where you're going to go, because it is between your feet. In fact, it appears that you probably won't even have to move the cyclic to do that — reducing the collective pitch will start you down that flight path almost automatically.

**Other Techniques**

There are undoubtedly other techniques for confined-area departures with a heavy load, but I haven't seen much written about them. And, there are probably as many techniques for this scenario as there are confined areas, so I'd hate to see someone try to promote a single procedure to be used for all confined areas. If you have a different idea for situations you've encountered, please send it along!

# CHAPTER 34 *Weather Just for Helicopter Pilots*

**Vertical** February / March 2009

*Comment: In this first in our new series on what we can learn from the fixed-wing world, we look at weather reporting.*

## *WHY AREN'T HELICOPTERS AS SAFE AS AIRLINERS?*

There's been quite a bit of discussion about raising the level of safety in helicopter operations to something approaching that of airliners. It is an admirable aim. Any way we can reduce the number of accidents and incidents will help us in many ways — fiscal (accidents are expensive), physical (people get hurt and/or killed in accidents), and status (accidents and incidents give us a bad reputation).

There is also, maybe most importantly, the human cost, which cannot be measured or included as a tidy statistic. Too many people I've known have gone west in helicopter accidents.

The next several columns in this department are going to look at the differences between helicopters and fixed-wing ships, particularly as they pertain to airline operations. Why airliners? Because they're the safest form of aerial transportation, and the standard to which we're being held.

In each of the successive issues, I will try to point out ways in which we can perhaps improve our situation. I'm sure ****both**** of the readers of this column can contribute other insights and suggest ways we can improve, so I look forward to hearing from you... and anyone else who may have stumbled upon this space.

## *AIRLINERS VS. HELICOPTERS*

Some things that are very relevant to airliners are not relevant to helicopters, yet we are expected to use the same systems. From this, several helicopter-unique observations and answers can arise. Some of those observations might appear, at first glance, to be, "Duh, that's so obvious," but their implications are huge.

The very first observation, and one that will have an effect throughout is that airliners operate from airports. ****The devil, you say.**** Helicopters, of course, often never see an airport. So, what's the effect of this?

Consider any airport that an airline operates to and from. It contains, at a minimum, radio communication. It also has navigation equipment, normally an instrument landing system, along with runways that have a glide-path-angle indicating system and lead-in approach lights and edge lights. Wind information is available in the form of windsocks (lighted), and often the actual direction and strength in the form of numbers provided by air traffic control (ATC). And, of course, there is weather information.

The airliners themselves all have dual navigation equipment, dual radios and probably weather radar. The aircraft and crew are certified for instrument flight rules (IFR), while the aircraft is certified for flight in icing conditions and has autopilot. Specific procedures for single-engine failure are defined and detailed relevant performance charts for the ship are available.

How about the crew? Well, there is normally two pilots, both with multi-engine and instrument ratings, and who've had regular training in simulators. Both of these pilots are also trained in crew environment and have had not only significant experience before becoming captain, but are type rated on the aircraft they're flying and probably have significant experience in other airplane types as well.

Finally, there is the actually flying. That has, more or less, been scheduled and is ATC controlled. Dispatch has taken care of weight and balance issues and devised flight plans. The flight has known departure and arrival places and procedures, a routine nature of operations and legs of flight that are of significant duration. The fuel reserves for IFR flight are not a major penalty, and all flights are conducted as IFR.

Are you starting to get the picture?

Let's look at each of these features (and many others) and compare fixed-wing and helicopter operations to see what could be done on the helicopter side to improve our safety record. In an ideal world, everyone would instantly agree and sign up for these improvements. In the real world, well, we'll probably be retired before the authorities get around to actually acting on them. ****Does my cynicism show?****

## *Weather Reporting*

Although helicopter operations are mostly visual flight rules, it appears that we have more than our fair share of weather-related accidents.

Weather is seldom an issue for fixed-wing on their route of flight, except for thunderstorms. It's just something they have to fly through or over. They're on instruments from takeoff to touchdown. Weather at destination is pretty important, but, even then, aside from thunderstorms, it's merely a hindrance to getting to a position to land the airplane, or it means the rapidly vanishing in-flight service may be interrupted.

We, on the other hand, worry about weather en route… and have little to help us. We fly relatively low to the ground in comparison to the fixed-wing world, so even small changes in terrain affect our flight conditions significantly. What we need is more training in micro-climate and micro-weather. This includes training on how to predict the really local weather, how to judge when conditions will deteriorate, and knowledge things like upslope flow and winter or summer effects.

I remember at least a couple of places where we knew the local weather was going to be bad if there was an east wind. In my military days, at one base, if we could smell the local pulp and paper mill, we knew it was probably not a day we would be flying.

## *Predicting the Weather*

Helicopter accidents are seldom related to thunderstorms, but there are far too many accidents due to fog and low ceilings. Both fog and low ceilings are closely related to a very simple, but often-neglected concept — the temperature/dew-point spread. Sadly, all too often I've read accident reports of emergency medical service (EMS) missions where the temperature/dew-point spread was either zero or a very small number. When there's less than 2 degrees C (3.6 F) difference between the two numbers, you know the ceiling is going to be less than 1,000 feet above ground. If you're flying toward higher ground, you're going to rapidly run out of visibility and flying room.

Fog and low ceilings could more easily be predicted if there were more places reporting just air temperature and dew point. Given that you can buy a good system that shows both temperature and dew point, as well as relative humidity, for less than $100 at a big box store, I have to ask why we haven't got this equipment at every police and fire station, and have it integrated into the weather system? It shouldn't be that difficult or expensive to do.

Every fire engine could have one. Most of the time there are fire engines at EMS scene calls, and that would be useful information to know when you're heading into a relatively unknown area at night in less than ideal conditions. That way, the lapse rate and temperature/dew-point spread could be used to calculate where a cloud base should be for all those places. For areas with mountain passes, this would be a good way to check to see if the passes are clear of cloud and fog.

We get the same basic weather training as airline pilots, with lots of emphasis on upper-level stuff helicopter pilots seldom, if ever, encounter. What we need is a little more emphasis on weather predictions in training, and operational procedures that help educate pilots on what to expect.

Recently, I had a question from this column's other reader (now I know who both of you are), asking whether a a guideline for using carburetor heat on a piston-engine helicopter that relied on an air temperature/dew-point spread of less than 5 C (9 F) might be useful. I was impressed that someone might have thought of that in the first place.

Then, this same reader brought up the issue of local variations in weather that were human made. It was pointed out that if you fly downwind of a large cooling tower, you'll encounter very high humidity levels, even if you don't see any clouds of steam where you are. Not only high humidity levels, but also higher than normal temperatures. After all, they are cooling something by exchanging heat.

Why is this important? Simply to reiterate that helicopters constantly encounter micro-climate issues and issues of weather that fixed-wing (especially airline) pilots never do. If we want to be as safe as they are, we must be vigilant and knowledgeable in how to recognize and predict these instances of weather change.

In the next issue, we look at how the concept standardized procedures might help make our lives a little more boring… but safer.

| Airline Situation | Helicopter Situation | Remarks |
|---|---|---|
| Detailed weather reporting is available at all airports through trained observers or automated data. | Operate a long way away from weather reporting stations. Pilots must observe weather and try to predict what will happen. | Need a suitable way to observe the weather and make predictions based on what we see.<br>Need good instruction on how to do micro-climate weather observations and make short-term predictions.<br>Lots of mini-weather stations are now available and connected to the Internet. We need to find a way to use that information for helicopters. |
| Weather reports for departure and destination and alternate routes are provided. | Weather en route, rather than at takeoff and landing sites is major concern. | Need better en route local weather reporting. |
| Weather radar is available at each airport. | Very seldom is weather radar coverage available in most areas where helicopters operate. | XM Satellite weather is nearly instantaneously available anywhere in North America. Need to find way to utilize this. |
| Wx weather radar available | Wx weather radar seldom installed | Not a major factor for most helicopter accidents. Helicopters are more concerned with sudden changes in localized weather. |
| Wind direction always reliably known prior to landing and takeoff. | There is no way to accurately know the wind's direction in unprepared landing sites. (The situation is even worse at night.) | Need accurate low-airspeed sensor for speeds below 40 knots indicated airspeed (discussed later). |
| Airlines have relatively few accidents caused by weather. | There have been quite a few accidents where helicopter pilots didn't understand implications of flying in less than desirable conditions. | Need to institute training scenarios in simulator for: night encounters with bad weather, and whiteout/flat-light conditions. |

Table 1 – Weather issue differences between helicopters and airlines, and how helicopters handling of weather can be improved.

.

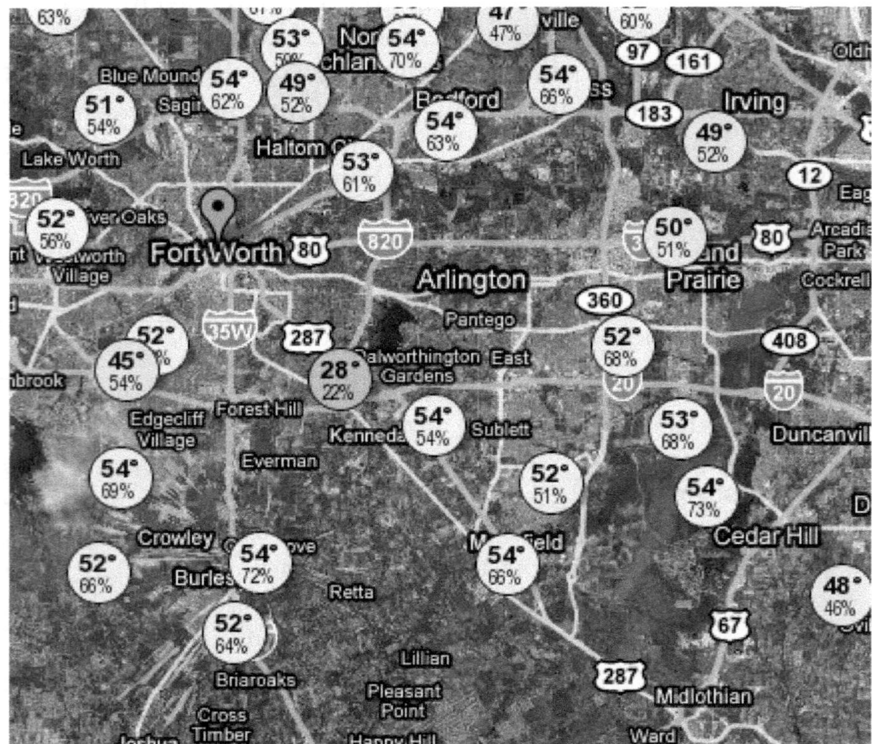

Figure 34-1 **Wunderground Local area map with Temperature and dewpoint**

# CHAPTER 35 *Night is Not VFR*

**Vertical** 2010

*Comment: The Real and Complete Definition of VFR*

One of the problems with discussing this subject is the FAA definition of VFR – it only discusses visibility and distances from clouds. This article should show this definition is sadly lacking.

Let's look at what must lie behind a complete definition of VFR (or Visual Meteorological Conditions (VMC), if you want to be really correct). We might also look at the definition used in other countries in order to come to a more complete understanding of what flying visually really means.

One of the places to look is the airworthiness certification requirements for helicopters. 14 CFR (the correct title for what we used to call FARs) Part 27 and Part 29 are set up for only day and night VFR certification – if you want to certify a helicopter for IFR, there are appendices that dictate equipment and handling needed. All that's needed is an airspeed indicator, altimeter and wet compass. What is interesting is what is missing from the requirement – namely, an attitude indicator or turn needle or even slip ball.

Yep, you read that right. There is no requirement for an attitude indicator to certify a helicopter for day and night VFR as far as the airworthiness people are concerned. Operation requirements for commercial operations in many countries cover this omission by requiring attitude indicators, but not the airworthiness rules. You could fly a helicopter at night in a private operation without an attitude indicator.

Same thing for navigation equipment – only a wet compass is required by the airworthiness rules.

So what are we supposed to do with this information? From this, we can imply that someone assumed that if you're VFR you can determine the attitude of the helicopter from looking outside. And navigate by looking outside – navigation includes determining height above ground, as it's hard to navigate when you're on (or in) the ground, and certainly needs more than a wet compass – you can't make corrections to heading without knowing where you are with respect to a planned course.

We can put the navigation issue to rest now – GPS has solved that problem, but we're left with the (unstated by the FAA) requirement to orient the helicopter (attitude and height above ground) by using visual references.

Let's look at a couple of examples of where the FAA definition falls apart unless you understand the underlying assumptions.

You're cruising along at 500 feet above ground and have to cross a large lake (20 miles across) in your minimally equipped helicopter (airspeed indicator, wet compass, altimeter, hand held GPS). As you come up to the lake, you've determined that you have an average of 5 miles of visibility and that while it's murky, there are no clouds to speak of except a high overcast layer that only jets might worry about. It's a flat calm day – not a breath of wind. Great VFR weather – right?

You leave the shoreline behind and now you're over the middle of the lake – no shoreline to be seen in any direction. No waves on the water, no shadows. This is called the fishbowl effect, in case you didn't know. You think you're inside a fishbowl. Navigation is not a problem as you have GPS. But I defy you to fly this without some adventure you might not wish to repeat.

There is no horizon to orient the helicopter's attitude, and no way to tell your height above the water except the altimeter. (You do have the correct altimeter setting, don't you?) Instrument flying with only an airspeed indicator, wet compass (down by your right foot) and altimeter (not even a turn needle) is quite an adventure. Pitch control isn't much of a problem as airspeed and altitude co-relate. Roll control and heading become quite a handful as there is no discernible horizon. One manufacturer even state 'Lose sight of the horizon and you die.'

You can repeat the scenario in a variety of ways – snow covered lake with overcast sky, night over the middle of the desert with no lights. I'm sure you get the picture.

Now, let's throw a bit more into the picture - what if the visibility starts to decrease as you cross the lake – un-forecast weather has moved in. Would you know it was getting worse? With no visual references, you can't know what the visibility was. You might not even be legal from the visibility point of view, and not know it.

A case can be made that even in great visibility and a clearly defined horizon but no other references (over the middle of the ocean) you can't tell height above the ground or heading (without a compass). A tuna spotting helicopter pilot told this was really quite a problem.

At this point, I hope you agree that there's a lot more to VFR than just visibility and distance from clouds. A horizon is needed, as are other references.

So what about at night? Over a city or town, it's pretty easy to orient a helicopter by virtue of the lights below. Visibility is easy to judge, as is height above the ground.

Go a short distance away – over a lake or the ocean or a large expense of forest or desert, with no lights, with a high overcast and no moon, and all the visibility and cloud clearance in the world won't help you. You have no way to orient the helicopter without reference to instruments.

Looking farther abroad, it is interesting to note that other countries have more complete definitions of VFR that include the requirement to orient by reference to the ground. And most European countries don't have night VFR. Night is IFR with appropriate rules and equipment requirements.

It is interesting to note that long ago, the US regulations contained something called 'Contact Flight', which was defined as

"flight ...in which the attitude of the aircraft and its flight path can at all times be controlled by means of visual reference to the ground or water."

I wonder why this very useful definition went away. Perhaps someone at the FAA can enlighten us.

The accident rate for helicopters (and light fixed wing) at night and in less than ideal visual conditions shows that the real definition of VFR isn't well understood.

So the next time you're tempted to fly VFR at night, over the water or other large unlit areas, think twice. VFR isn't just visibility and distance from clouds – you need some sort of clear visual reference.

## CHAPTER 36 *Night Light*

ROTOR&WING INTERNATIONAL 1995

*Comment: FLYING HELICOPTERS at night · has long been a feature of military operations.*

**Figure 36-1 An Assortment of Night Lighting Light**

Turning darkness into daylight by using night vision goggles (NVGs) has transformed the helicopter into an around-the-clock transport and weapons system. It hasn't always been easy or inexpensive to do this, and we have often had to use technology that was not always appropriate. Consider, for example, helicopter cockpit lighting to complement NVGs. I have seen some badly arranged setups. One major program left all radios and navigation aids without any lighting. It was judged too expensive to fit suitable filters to the radios, so the light's wiring was disconnected. Easy, but of no use to the crew who had to change radio frequencies when they weren't using NVGs or when they were looking under the new generation of goggles. Solutions included the use of a normal flashlight or a special map light. Neither was satisfactory. Sometimes map lights were used as an infrared (IR) floodlight by fitting a filter over the lamp. It could be seen over a distance-by friend or foe.

Recently, the UK military allowed one of its contractors, LFD Ltd., of Portsmouth, Hampshire, UK, to show off new helicopter night-lighting wares. LFD has long designed specialist night vision equipment, and LFD's new designs are manufactured by Basys Technology Ltd. In a nutshell, what makes the LFD/Basys line of infrared (IR) equipment special is the use of IR-only diodes.

These produce light that is easily picked up by NVGs, but requires very little electrical power and is nearly inVIs1ble to the naked eye. Obviously, such technology is useful for a range of military night flying products. The new LFD/Basys products address many of them. For example, there is the Fingerstar. A small, lightweight light that easily straps onto the index finger of either hand, it can produce two types of illumination. The low level of 'normal' light is NVG-compatible and useful for map reading or looking at radio controls. Or the IR light can be used for signaling to NVG-equipped troops on the ground. The Fingerstar has a switch that works as a typical (on-off) switch in the normal light mode and a momentary switch (on-while-pressed) in the IR mode. This permits its use as a flashlight in the normal mode, while preventing it from being left on in the covert IR mode. Another new LFD/Basys item is a set of electroluminescent (EL) panels for NVG-compatibility, called Glowstar. For older helicopter cockpits that don't take to retrofitting for NVGs cheaply, these EL 'eyebrow' panels offer an economical compromise solution. They are easily installed on the underside of the existing glare shields to provide illumination for the panel instruments below.

What about lighting up the outside world to see objects in detail? On really dark nights, NVGs can't pick up essential details like wires and small poles. Up to now, the only workable device was to use a permanent or temporary IR filter placed across a standard landing light or a high-power searchlight. _ This has drawbacks. To make this arrangement suitable for NVGs, most of the white light has to be filtered out, and the 1% that is left. is quite concentrated. It also takes a lot of power to generate the white light, and this can be easily detected by the naked eye or a simple thermal imager. Again, a big 'Shoot Here' sign in the sky.

A less well-understood problem is that the filtered light has quite a high intensity around the center of the beam. The NVGs have to adjust their gain for this light level, and as the light drops off rapidly away from the center, the images in the NVGs drop off even more rapidly. If something is not iii the central cone, it won't be seen.

LFD/Basys has developed an IR floodlight, called BrightStar. The stationary floodlight can light up a large area immediately in front of or underneath the helicopter. It puts out a large field of light that has no bright central spot; thus, NVGs can see everything with a more or less even level of illumination. Because it is an IR light, it uses very little power and has little heat signature.

Brightstar was recently fitted to Royal Navy Sea King Mk 4 and reports Mick Jarvil, LFD/Basys' marketing manager, and operational trials have shown it to be most useful for illuminating clearings when the helicopter is on short final or when hovering over an underslung load. Two versions of Brightstar exist. Brightstar II is a twin-beam, forward facing version, and Brightstar III is a smaller, single-beam version, for shining directly down. So if helicopters can fly around with no lights and no one can see them, how do you avoid mid-air collisions or maintain separation in formations? As an anti-collision device, LFD/Basys developed a low-profile IR light, called Starflash, that complements existing anti-collision lights. It consists of a short collar of IR strobes that sits around the base of the existing light. Starflash quietly puts out an IR signal that is as detectable as the normal strobe light when pilots wear NVGs. It can be set to strobe or flash in a coded pattern to permit identification of individual aircraft or formations. (For example, tonight, all aircraft. in B Squadron are known as dot-dot-dash-dash.) What about position-keeping lighting for' tactical formation flights? At night, the exterior EL panels currently used are difficult to see from far away; as a result, they are only useful for tight, fly-past formations. This flying is very stressful and can give the enemy a concentrated bunch of metal to shoot at. Also, the difficulty in seeing the EL panels from far away means that the joining up of a night formation flight can be 'entertaining,' to say the least. To overcome these problems, LFD/Basys developed the Starpoint and FLIR-1D Wingstar IR formation lights. The battery-powered Starpoint lights simply bolt onto an airframe bracket, as a temporary fit. The FLIR-1D light replaces the normal light bulb on wing and tail-tip lights to supplement the existing g navigation and formation lights.

One more are a LFD/B a sys has addressed concerns NVG-compatible ground-level lighting for helicopter operations to pick up loads or drop off troops. Some cyclo-luminescent once-only lights, particularly the blue ones, don't show up on NVGs, so they're not much use. And if you have more than one point of pickup, how can you identify it from the others? The answer from LFD/Basys is a series of pole-mounted marker lights. Polestar I offers bright and dim settings and fast or slow flash of an IR-only light. Taking the same technology farther, Polestar II and III provide a small NATO T-equivalent landing site, powered by a nine-volt battery. The light ca be detected up to three miles (5 km) away in IR, visible red, or NVG-compatible green light. It also features flashing modes of slow or fast flash or bright or dim settings. Polestar III adds in letter coding of the flashes and other features. The LFD/Basys line of lighting has already seen 'action' in Northern Ireland, the Gulf War, Bosnia, and other places. The operators have all been very happy with the new equipment, and in one case, an NVG capability was fitted to a helicopter within a matter of days. The small, add-on devices like Fingerstar and Polestar show what can be done with the innovative use of a particular technology. May they light up the night in a quiet manner. •

Figure 36-2 LED landing Light

# CHAPTER 37 *Firefly- Solving the Night Landing ProblemProblem*

ROTOR&WING INTERNATIONAL April 1'995

Comment: Helicopters are unique vehicles- they can land literally anywhere there is space for the rotors.

.

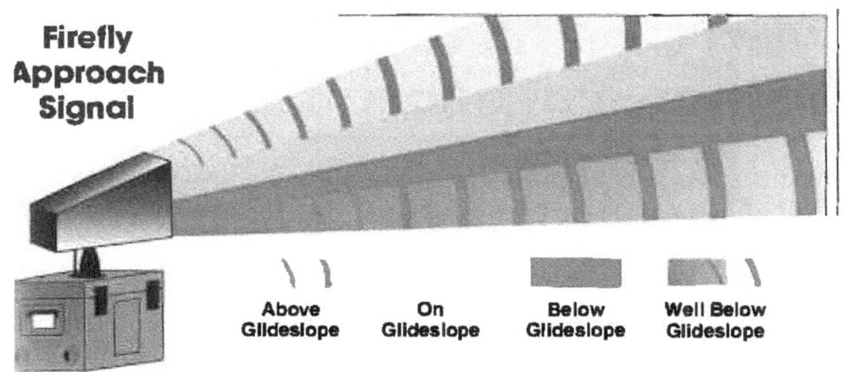


Figure 37-1 **What The Approach Lighting Looks Like**

This is however, a double edged sword.It leads to landings in places where the things the rest of the aviation community takes for granted like runways, air traffic control, weather observations and so on are missing.For many operations, one of the most missed items is lights for the approach.Trying to do an approach to an unlit field, using only your searchlight is not conducive to low blood pressure, but if you're a police or EMS helicopter pilot, this might be all to common.If you're a military special operations covert mission kind of guy, the problem is made slightly worse, by not wanting the opposition to see your landing system either.Night Vision Goggles on partly solve this problem.

A solution may be at hand.In-flight Research has been working on the problem for several years, and in an exclusive interview to Rotor and Wing, revealed their latest efforts, called the ACS 20/20 or, more commonly, the Firefly.

The concept is simple, but the execution was not, and it took Richard Walker and his team several years of work to get this far.By taking a modular, staged approach from the outset, they have developed a unique system. To describe it, lets look at a typical scenario for it's use.

There's been a requirement for helicopters to land in a remote field for a long time (police, medical emergency whatever).How this is done with the new system is very simple.

## *Typical Use for the Portable System*

The ground personnel take out the Firefly from the back of their vehicle, and carry the two small boxes to a suitable spot in the field.They join the smaller lamp section to the combined battery pack/master unit.They check with their searchlights for any obstacles such as wires or tress, and then pick a suitable approach path, looking through the optics of the Firefly to verify where they have aimed the system.The system has a built-in, no moving parts level detection system, so it is easy to ensure the lamp is leveled laterally before adjusting the glide path.Radio controlled perimeter lights can be placed around the touchdown area and switched on by the main box.(in fact, if it can be controlled by an RS-

422 signal -pretty standard for computer controlled things, it can be controlled by this box).The system is armed, and they radio the helicopter to tell the approach direction and location of the landing site.When the helicopter is ready to land, the pilot keys in a number on a hand-held keypad, which transmits through any of the radios on board, and it turns on the glide path light, and also the lights on the ground.When the pilot has landed, he can turn it all off again using the same keypad.

If a really portable system is wanted, the head unit can be used alone, with a suitable power supply (car cigarette lighter works fine), as there is small processor in the head which will determine the 'level' position.

## *Four Basic Angles for the Glide Slope*

The projected light beam is split into 4 basic areas- above the desired glidepath is a flashing green light, on the desired glidepath is steady green, slightly below the glidepath is steady red, and well below the glidepath is flashing red.These are the same as required by the international lighting standards laid down by ICAO Annex 14 requirements.

Aside from the variability of the glidepath angle, it's the same type of light signals the pilot would see on any visual approach at a major airport.The beam is sharply defined- ± 8° laterally and ±8° for the glide path.

If the landing site is more permanent, but infrequently used, the system can be pre-configured for a variety of directions, including different glide path angles for different directions.Obviously in this case, a servo motor would be needed to control the azimuth and elevation, but this is simply installed between the master unit and the lightbox.

The secret of the system lies in the use of microprocessors to control the lamp and the other devices.Exact details of how the lamp system works are classified, as it took a military organization over 5 years and bags of money to come up with something similar in concept, but over 10 times the weight, and infinitely more complex, which didn't work. Suffice to say, the Firefly has are no moving parts in the light system.This means there are fewer things to break!

## *Background to the reasons for Firefly*

In 1985, Walker was involved in developing a replacement for a British military night landing light system for helicopters (call Bardic) which was very heavy and not man portable.After developing and successfully marketing the Glowworm system, he set out on what became a long journey to develop a better system.The design aim he set for his team of engineers was to develop a light-weight, adaptable night landing system for aviation (not just helicopters, you'll see). Two prototype units have been installed in hospital helipads in the UK, where the rules about such operations are quite a bit more strict that in the USA. (That's another story in itself...).The end product is called the ACS 20/20 (for Airfield Control System with 20/20 vision, of course)

## *Self-Contained*

One of the requirements was for self-power.While it is capable of handling any input voltage (from 10 to 14vDC and 85 to 264VAC), the system can operate for extended periods just on battery power.How long will depend on the size of the battery and the output required for the approach light.Presently, a 35 amp-hour battery will give 7 hours of continuous projection of the light, however in intermittent use, such as an intelligent pilot would give, it will last much longer).If just the head unit or lightbox is used as a starting block, the costs are lower, but the possibility to upgrade to more complex systems is retained.

Some interesting options are for covert military operations, particularly using NVG's.In this case, different colors are of little use, so a flashing light method is used to tell the pilot when the helicopter is above, on or below glidepath.The present light is easily converted to an NVG suitable light.

The basics having been covered, the possibilities are endless.First of all, the radio, presently only a receiver, (but easily changed to a transceiver), handles any frequency from 100Khz to 1.4 Ghz, which pretty well covers the spectrum.The portable keypad, using standard telephone tone signals hooks into the helicopter's intercom system with a T connector.When the pilot transmits on the pre-sleeted frequency the keypad squirts down the necessary tones to activate the microprocessor.The microprocessor will be set up to recognize the command signal and perform any one of 99 different, customizable commands, again depending upon the configuration of the system.You can literally make the system do anything you want it to.

Since a microprocessor is used to control everything, it can serve a whole host of functions relating to security- like special codes to turn the system on, recording who used the system and when, the ability to control other external devices and so on.Control is through a special port which can plug into a personal digital assistant or other computer.

One rather rich client, who had a very expensive house, regularly flies guests to his private heliport at night and wanted to be able to show off the house with some dramatic effect.He didn't want the gardener waiting around to hear the helicopter, so by using Firefly he can turn on the house floodlights, and the lights in the swimming pool when on short final.Easily done, and much more dramatic as well- the Firefly can control anything that can be plugged into it!

As if another show of the flexibility of the concept is needed, the problem of landing on pitching rolling heaving ships and oil rigs was mentioned.By adding a gyroscope package between the control box and the light box, it would be possible to stabilize the light beam in space for pitch and roll.Heave is another, (probably insurmountable problem), but eliminating pitch and roll movement is a major step forward.

The mind boggles at the possibilities, which appear to be limited only by the imagination of the end-user.In-Flight Research also showed me a much smaller, more portable (but less packed with options) version they had developed for covert operations which was about the size of a very small shoe box, and weighed less than 2 kg.

## *SUMMARY*

GPS has solved nearly all the problems of navigation to a remote site with great accuracy, however, there is still the problem of making a visual landing.Firefly solves many parts of this final critical aspect of the flight, and should make life much easier for it's users.

Figure 37-2 **The Box complete**

# CHAPTER 38 *$2,000 per second!*

ROTOR&WING INTERNATIONAL May 1995

*Comment: Still valid points 20 years later*

It's impossible to get away from digital computers. They have transformed many aspects of our lives, and are certainly no stranger to the modern helicopter cockpit. More recently, they have been applied to controlling engines with some surprising results. The digital fuel control has mostly appeared on new engines, but recently have been tried on older, more well known engines, with some surprising results.

This article will discuss some of the reasons for the changes, the benefits and potential problems. To begin with, please hold firmly in your mind that everything is a compromise. The turbine engine itself is a compromise, but we have grown to accept it's strengths and work around most of the weaknesses.

## BEFORE YOU READ ANY FARTHER-

Pilots - think about how much time you spend monitoring engine and transmission parameters, matching torques, setting up engines, performing power checks and so on. Mechanics- think about how much time you spend setting up engines, (especially multi-engine installations with different time engines), troubleshooting gripes about the engine response and so on.

If you fly a helicopter with two engines- think of the problems when one engine fails- new limits to monitor and obey, exactly at a time when you have other things on your mind. I know of one helicopter that has 5 different limitation levels (continuous twin, takeoff twin, continuous One Engine Inoperative (OEI), 30 minute OEI, 2.5 minute OEI) with three different parameters (TOT, torque and N1) to be monitored in each- of course, none of the numbers are the same between the limits. In a rapidly changing situation such as an engine failure on takeoff it was not possible to fly the helicopter and respect many of these limits, even in a training environment.

## TYPICAL HYDRO- MECHANICAL ENGINE CONTROLS (OR GOVERNORS)

The majority of helicopter engine fuel controls are of the hydro-mechanical type- they sense free turbine speed and attempt to maintain it at a constant value. This is accomplished by changing the fuel flow and compressor speed. There may be 'stops' to prevent compressor speed from exceeding limits, and possibly an overspeed system to prevent the power (or free) and compressor turbines from running away and disintegrating. In multi-engine installations, the fuel control system may provide automatic torque matching. A few have torque limiters to prevent overtorquing. There may be small differences in individual helicopters, but by and large, that is normally all you get with a hydro-mechanical (steam driven) fuel control.

Because the hydro-mechanical fuel control will not respond unless there is an error in power turbine speed, the response to power changes is slow. Rapid power changes are not well liked as the engine had to accelerate or decelerate in a predictable manner to avoid compressor stalling or flaming out respectively.

Why weren't the engines responding fast enough? Consider the pilot applying a large collective up application at the end of a quick stop, when the power is low and the rotor is nearly in autorotation. The compressor is winding down in speed because the fuel control sees that the power turbine is running too fast and wants to get it back to 'normal' speed.

Remember that the fuel control won't think it should start increasing compressor speed until it sees the power turbine RPM below where it should be- by which time it is fighting not just to get back to the datum RPM, but also against the increasing power demand. There are various attempts to improve the situation by feeding in an anticipator signal from the collective, but the problem is that the engine really needs rate of collective change, not just position to make it's response better.

The response of a turbine engine response to a rapid power demand is a compromise. Get the rates wrong and response can compressor stall. Given that the effects of a compressor stall are worse than slowish acceleration, the designers will always err on the side of safety- the acceleration may be slow, but the engine won't cough at a bad time. Similarly, when the power is reduced rapidly, the engine can only decelerate so quickly because if the fuel were cut off too quickly, the engine would flame out.

## *CONSIDER THE INPUTS!*

For those who have spent some time trying to explore the plumbing of a hydro-mechanical fuel control unit, the number of pipes in and out, adjustments and so on is bad enough, but ask yourself- even if the designers wanted to- where would they put any more sensing inputs and outputs? How would they end up marrying signals of rotor RPM and power turbine speed? The hydro-mechanical fuel control might end up being bigger than the engine it was controlling! Look at the diagram of the inputs and outputs of a typical fuel control system. All this just to control the amount of fuel that is going to the engine.

## *EARLY ELECTRONIC CONTROLS*

Electronic controls for turbine engines are not new- they have been around in part since the early 1970's, but generally only in piecemeal fashion. Early models were analog in construction, and needed as much attention as the hydro-mechanical components they replaced. Failures were often mystifying and frequent. Like many aspects of aviation, many things were learned that have been applied to the current generation of digital computers.

## *RECENT CHANGES.*

Digital computers have increased in capability for memory, speed and hence computation, as well as reliability, resistance to electro-magnetic interference, and cost. All of this equates to a capable, reliable method of controlling engines.

Recent changes to the FAR's that cover engine certification for helicopters have required that new engine limits be automatically controlled and recorded- given the level of extra power the market is demanding for these limits (up to 35% above the takeoff limits) the only sensible way to approach the problem of control and monitoring is with a computer. 30 minute and 2.5 minute OEI ratings are the norm on existing helicopters, but 2 minute and 30 second ratings are coming for new engines. There is some comment in the engine industry that it is not possible to give these new limits without the use of advanced (i.e. non-hydro-mechanical) controls.

## *FADEC DEFINED*

FADEC means Full Authority Digital Fuel Control. "Full authority" because as some early computer fuel controls only had worked on a small part of the flow fuel to the engine- (conservative bunch, these engine designers). The early push for better governing came from the military who wanted more rapid engine response for aggressive NOE flight, and just weren't getting it from conventional hydro-mechanical governing systems. Adding to the problem is the trend towards lower rotor inertia, and increased engine inertia (heavier compressors, etc) These two items are working in opposition for rapid power changes. About this time someone made computers more available as well.

Once the though processes had started down the way of using a computer, other ideas started to surface. What if other sensors could be used- instead of a mechanical sensor of power turbine speed, what if a more accurate optical sensor could be used? Once questions like this start to be asked, it is more logical to use a digital computer to analyze these inputs and make intelligent decisions about the output.

## *Logic and such*

Digital computers are best at making decisions on a yes/no basis, and that is the basis for the operation of the FADEC. In the end, the over-simplified question comes down to - is the fuel flow where it should be for these conditions? If yes, continue with the present fuel flow- if no, change the fuel flow depending upon a whole range of conditions.

This is how the logic circuits that make the system work are set up- the computer takes the signals from the sensors, and then applies the logic laid out for by the designers, and moves a fuel valve to makes the engine meet the response. For example, instead of controlled explosion on start, the FADEC can schedule fuel to make a smooth, cool start repeatedly every time. It can record the start parameters, prevent over-temps and it may abort the whole start to prevent burning up the engine.

Another example of the logic used is shown in this simplified diagram (figure 2) of the relationship between rotor speed and free turbine speed. In this example, the two signals are compared, and if the rotor speed is higher than normal, and the free turbine speed is also high, it reduces fuel flow to keep the free turbine speed at the normal speed. If it sees the rotor RPM decaying from a needles split condition, and the collective being raised, it concludes that the pilot is going to apply power. To assist the engines to respond and to reduce the amount of rotor RPM decay, it will increase the free turbine speed to match the rotor speed by increasing the fuel flow to the engines, and start the compressor accelerating. The end result is a reduced transient rotor RPM droop. Co-incidentally, it also results in a very smooth free-wheel unit re-engagement.

What about limiting the output of the engine to make sure that it doesn't get abused? (Note to editor- get ready for lots of letters about this point!) Torque matching can be done with ease, and so on- literally, if you want something done with the engine, it can be done- just ask, but remember- everything is a compromise.

**Overtorques - Begone!**

It is in the protection of limits (TOT, torque and N1) that FADECs are really showing their worth. On one FADEC engine/ airframe combination I know of, it is not possible to get to the OEI limits unless the other engine is stopped or the N1 is well below the self-sustaining idle speed. Literally, it is not possible to hurt the engine or helicopter anytime (even when training), and the performance that is obtained in a real engine failure is always better than what you practiced with.

Another engine FADEC system has a training mode, where the 'good' engines limits are artificially lowered for single engine training. With this system when training, ECL's (or throttles) will not be pulled back The reason for this is that when training if the 'good' engine fails, the other engine will instantly respond with full power, not limited. Clever logic, but definitely different from what we are used to.

Since the higher OEI limits are not ever reached in day to day operation, the engine manufacturer can make these limits higher than before, giving better single engine capability, and security that when you need the power, it will be there.

Overtorques? Overtemps? A thing of the past- if you want them to be- the boss will love it, because the cost of owning the engine has just gone down, but if you as the pilot need the power in an emergency, it might not be there, unless the logic has made allowance for this.

The list of benefits is just starting- no more engine set ups- if the FADEC needs replacing, just plug it in and go. No idle adjustments, torque matching adjustments, acceleration time adjustments and so on. Several FADEC systems automatically do a built–in–test when electrical power is applied to the engine, and test sensors and internal logic continually.

Most of the systems record data about exceedances of limits and let the maintenance people take note of them. Some FADEC systems even are capable of continuous engine trend monitoring, so that compressor washes can be scheduled more precisely, and even rapid degradation (power loss over an hour or so) could be detected.

Engine start cycles can be counted accurately, so that the number of times the engine has gone from 'off' to idle RPM is counted, not just a count of the number of times the start button has been pressed.

## *The Inevitable Failure Question*

Ah, you ask, but what if they fail? The good news - First of all, since there are fewer connections and fittings, (i.e. less plumbing) they are less likely to fail. Secondly, because of internal logic checks, the system will probably warn the pilot before it fails completely.

Thirdly, the types of failures are actually very small- the FADEC can freeze the fuel flow on the engine, run it up or run it down. The most common failure mode will be the 'freeze' in power, as that has the least drama associated with it, and that is what the designers have set the computer to do- if anything goes wrong, freeze the fuel flow. Nearly all the engines with FADEC I am aware of have a manual reversion, and controlling the engine in this case is the same as a piston engine helicopter. One type without a manual reversion has a dual computer/ sensor suite.

As an example of the level of logic and testing, let me relate one example. The design engineers raised a warning that there was one remotely possible internal failure that could run the engine up in manual mode, without warning the pilot first. Upon detailed questioning, it was revealed that the maximum time that would elapse before anything happened and the pilot was warned of a failure was about 1/2 second, and that even then the worst the engine would do was run up to a moderate power setting in three seconds. Since the worst time for this to happen was on the ground at flat pitch, with the pilot not looking inside- it was decided to make the governor failure warning an audio as well as visual cue. Testing showed that there was ample time to chop the ECL and not have a large rotor overspeed.

## *Practical Benefits for Pilots*

So what are the practical benefits- for a beginning, starts will be more predictable, probably cooler and quicker. Once started, you may be able to literally ignore engine parameters as the FADEC will take care of them. You may also have a choice of which way to match the engines- either TOT or torque matching. All the power will be available from both engines at all times. Since this statement was not understood in a previous article, a bit more explanation- with a normal torque matching system, when one engine reaches it's limits, (say TOT) you have to stop pulling up on the collective, and the power from the other engine will be unavailable. The FADEC systems I have seen will match torques until the TOT limit is reached, and then limit only the high TOT engine. Pulling up on the collective will demand power from the other engine until it too reaches it's limit. With one helicopter with a FADEC, the advice to the pilot is that you know you are at takeoff power when the rotor RPM starts to droop. During critical situations, such as practicing for single engine failures, the pilot can concentrate on looking outside and let the computer monitor the limits. There is no need to look inside to monitor the good engine, so that you don't literally pull the guts out of it when you are staking everything on it.

Needless to say, since the main reason for starting down the electronic road was more rapid response to power changes, FADECs should be good at that. To be honest, I am amazed at the engine responses. As a test pilot, there are times when you have to do nasty things to fine pieces of engineering, and this is one of them- rapid power demands from low power to maximum in very short times- some less than a second, and the FADEC engines have handled them very well. So far, I have found it impossible to trick them with varying frequencies of collective inputs, or rejected landings, or anything else perverse.

## *A Note of Caution*

It should be evident from the tone of the writing that I am impressed- for the most part yes. A point that I am slightly concerned about is the desire of the engineers to protect the engine and helicopter at all costs from being over-powered. I would suggest a slight change in logic here- there have been times in my flying career when extra power was needed - more that I was allowed to normally use. Rather than deny the pilot this power (The helicopter was protecting itself from being overtorqued when it crashed...) may I suggest some 'last chance' logic? When the pilot pulls to twin engine takeoff power limits and the system protects itself, and the rotor RPM decays- the system should permit the rotor RPM to decay until it reaches a minimum value and then not let it go any lower.

Engines, transmissions and dynamic components are much cheaper than airframes, lawsuits or human lives. Since the FADEC system is recording all these parameters anyway, this should be viewed as a one-time save–the–bacon affair.

**It won't be the Same Anymore**

What has to change from a piloting point of view? First of all, don't leap into a machine with FADEC and expect things to be the same- engines may be started with the throttles at Idle or perhaps even at the "Flight" position. The "Flight" position may not be the full forward position, and advancing the throttle beyond this position may have no effect in the normal (automatic) mode.

One of the things that will certainly change is the way that engine failures will be simulated- anyone who reaches up and grabs a throttle and yanks it back may be unpleasantly surprised. This is where the $2,000 per second figure comes from. The engine manufacturers have gone to a lot of work to get very high contingency ratings, and these are not like the previous OEI ratings in that you only have so much time with these power settings and then it's time to replace the engine. If a typical new engine costs $250,000 and it has 4 applications of 30 second power (2 minutes or 120 seconds total time at that rating), then it's not hard to see how the cost per second of $2,000 is arrived at.

Anyone who has one of these engines without an OEI training mode, or some other logic to protect the engines from inadvertent use (i.e. training) is asking for some very expensive training time.

## *PRICE ETC.*

Nothing is free, and there will be a price for a FADEC system. It will not however be as much as the cost of an engine or transmission, and over the TBO of an engine it may result in the engine reaching it's overhaul life instead of being burnt out in a hot start. Since parameters are more closely matched, it may permit the overhaul life of engines to be extended, resulting in lower costs of operation, but this is conjecture. For multi-engine operations that work to Category A standards, the higher 'burn-out' ratings may mean that more payload can be carried, resulting in greater profits. Lower maintenance man-hour costs and higher availability may result from less adjustments to the engine, and so on. The benefits are just beginning to be understood.

It will be interesting to look back in 5 or 10 years to see what the real benefits have been of this technology. Perhaps by then, engines will be treated the same as the transmission- a hunk of very precise metal that does it's job without a lot of pampering and attention. St. Exupry stated it well, over 50 years ago:

*"...in the machine of today, we forget that motors are whirring:, the motor, finally has come to fulfill its function, which is to whirr as a heart beats- and we give no thought to the beating of our heart."*

Wind Sand and Stars by Anton St. Expury,

$2,000 per second!

# CHAPTER 39 *Winter Operations*

**Vertical** 71 December 2008/January 2009

*Comment: It's that time of year again. The sun is lower in the horizon and the days are shorter, or are the nights just longer? The air is definitely colder, and snow prevails for the next few months just about anywhere north of the Mason-Dixon Line.*

**Figure 39-1 Watch out for Blowing Snow**

With this change in climate, how should we change our thinking about flying helicopters? To start, realize that open-toed sandals and cutoff shorts probably aren't a good idea for flying clothing. Perhaps more than fixed-wing, we know that we may not be landing in a place of our choice, particularly not close to a place with all the civilized amenities. So, dressing like we would be walking around in the wilds is now an even better idea than in the summer time.

The preparation for winter operations, though, goes way beyond just wearing the right clothes. It's the minutiae of things that living in a cold climate teaches us that needs to be translated to operating helicopters. At the risk of telling you who actually do this for a living (those who can't do teach, and those who have difficulty teaching write about doing it, or something like that) here are some loosely collected thoughts that have, at one time or another, passed briefly through my mostly vacant brain, lodging just long enough to be written down...

## *The Simple Things*

When coming in to land, turn the defroster off for the last few minutes of flight if you can. This ensures the windshield doesn't stay warm and let snowflakes melt and refreeze later. Of course, when you're parked, windshield covers stop ice and snow from forming on the windshield in the first place.

Don't even think about trying to scrape a frosted blade with anything more rigid than a credit card. (I heard of someone using a hammer to get rid of really thick ice once. Needless to say, all the blades needed to be replaced).

Leaving the helicopter outside may be easier on the metal and other bits than moving it from a heated hangar to the cold outside, and then back again. If you have to, though, covers are mandatory for this exercise.

Before you get in the cockpit, bang your boots against the door frame to knock off excess snow. That way, you don't have puddles of water on the floor. On the helicopter itself, check the intake and roof area for snow build-up. Even check inside the intakes. If you go to the trouble of closing up the helicopter, make sure you have very tight-fitting plugs or bungs for those engine air intakes.

On startup, warm the oil up to minimum operating temperature before advancing the throttle to fly. And, use your pitot heat religiously. Snow can block the pitot tube without much warning.

The power from batteries will be lower in cold temperatures. Some pilots who have no hangars for the airframe, end up keeping the battery warm at night (when a significant other would probably be preferable).

Water is always an issue in the fuel used in helicopters, and, in winter, it can become ice and clog fuel filters. As ice, it may also not show up when draining fuel from the sump before the first flight of the day. Pay attention to fuel quality.

## *Icing Considerations*

Know how accurate your outside air temperature gauge is. They can be off by a couple of degrees, and you may think you're not in icing conditions when parts of the airframe can already be accumulating ice.

Know what the signs of freezing drizzle are. Most pilots don't know that even if you have clearance to fly in 'known' icing conditions, this only applies to droplets that are smaller than the diameter of a 0.5-millimeter mechanical pencil. If you see dots of ice, of any size, forming on your windshield - vacate the area, pronto. Nothing is cleared for flight in freezing precipitation. Nothing!

Many years ago, someone in the air force tried to convince me it was okay to fly in 'trace' icing. Trace icing is never forecast, and it's impossible to be sure things are not going to get much worse. In case you're foolish enough to try, it helps to remember that icing can be particularly dangerous in innocuous appearing laminar clouds.

Apply heat to the windshield as soon as power is available to stop the windshield from frosting up. You can also leave the doors and windows open until the defroster is able to heat up the windshield. A load of passengers will put out a large volume of moist breath that will stick to windows very effectively, so leave the heater off if you're carrying folks who have just come from working outside and who are going to back to working outside as soon as you drop them off.

A small fan heater in the cockpit will keep the inside and outside of the windows clear of frost, and even a light bulb in a enclosed engine compartment can keep the engine warm.

## *Landings and Takeoffs*

Expect snow clouds and whiteout when landing, and plan accordingly. Know what you're going to do if you encounter whiteout on landing (during flight too).

Snow is deceptive, it can smooth out a very uneven surface and hide things like stumps and other dangers that may make life unpleasantly off level or which can reach up and puncture the underside of the helicopter. Snow can also be uneven in its ability to carry a load, so 'seating checks' (a few vigorous up and down movements of the collective on landing, prior to lowering the collective all the way) may be in order.

Skids can get frozen to a landing surface. A nasty way of finding that out is getting dynamic rollover on a level surface when one skid refuses to relinquish its grasp on the earth. A small yaw input to make sure the skids are free of the ground before applying collective seems to be the preferred method for eliminating this surprise.

Snow can often have a pretty thick crust, which can catch a skid on liftoff and also cause dynamic rollover. If you suspect a crust of snow is around your skids, better stomp around and break it up before you attempt to lift off. You may think you're coming straight up from the hole you just made from landing, but it doesn't take much crust to produce the pivot point necessary for the rollover to start. Some helicopters don't take kindly to even small yawing movements on the ground, though. And, of course, you know what to do when you encounter the first signs of dynamic rollover… don't you?

## Pluses and Minuses

On the plus side, visibility is generally very good in cold conditions, and certainly sun can be surprisingly bright on snow. Have sunglasses handy. Of course, those of us with more years and poorer eyesight than we'd care to admit know about wearing glasses and going from a cold environment to a warmer one, and the temporary embarrassment of vision that entails.

On the downside, a snow-covered surface when there is overcast cloud cover is an ideal condition for flat light. This means you are unable to tell your height above the uniform surface, as there are no shadows. Flying over snow-covered lakes under overcast skies or with falling snow will probably claim at least one helicopter this winter. (I nearly said I'd buy a beer for those who avoid it based on this warning, but how could I check that the resulting hundreds of you who write in or call are telling the truth?)

One plus found in cold weather is that engine power available will be better than in hot temperatures for the same pressure altitude. As such, some engines may reach fuel flow limit before they reach other limitations that you would normally expect. So, pay attention to how much power you're going to get and use the power check charts to confirm this.

There is one other note related to performance, a big minus, but it's only for multi-engine helicopters. It's a very clever feature that may leave you slightly uncomfortable. Some multi-engine helicopters incorporate an automatic shutoff of bleed air systems in the event of an engine failure. This is great if you're in a warm climate and need the extra power from the remaining engine in a moment of extremes. It's not so great if you've managed to get everything sorted out and are in single-engine cruise in really cold weather. You have no way to turn the heat back on or keep the windshield defrosted, unless you know a trick to fool the protection feature. Since there are quite a few different systems out there, I'm not going to suggest specific ways to do this. What I will say is that if you don't know how, it would be wise to find out before it happens.

## Other Tidbits

When instrument flying in very cold weather, pay attention to the effect that has on altimeter errors. Anything below -20 degrees Celsius (-4 degrees Fahrenheit) really needs to be looked at carefully.

Really cold weather also invites inversions, especially in mountain valleys. It happens in flat areas too, as it may be very cold on the ground, but surprisingly warm aloft.

Time and weight are also important considerations in cold weather. Your passengers and other essential crew who get in and out of helicopters will be moving more slowly than in the summer - all those bulky clothes slows them down. It also adds weight. Standard passenger weights in the winter are about 10 pounds heavier than in the summer.

Finally, and perhaps most importantly, especially for those who have formed a very tight and personal bond with their airframe, one that goes beyond the normal human-machine interface - don't kiss or lick your helicopter when it's cold. Wait until you're in the privacy of a warm hangar.

Figure 39-2 **Clean Before Flight!**

# CHAPTER 40 *Cold Hearted Liars*

Published under a Pseudonym...

*Comment: I had to use a pseudonym as I was working for Transport Canada at the time.No, this*

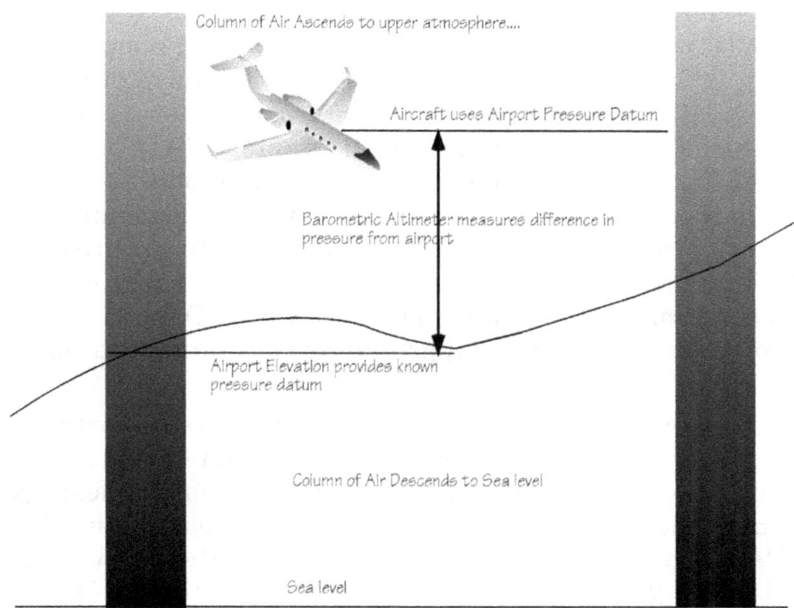


**Figure 40-1 Altimeter Errors ij Cold Weather**

*isn't about your ex-spouse nor mine for that matter! Baseball season is over and football season is in full swing. For many of us this indicates the time of year where the winter sweaters come out of hiding for yet another long and cold winter season. With the beauty of winter season comes many caveats we deal with in aviation including better performance, (generally speaking), pre-heating of our aircraft, an increased awareness of icing, etc. However, what many often overlook is the lies or inaccurate indications that our pressure altimeter can and WILL tell us on a blustery cold day. Think this issue only concerns Instrument Rated Pilots and IFR capable helicopters? Think Again!*

## *THE PROBLEM*

The pressure altimeter in your helicopter is calibrated for a 'standard-day' pressure condition. It is important to note the 'pressure condition' and not condition(s) i.e. pressure AND temperature. That is correct! Your pressure altimeter DOES NOT correct for non-standard temperature! However, we correct for non-standard pressure every time we fly! We call on ole' man Kohlsman and adjust him accordingly to the local setting.

Does this really matter to us as helicopter pilots? YES! Cold temperatures can have a dramatic effect on helicopter operations; not necessarily your everyday VFR [DAY] operations but it can affect you. Strolling along too low on an MDA or breaking out a tad too far down the ILS on a DH could ruin your day. And both of these can happen on a cold day!

## *THE MECHANICS*

Let's keep it simple. We know that cold air is more dense; heavier than warmer air. While flying, our pressure altimeter setting is based on the column of air in which we are flying. In this colder, denser, heavier air the helicopter is more or less pushed down below a datum. This datum would be found at a standard temperature of 15°C. Translation; when the air is colder than standard [datum] the helicopter is actually lower than the altimeter is indicating. Inversely, when warmer than standard the helicopter is higher than indicated by the pressure altimeter.

Being closer to the ground than your altimeter is indicating should be of concern to you. How much concern? It depends on how cold it is and your current flight regime. As previously mentioned, day VFR conditions is not the time to remember the most important parts of this article. But, find yourself having to perform an instrument approach after an inadvertent IMC situation in much colder than standard and you'll be glad you know how to read and adjust for altimeter lies.

In the above situation don't count on ATC to make adjustments for non-standard temperatures. If you are getting vectored such as in the case of an inadvertent IMC or maybe even during the course of a 'normal' IFR helicopter approach in an IFR capable and certified operation, ATC does not factor in temperature corrections. The actual Mode C signal sent from your helicopter to ATC is always based on an altimeter setting of 29.92. The ATC computers make adjustments based on the local altimeter settings but DOES NOT correct for non-standard temperature. This is where a little math, or in the practical case of helicopter flying, a quick-reference chart comes into play to help us with cold temperature corrections. When using the chart it is paramount that the correction be made based on The Helicopter Height Above Reporting Source, normally the airport (ATIS, AWOS, etc.) Or, the correction is made based on the height above an important point in the approach like the procedure turn, final approach fix, etc.

As an example, looking at the chart above (available in chapter 7 of the AIM) we see with a temperature of -20°C while at a height of 900 feet above the airport reporting the altimeter setting the correction factor is: 120 feet. Under these conditions you should be flying an additional 120 feet above what is required for that particular segment of the approach. Example: if you have passed the Final Approach Fix (FAF) and have an MDA of 1420 above the altimeter setting location YOU should fly the helicopter as necessary to maintain 1540 on your altimeter until reaching the Missed Approach Point (MAP).

Let's look at another practical example with a snapshot of an ILS approach. Note the Decision Height (DH) of 819 feet (circled in red) and also note the Touchdown Zone Elevation of 619 (again circled in red). Simple math shows us this yields a difference of a 200 foot minimums ILS approach (circled in blue).

Now, consider this: the AWOS is reporting a temperature of -15°C. Under this non-standard (temperature) condition and based upon the chart above, at minimums of 200 feet (DH) your helicopter is actually 20 feet lower than indicated. Therefore, you should fly the final approach segment down to a Decision Height of 839 as opposed to 819 indicated on the approach chart.

Let's expand on this same point to include other parts of the approach - again based on the approach snapshot from above - however this time the reported temperature at the airport is -25°C: (temp

**TABLE 1.**

| *PART OF APPROACH* | *ALTITUDE (MSL* | *HEIGHT ABOVE AIRPORT* | *CORRECTION TO BE ADD* | *ALTITUDE TO FLY* |
|---|---|---|---|---|
| Procedure Turn | 2600 | *2000* | *320* | *2920* |
| Final Approach Fix | 2600 | *2000* | *320* | *2920* |
| Missed Approach Point (DH) | 819 | *200* | *30* | *849* |

reporting source)

*Roughly

For those math junkies out there, who can actually fly an instrument approach in a helicopter and do the math at the same time....our fellow Canadian aviators have long used a published formula that looks like this:

From our example above (-25°C reported at the airport) it looks like this:

0.004 x 40 (-25°C is 40°C from ISA) x 200 = 32 feet

(do the math it works!)

## BEYOND IFR

Say this information isn't for you? Think again! The next time you come in for landing to the runway numbers on a DARK night and it is well below standard temperature take the information above into account. You may see the runway numbers and think you are at a 'safe altitude' but as you can see from above you may be lower than your pressure altimeter indicates. And just because you see the runway numbers doesn't mean you see what is below you!

Even consider daytime VFR operations for that matter; add the factor of a cold weather altimeter error and maybe a fresh layer of snow that really reeks havoc on your depth perception and you may just have enough links to complete an accident chain.

CFI's and especially CFI-I's take note of this information and educate your students. Just because you are doing instrument training in 'simulated' conditions in your faster than light piston helicopter doesn't mean that your student or YOU may not find yourself in need of this information whether it be an inadvertent IMC situation or down the road as their careers progress to flying actual IFR Helicopter operations/approaches.

## CONCLUSION

This information shouldn't scare you or seem like another burden of 'one more thing to remember'. It is just something to consider during these cold winter days. Do yourself a favor and make a copy of the Temperature Correction Chart found in the AIM and put it in your nifty little knee board to keep the information handy. Unless of course you are one of those special math junkie kinda people.

.

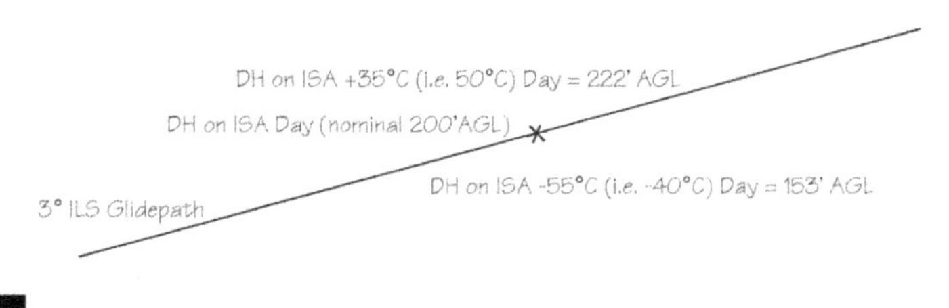


**Figure 40-2 Altimeter in Cold Weather during Approach**

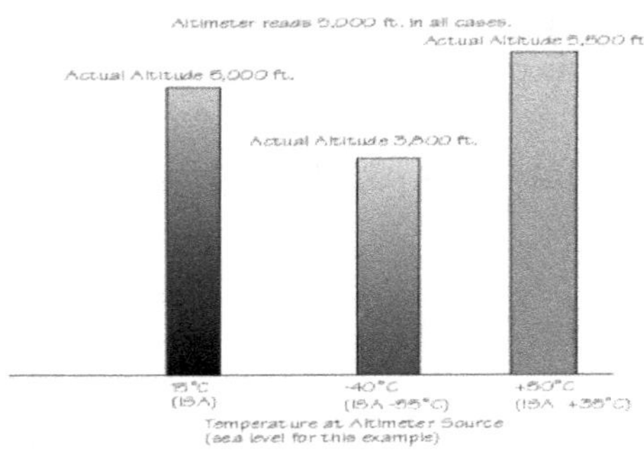


**Figure 40-3 Difference in height for same weight of air at different air temperatures**

After word:

After this was published, I was flying one very cold night, and on intercepting an ILS gliepath, noticed another area of cold-weather effects I had missed in the article. I sent a Letter to the Editor under my real name, which caused great amusement to the editor and those who knew...

# CHAPTER 41 *Low Speed Disorientation*

**Vertical** October / November 2013

*Comment: In daylight, with good visual references, it's pretty hard to get your perception divorced from the reality of what's going on around you.*

In the clouds, or at night, it's a different story. The lack of things in the real world for your eyes to use to perceive motion means we have to rely on instruments — which being of earthly construction have significant limitations on how well they work and what they can tell us.

For example, an artificial horizon (whether mechanical or electronic) reflects (or projects) the same amount of light back to us whether we're in level flight or nose up or nose down. We have to interpret this information and compare it to what we want the attitude of the helicopter to be. If the change of pitch attitude up or down is rapid, our inner ear might help with putting the total picture together, but this can be masked by turbulence, and if the rate of pitch is slow, we may not get warned by that inner ear. We can also use other information such as rate of change of altitude, vertical speed, change of airspeed, wind noise and so on to help us understand what's happening to our aircraft, but if we find ourselves in an unexpected situation, adrenaline may mask any or all of these symptoms.

So, it's easy to see why we can get fooled — and it happens to every type of aerial device from small fixed-wing airplanes to airliners, and helicopters are especially prone by virtue of the proliferation of glass (which permits more distracting visual cues to be thrown at the crew) and the ability to fly at low speeds. The inherent instability of the helicopter doesn't help, and the ability to lift off into very poor visual conditions with little (or no) forward airspeed rounds off the list of reasons why helicopters are perhaps the most likely flying machines to cause disorientation.

Different Aircraft, Different Problem

Consider a fixed-wing airplane taking off. It won't lift off the ground, let alone climb until it has considerable forward speed. Assuming the airplane never gets close to the stall, there's really only one or two ways that the aircraft can wander away from a "controlled" situation — in pitch, it can only go to a nose-high, airspeed decreasing; or nose-low, airspeed increasing situation. In roll, it can go left or right. Hardly anything would ever cause an airplane to establish an unusual attitude in yaw in forward flight. So the fixed-wing pilot is faced with a relatively small number of situations that could be classified as disorienting, and can thus pretty easily be trained to recognize and recover from those situations. Even this relatively simple set of conditions, however, has caused significant grief in the fixed-wing world. Consider the crash of the Air France Airbus A330-203 over the middle of the Atlantic in the middle of night — following loss of pitot static information — as just one example. So the emphasis on disorientation that we've inherited in the helicopter world has a distinct fixed-wing bias. And since nearly all helicopter instrument flight rules (IFR) flying and night flying is at speeds above $V_Y$ (minimum power speed), it's pretty reasonable to expect that this is all we need.

Unfortunately some recent incidents have shown where things really do start to fall apart in the helicopter-only regime of flying — namely at speeds near and below $V_Y$. Say, for example, a helicopter is on an instrument approach, with the autopilot fully coupled maintaining glideslope and track. For reasons that are not clear, the machine is permitted to slow below $V_Y$. What the crew hasn't noticed (or realized) is that as the aircraft falls below a certain relatively slow airspeed, the yaw channel reverts to heading hold — not turn coordination — and as they try to turn (using cyclic to change angle of bank), the helicopter is suddenly maintaining heading but with an angle of bank and not turning. Confusion multiplies upon confusion, and pretty soon they are out of control.

Heading is a difficult parameter to monitor at slow speeds, because small inputs can cause relatively large heading changes, but with few noticeable cues to the pilots. The Royal Air Force used to demonstrate this by putting student pilots in a box that was on a turntable with very smooth bearings. After the lid was closed, the student would be talking to the instructor for several minutes and at some point during this conversation, the box would be rotated, but at a very, very slow acceleration, below the threshold of perception of yaw. After several minutes of acceleration, the rate of rotation would be quite high, but not perceivable by the pilot. The box's lid would then be quickly removed and the pilot presented with a rapid rotation, but with an inner ear quite convinced it was not rotating. The scrambled signals between the two sensors often resulted in a display of the contents of the pilot's stomach. There are other equally compelling ways to show how our senses can be scrambled — and hence the need for training to believe your instruments instead of your senses.

## Diagnosing Disorientation

For those who haven't been disorientated in an aircraft before, you need to learn to believe the instruments — after learning to recognize the symptoms of "not so controlled" flight. And herein lies a problem for the helicopter world. While we know and practice unusual attitude recovery in forward flight (i.e. nose high, airspeed decreasing or nose low, airspeed increasing), we seldom think about how we can get disoriented in the region between liftoff and $V_Y$. A recent incident offshore showed this problem with nearly disastrous results. The large, two-crew helicopter was taking off from the back of an oil support ship at night in relatively rough weather. After clearing the deck, and an initial nose down pitch to accelerate, something must have triggered the flying pilot to put in a very large aft stick input — perhaps the pattern of lights of the oil support vessel that was on his side of the helicopter, or something else we'll never know. Regardless of the source, it was compelling enough to cause him to put in a very large aft stick input, and the helicopter suddenly pitched to about 20-degrees nose up — an attitude that would never normally be seen in any flight regime. The helicopter decelerated to zero airspeed as it climbed and then started to slide backwards and down towards the water. For some reason the non-flying pilot did and said nothing — he may have been busy with other duties or so perplexed at what was going on as to be unable to offer any good advice. At some point during this, someone recognized the very unusual nature of things and attempted a recovery action — and recovery was started. But it was such a close call that the safety watch on the oil supply vessel was ready to press the crash button when he saw the helicopter rapidly descending backwards towards the water and only when it emerged seconds later from the spray that was sent up by the rotor downwash did he start to breathe again. Some post-flight analysis of the angles used and heights above the waves convinced many that there had been some divine intervention that night.

When I was told of this incident, I wondered if no-one was teaching the instrument takeoff technique any longer. That technique had certainly saved my bacon when I encountered disorientation at low level over the water, even though that had not been the intended teaching point! I was flying a Royal Navy Lynx, and we were supposed to be firing a missile on a test range that morning. The test range was in the Irish Sea, and that morning it was covered in mist and fog. There was also a sailboat transiting the range, and we were going to see if we could identify it for some further visit by the constabulary. The navigator was giving me headings and airspeeds to fly, and I knew we were getting quite close to the boat, even though I was flying solely on instruments. The speeds kept getting slower and slower, and the turns larger and larger. Suddenly, I saw the sail go by just below us to the left, and the navigator gave a very large turn, and... I lost it! I had no idea where we were spatially, there was no airspeed, and we were at a steady height of about 100 feet above the waves. I immediately reverted to the instrument takeoff technique of "wings level, heading constant, apply power — and then looked for rates of climb on the vertical speed indicator, followed by climb on the altimeter. When I had both of those, I lowered the nose five degrees while continuing to climb, and maintained heading. When we got to 60 knots, I raised the nose and continued to climb. And restarted my heart.

Only later that day in the bar did I thank those instructors and check pilots who made me fly this procedure again and again, because back then, I considered the procedure quaint but useless — if the weather was that bad, I wouldn't be flying, so why was an instrument takeoff something I needed to do?

So, perhaps we need to rethink our emphasis on disorientation and unusual attitudes in helicopters — the slow speed stuff could be more important than the high-speed.

# CHAPTER 42 *Digital Fuel Controls*

ROTOR&WING INTERNATIONAL May 1995

*Comment: REDLINE! You've just overtemped your helicopter's engine, and it's going to cost you money. Too bad the engine didn't have a full authority digital engine control (FADEC). The computerized device could have saved you a tidy sum of money.*

Digital computers have transformed many aspects of our lives and are no stranger to the modern helicopter cockpit. They are now being applied to controlling engines with some surprising results. FADECs have mostly appeared on new engines, but now is being tried on earlier models.

## *WHAT'S THE IMPORT?*

Most of us have heard about FADECs, but it's likely many don't fully understand them or their use. This article aims to clarify why FADECs are appearing in helicopter engines, there are some concerns. To begin with, hold firmly in your mind that everything is a compromise. The turbine engine itself represents a compromise, but we have grown to accept its strengths and work around most of the weaknesses.

Mechanics, think about how much time you spend setting up engines (especially multiengine installations with different time engines), troubleshooting gripes about engine response, and so on.

Pilots, think about how much time you spend monitoring engine and transmission parameters, matching torques, setting up engines, performing power checks, and so on. If you fly a multiengine helicopter, think of the workload when one engine fails-new limits to monitor and obey; at a very stressful time.

One helicopter I know of has five limitation levels (continuous twin, takeoff twin, continuous one-engine inoperative [OEI], 30-minute OEI, 2.5-minute, with three parameters (TOT, torque, and $N_l$) to monitor for each engine. Of course, none of the numbers are the same between the limits. In a rapidly changing situation (such as an engine failure on takeoff), it was impossible to fly the helicopter and respect many of the limits.

FADECs offer a means to precisely automate these functions, plus deliver many other capabilities not afforded by the hydromechanical fuel control, otherwise known as a governor.

## *HYDROMECHANICAL CONTROLS*

The most prominent type of fuel control on helicopter engines, the hydromechanical fuel control senses the speed of the power (or free) turbine and, by regulating fuel flow and compressor speed, it attempts to maintain the free-turbine speed at a certain value. The value basically depends on power demands balanced against the need to avoid compressor stalls or flameouts.

The fuel control unit may offer "stops" to prevent compressor speed from exceeding limits and possibly have an overspeed system to prevent the free and compressor turbines from running away and disintegrating.

In multiengine installations, the fuel control system may also provide automatic torque matching. A few have torque limiters to prevent overtorquing. Other small differences may exist on certain helicopters, but by and large, that is normally all you get with a hydromechanical fuel control.

A key complaint from pilots about hydromechanical fuel controls is that they inhibit engine response to demands for power changes. Why don't the engines respond fast enough? One reason is that (one of those compromises) turbines just take longer to spool up or down in reaction to throttle movements.

For its part, the hydromechanical fuel control does not like rapid power changes. Its job is to assure the engine accelerates or decelerates in a manner to avoid compressor stalling or flaming out, respectively. By design, its job of avoiding stalls or flameouts "outranks" pilot demand for power. The acceleration may be slow but the engine. won't cough at a bad time.

Here's an example. Consider that a pilot applies a large collective -up at the end of a quick stop, when engine power is low and the rotor is nearly in autorotation. The fuel control, meanwhile responding to the quick stop, is letting the compressor wind down in speed because the power turbine is running too fast. The fuel control wants to get the power turbine back down to a "correct" speed. The fuel control won't think it should start increasing compressor speed until it sees the power turbine rpm is reduced to just below the correct value. Then it responds to the demand for power and has to make a major effort to get back to the required value.

One attempt to improve the situation is to feed in an anticipator signal from the collective-as a way to forewarn the fuel control of the pilot's next "move." But the problem is that the fuel control really needs rate of collective change, not just position of collective to make its response better.

Similarly, when the power is reduced rapidly, the fuel control can allow the engine to decelerate only so quickly. If the fuel were cut off too abruptly, the engine would flame out.

We've just explained one problem- what about the others mentioned earlier; that add to mechanic and pilot workloads? Furthermore, new engine certification regulations that allow new engine limits, such as two-minute and 30-second OEI ratings, require automatic control and recording of the limits.

To do a better job, the fuel control unit needs more inputs and capabilities But the plumbing of hydro-mechanical fuel control units is already awesome. Just look at a diagram of the typical fuel control system's inputs and outputs (above).

## *ADVENT OF FADEC*

Getting more inputs meant "going electronic". Electronic controls for turbine engines have been around, in piecemeal fashion, since the early 1970s. Early models were analog in construction and needed as much attention as the hydromechanical components they replaced. Failures were often mystifying and frequent.

Yet work progressed, as the push for better fuel control/governing came from military aviators. They wanted more rapid engine response for aggressive nap-of-the-earth flight and just weren't getting it fast enough from conventional hydromechanical fuel control systems.

Adding to the problem was the trend toward lower rotor inertia and increased engine inertia (heavier compressors, etc.), These two items work against power changes.

Thought processes started down the way of using a computer, and other ideas started to surface. What if other sensors could be used? Instead of a mechanical sensor of power turbine what if a more-accurate, optical sensor could be used?

The gateway to such capability came through digital computers, resulting in the advent of FADECs. They possess vastly increased capability, speed, reliability, and resistance to electromagnetic interference. All at a much lower cost than before.

The term FADEC means Full Authority Digital Engine Control. It is termed "full authority" because some early computerized fuel controls only worked on a small part of the fuel flow to the engine (conservative bunch, these engine designers).

Note also that it is not merely a "fuel" control, but a broader "engine" applications. Digital computer logic enables FADECs to accept and analyze a seemingly infinite number of inputs and make intelligent decisions about responses. Is the fuel flow where it should be for these conditions? If yes, continue with the present fuel flow · if no, change the fuel flow depending upon a whole range of conditions

In basic terms, the FADEC computer receives signals from sensors, applies the logic laid out by the designers and causes a fuel valve to move to make the engine deliver the required response.

For example, instead of a "controlled explosion" on start, the FADEC can schedule fuel to make a smooth, cool start repeatedly every time. It can record the start parameters prevent overtemps, and it may abort the whole start to prevent burning up the engine.

Another example of the logic concerns the relationship between rotor speed and free turbine speed. FADEC compares the two signals, and if the rotor speed is higher than normal and the free turbine speed is also high, FADEC reduces fuel flow to keep the free turbine speed at the normal speed.

If it sees the rotor rpm decaying from needles-split condition and the collective being raised, the FADEC concludes that the pilot is going to apply power. To assist the engine s to respond and to reduce the amount of rotor rpm decay the FADEC will increase the free turbine speed to match the rotor speed by increasing the fuel flow to the engines and starting compressor acceleration. The end result is a reduced transient rotor rpm droop. It also results in a very smooth free-wheel reengagement.

## *EXCEEDANCES, BEGONE!*

It is in the protection of limits (TOT torque, and Nl) that FADECs are really showing their worth. And torque matching is provided with ease. On at least one F ADEC engine /airframe combination, it is impossible to get to the OEI limits unless the other engine is stopped or its Nl is well below the self-sustaining idle speed.

Another FADEC system has a training mode, where the "Goodwin's limits are artificially lowered for single-engine training. During training with this system, engine control lever s are not pulled back. The reason: if the "good" engine fails, the other engine will instantly respond with full power, not limited. Clever logic, but much different from what we are used to. Since the higher OEI limits are never reached in day-to-day operation, the engine manufacturer can increase these limits, giving better single-engine capability. This has to give pilots a level of security, in knowing that power -will be there when it's needed.

Eliminating overtorques and overtemps -even limiting the output of the engine to assure it doesn't get abused -is possible. Aircraft owners will love it, because the cost of engine maintenance for "abuse" has just gone down. But remember, what we said about compromise. Pilots understandably want power available in cases of emergency. So any FADEC programming to eliminate exceedances should also be programmed to address legitimate needs to "pull power and go."

The list of FADEC benefits is just starting. Another example, no more engine set ups-if the FADEC needs replacing, Just plug it in and go. No idle adjustments, torque-matching adjustments, acceleration time adjustments and so on.

Several FADECs automatically perform a built-in test when electrical power is applied to the engine. And they also test sensors and internal logic continually. Most FADECs record data on exceedances of limits and let the maintenance people take note of them.

Some FADEC systems even are capable of continuous engine-trend monitoring, opening the door for many other ways to lower maintenance costs and workload.

Engine start cycles can be counted accurately. The number of times the engine has gone from "off' to idle rpm is counted, not just the number of times the start button has been pressed.

Ah, you ask, what if they fail? First they are less likely to fail, since there are fewer connections and fittings (i e less plumbing). Second, the system is designed to warn the pilot before it fails complete ly. Third, the types of failures are actually very limited. If anything goes wrong, the FADEC can freeze the fuel flow, run it up, or run it down. The most common failure mode wi ll be the "freeze" in power; FADEC designers programmed the computer to pick this path (it has the least "drama"). Nearly all the engines with FADEC I am aware of offer a reversion to manual control. Controlling the engine in this case is the same as a piston engine helicopter. The one type I know of without a manual reversion has a dual computer/sensor suite FADEC.

FADEC designers have been very cautious in addressing possibilities of failures and warnings to pilots. For example, they found one remotely possible internal failure that could run the engine up in manual mode, and a maximum of a half-second could elapse before the pilot was warned.

Even then, the worst the engine could do was run up to a moderate power set- ting in three seconds. Since this could occur while the pilot was not looking at instruments, it was decided to make the failure warning both aural and visual. Testing showed that there was ample time to chop the engine control lever and not have a large rotor overspeed.

Benefits and cautions

What are the practical benefits for pilots? Starts will be more predictable, probably cooler and quicker. Once engines are started, you may be able to ignore engine parameters, as the FADEC will tend to them. You may also have a choice of which way to match the engines-either TOT or torque.

All power will be available from both engines at all times. With a normal · torque-matching system, when one engine reaches its limits (say TOT), you have to stop pulling up on the collective, and the power from the other engine will be unavailable.

The FADEC systems I have seen will match torques until the TOT limit is reached and then limit only the high TOT engine. Pulling up on the collective will demand power from the other engine until it too reaches its limit.

In one particular helicopter with a FADEC, the advice to the pilot is that you know you are at takeoff power when the rotor rpm starts to droop. During critical situations, such as practicing for single-engine failures, the pilot can concentrate on looking outside and let the computer monitor the limits. There is no need to look inside to monitor the good engine, so that you don't literally pull the guts out of it when you are staking everything on it.

Since the main reason for starting down the electronic road was more rapid response to power changes, FADECs should be good at that. The turbine engine still requires time to spool up or down, but the multi-sensored, computerized FADEC is an immensely better "time manager" than its hydro-mechanical counterpart.

To be honest, I am amazed at the engine responses. As a test pilot, sometimes you have to do nasty things to fine pieces of engineering. One of them is rapid power demands from low power to maximum in very short times, in less than a second. The FADEC engines have handled them very well. So far, I have found it impossible to trick them with varying frequencies of collective inputs, or rejected landings, or anything else perverse.

## *Concern Remain*

Yes, FADECs are impressive, but some concerns remain. One is the desire of engineers to protect the engine and helicopter, sometimes at all costs, from being overpowered. Yet extra power-more than a pilot is "allowed" to use--is sometimes needed. Rather than deny the pilot this power ("The engine was protecting itself from being overtorqued when it crashed...)

May I suggest some "last chance" logic? When the pilot pulls to twin-engine takeoff power limits, the system protects itself and the rotor rpm decays I suggest that the system should permit the rotor rpm to decay-but only until it reaches a minimum value and then not let it go any lower.

Engines, transmissions, and components are much cheaper than airframes, lawsuits, or human lives. Since the FADEC is recording all these parameters anyway, this should be viewed as a one-time, save-the-bacon affair.

What has to change from a piloting point of view?

First, don't leap into a machine with FADEG and expect things to be the same. Engines may be started with the throttles at Idle or perhaps even at the Flight position. The Flight position may not be the maximum travel available, and advancing the throttle beyond this position may have no effect in the normal, automatic mode.

One certain change is the way that engine failures will be simulated- Anyone who reaches up and grabs a throttle and yanks it back may be unpleasantly surprised. They may not get to super contingency ratings or if they do, they may not like the cost of using them. The new engines may only allow so many "pulls" to the super contingency rating before you have to overhaul the engine.

Finally, pilots need to be very vocal about the requirement to have power in an emergency. Looking at the cost of FADECs, well, nothing is free. But the cost of a FADEC system will not be as much as the cost of an engine or transmission.

Since parameters are more closely matched and the potential for "abuse" is reduced, the engine has a better chance of reaching its overhaul life. Perhaps FADECs could result in longer engine overhaul lives. It offers to also reduce day-to-day maintenance hours and costs, resulting in higher airframe availability.

The benefits are just beginning to be understood and will be clearer in near-term future. Perhaps by then, engine' s will be treated the same as the transmission -a hunk of very precise metal that does its job without a lot of pampering

# CHAPTER 43 *Digital Engine Control Failures*

**Vertical** 2007

*Comment: Part of my attempt to keep the mortgage paid involves working with lawyers to help delve into various rotorcraft accidents.*

While the financial aspect is part of the draw, I'm also fascinated by being able to find an accident's root cause. As an ex-certification test pilot for Transport Canada, I have maintained my interest in failure cases (although some have argued that this interest borders on being perverse... but that's a story for another issue). My interest is aided (or depending on how you look at it, my obsession encouraged), by having lots of contacts around the industry who provide me with deep background into interesting incidents or accidents. From this and other insights and information, I've begun to notice a trend regarding the failure of digital engine controls. It is a trend that appears to have begun about 10 years ago and has continued unabated. These are not engine failures per se, but digital fuel control failures. Perhaps better stated: they are failures resulting from the unusual aspects of digital engine controls, coupled with the lack of proper training on these devices. At the end of the day, the digital system was doing pretty much what it was supposed to be doing, but the pilot failed to know what to do.

## The Origins of the Problem

The trend appears to have started with a helicopter retrofitted with an engine featuring a digital fuel control. Shortly after the pilot got checked out in the machine, at night, the digital fuel control had a minor malfunction. Properly handled, the pilot should have reverted to manual control, come back and landed. Non-digital fuel control versions of the engine had a manual reversion mode, so this should have been a complete nonevent — but only if the pilot had been trained properly. This pilot, unfortunately, couldn't sort out the fuel control malfunction, and elected to do a night autorotation. The result was that the helicopter ended up being written off. Not much later, another type of helicopter (a new model this time) came onto the market. It was also fitted with a digital fuel control. Several incidents and accidents later, the fuel control architecture had to be significantly revamped to make it easier to understand and capable of dealing with malfunctions. Some of the blame for this could be laid on the design of the fuel control and its installation in the helicopter, but consider that the first incidents happened to instructors at the factory training school (they didn't understand the system). Oddly enough, years later, there is still no requirement in the United States that anyone need have detailed knowledge of how the system works in order to fly the machine safely. (Other countries have type ratings for each model of helicopter, which solves the problem in those countries.) Not surprisingly, incidents are still happening with this model in the U.S., mostly due to pilot error in not knowing how to handle relatively minor failures.

## The Problem Expands

Fast forward several years and we encounter several different light-twin helicopters that arrive on the market at the same time. All of these models have variations of the same engine and all have digital fuel controls. Different variations of engine controls appear, most with rotary knobs to set the condition of the engine. Some also incorporate throttles that are the same as those used in earlier models of the same helicopter. Others have just throttles but no knobs. Not long after these models come into service, strange failures start to happen — and not just to one brand of these airframes. Most of the manufacturers report pilots taking off with one engine at fly and one at idle. One report even has someone trying to takeoff with both engines at idle! The only manufacturer who didn't report the one-at-idle, one-at-fly problem is the only one that doesn't use the three-position rotary knobs to control the engine condition. This manufacturer has only throttles and the throttles are used all the time. In the other machines, the ones with the problems, there are either no throttles, or the throttles are used only in emergency procedures. Meanwhile, the three position, engine-condition knobs

are not prominently located in the pilot's field of view, nor are they reachable with hands on the flight controls. To make matters worse, for the helicopters that had the engine problems with one-at-idle and one-at-fly, all of those have at least six or seven separate indications of the situation — indications that go beyond different compressor speeds, power turbine speed, torque and turbine temperature. These include indications like OEI (one engine inoperative) in big red lettering, no less; or "IDLE" on the display. Interestingly, all the reported incidents involved single-pilot operations, but more on that later. Why did some, but not all, manufacturers use the three-position knob instead of the throttles? It's difficult to say, but it appears they erred on the side of engineering convenience. Setting up the throttles as the only way to control the engine required integrating mechanical and electrical mechanisms, and was not as easy as only using an electrical switch for normal operation and the throttles for only emergency, mechanical operation. (One company did manage to solve this problem satisfactorily, though.)

## *The Heart of the Issue*

When I think of these incidents, I recall the discipline drilled into me during my military training. I trained on a military version of the Bell 212. Our takeoff check consisted of physically checking that both throttles were in the flight (fully open) position, rotor RPM was 100 per cent, engine indications were matched, temperatures and pressures were in the green range, and there were no caution lights. (This I remember from 30 years ago, so it must have been pretty good training and memory work: "Two full, 100 per cent, matched, Ts and Ps in the green, no lights.") Has no one ever demanded a check like this of the pilots who had these incidents/accidents? Evidently not. When questioned, one of the pilots, who had taken off with one at idle and one at fly, responded that his pre-takeoff check was "three in the green." When questioned further about three in the green, he indicated it had nothing to do with the engine situation... I'll save him the embarrassment of not repeating what he said he was checking, but suffice it to say that if those three things had not been green, he would be sitting much lower to the ground. What was perhaps even more amazing was that none of his supervisors or medical crews had ever questioned what it was he was checking. The other person in the front seat didn't know what the pilot was supposed to be checking prior to takeoff, so he had no way to know what was right or wrong. The pre-takeoff check from my military days was simple, used by everyone and took mere seconds to accomplish. It double-checked the situation without making too much of a meal of things (e.g., you wouldn't have 100 per cent rotor RPM without both throttles being at flight).

A suggestion put forward by one manufacturer was that pilots should use the flight manual procedure. Since no manufacturer in this weight range publishes a cockpit-sized checklist, this means using the normal flight manual. Anyone who has ever tried to manhandle any flight manual while just sitting in the cockpit, let alone while trying to control the helicopter, will realize this is an incredibly head-in-the-clouds approach. For the manufacturer who suggested it, their pre-takeoff checks cover two pages in the manual, when less than half a page would have been sufficient. But even a simple checklist is difficult to handle in a single-pilot helicopter when you need both hands on the flight controls. The common thread running through all these incidents and accidents is the pilots themselves. Either they were not trained properly, or were not following what should be simple, easy-to-follow practice.

## *Overcoming the Problem*

Now, I don't like to just point out a problem and then run away, so I'll ask the obvious question: What can be done about this? Pilots too often have to compensate for shortcomings or compromises in design. While we're used to that, we shouldn't have to be. So, let's start at the source. Manufacturers should engineer out possible sources of error. Don't use switches for engineering convenience. It takes a bit more design effort to incorporate the throttles so they become the normal way of controlling the engines, instead of only being used in emergencies, but it's worth it. Let's prevent mistakes before they happen. On the pilot side of things, if they are to overcome design shortcomings, they should at least have the proper training. Training required by the authorities and by the insurance companies. This training should also have definite training objectives, demonstrations of proficiency as requirements to pass the course, and be repeated at intervals. Above all, though, this training must be on the systems. Finally, we need checks that are going to be the last chance to stop mistakes from happening. Proper procedures should be developed by the manufacturers so that things like the pre-takeoff checks are simple, easy-to-follow and thorough. Supervisors could insist on memorized pre-takeoff checks said out loud (in single-pilot operations). Medical crews that know what should be said and what the instrument panel shouldn't look like (no red labels or lights!) could be another important link in the chain to prevent an incident or accident. Digital fuel controls are here to stay. We need to make sure we understand how they work and how to deal with potential problems if we want to make a dent in their related accident rates. argued than this interest borders on being perverse... but that's a story for another issue.

.

Figure 43-1 **Digital Fuel Control Boxes**

# CHAPTER 44 *Loss of Tail Rotor Effectiveness and the Engine Governor*

Not Previously Published

*Comment: Loss of Tail Rotor Effectiveness is a little understood subject, and I applaud anyone who attempts to shed more light on the subject. But most leave out a major part of the problem.*

I've done some pretty abrupt hover turns in my flight testing career in a wide variety of helicopters, and never seen anything untoward happen. Maybe I've just been very lucky.

The item that must be addressed is the myth of "tail rotor stall". All the investigations into this by Bell Helicopter (the only company to investigate it I know of), showed quite clearly that the tail rotor was not stalled. It was still producing thrust, but not enough thrust for the situation. Don't use the word stall, as it might lead some people to use the incorrect recovery technique.

That notwithstanding, there is another potential cause that was not considered. That is due to the engine governor. What follows is true only for a turbine engine helicopter (although it may be true for an R-22 or R-44 with a governor, I'm not in a position to say that I can prove it).

First of all, a question. If the pilot of a Bell 206 sitting in the hover on a light wind day (not at maximum weight or close to any limits) adds a reasonable amount of left pedal, will the helicopter climb or descend if the collective is not touched? To those who have not tried this, it will climb- and the answer is due to the governor. If you'd like to think of the governor as counting the rate of blades passing the centerline of the helicopter, then as you turn left (in the same direction as the main rotor rotation), the governor thinks the blades have slowed down, and it will add fuel to get the rotor RPM back to the datum value. In the cockpit, you'd see the rotor RPM slow down as you add the pedal, then a very short time later, all the engine parameters would increase and you would start to climb. Sitting in the cockpit, the rotor RPM may say 100%, but remember that's with respect to the helicopter.

The rotor speed may not have changed with respect to the helicopter, but it will have changed with respect to the earth, and that is what produces the increased lift.

The governor, unfortunately, works against you in a right turn, and I would not advise you to try this unless you are in very light wind conditions, start from a 10-12' AGL hover, and are prepared to recover quickly.

Adding a boastful of right pedal will result in the rotor RPM increasing and then a short time later, all the engine parameters and torque decreasing, and the helicopter descending. If you start into wind, you'll be translating downwind as you descend and turn - not a pretty feeling.

The governor is pretty accurate, and even a slow rate of turn is easily sensed by it. For example, 30 degrees per second is a very mild hover turn, and yet is about 5 RPM. For the governor, this is about 1.5%, and it will do it's best to correct for that.

The rates of yaw in any LTE incidents I've read about are pretty high- and the figure quoted in the article of 75 degrees per second reflects that, and the governor can certainly correct a lot for that.

The problem with the governor affecting the rotor RPM is that this also affects the tail rotor, and for a right turn that will decrease the rotor RPM with respect to the earth, also means the tail rotor will lose some of its capability to generate thrust.

I've tried this in nearly all of the 60 helicopter types I've flown, and it works in all of them (except tandems and coaxials or any pure piston engine with no governor). FADEC equipped engines have a 'tighter' governor and if anything a more pronounced effect.

Another item that deserves serious consideration is the effect of turning from into wind to downwind. And I don't want to get into a big discussion about this- it has been my experience that kinetic energy with respect to the ground has to be considered whenever maneuvering through a change in relative wind direction. That is also exactly what happens in most of these situations- at slow ground speed the helicopter has very little kinetic energy with respect to the ground, but the airspeed means that the power required is relatively low. Change the airspeed to zero or possibly a tailwind, and without a corresponding increase in power, the helicopter will settle. The change in the balance of moments is something that not even I can begin to figure out- perhaps Dennis' cousin the mechanical engineer could help.

One of the best solutions I've heard for preventing loss of tail rotor effectiveness in the Bell 206 series is to always turn left- it does several things- it keeps the airspeed in your field of regard, and forces you to know what it is. As far as is known, it has never happened in a turn to the left.

# CHAPTER 45 *Fuel Nozzle Clogging*

**Vertical** Not Sure

*Comment: Sometime we come upon stories in strange ways. Ways that are strange to us, but ways that make sense in the cosmic plan, somehow.*

This is one of those stories.

While researching a year's worth of helicopter accidents for a presentation, I noticed two accidents caused by fuel nozzle clogging. This appeared to be a bit unusual, and I filed the information away in that part of the brain reserved for odd socks, single shoelaces and the like.

Sometime later, I happened to be talking to one of the experts I work with frequently on legal cases. He's one of those multi-faceted folks who combines deep technical knowledge, a great memory and superb common sense. Somehow the subject of clogged fuel nozzles came up, and we talked for a while about the subject, and then he said – there's someone you really should talk to about this – a real expert. Coming from my friend, this recommendation was going to be a good to follow.

After the email address popped onto my screen, I sent an email and promised to follow up with a phone call. Several weeks passed, and the pressure of work pushed things into the background, until the name popped up in one of the all-too-infrequent computer cleanings.

With some trepedition, I phoned. Sometimes people don't want to talk to someone who is involved with legal cases. I understand, even when I promise that no names will be mentioned, it takes a bit of convincing that I protect my sources. So, having been put through, I introduced myself and explained the reason for the call. (The email hadn't ever got through).

The man at the other end of the line (we'll call him Combustion Bob, as he's deep into turbine engines, and the combustion chamber is about as deep as you can get in a turbine engine) was quite open, and so the conversation evolved.

The problem is quite widespread, and has just become more common in the past several years with the introduction of – wait for it, because you'll have difficulty believing it – low-sulphur diesel fuel. (as the owner of an old diesel Mercedes I was immediately interested in this).

Struggling to make the connection, Combustion Bob explained. Sulphur in diesel fuel was actually a bit of a lubrication (as well as a source of pollution). When it was removed from the fuel, something needed to be added to the fuel to restore the lubricating properties – and the something was lots of different chemicals. When used in diesel engines they work just fine. But what is the connection to turbine engines?

.

**Figure 45-1** xxxx

# CHAPTER 46 *Recuperation for Helicopter Engine*

**Vertical** Not Sure

*Comment: One of the things that I love about trade shows is looking for new technology, or new applications of existing technology.*

## *RECUPER WHAT?*

In fact, my perfect job would be 'Trade Show Junkie', and I'm still looking for the sugar daddy to bankroll it.

At Heli-Expo 2009, a small booth from Frontline Aerospace had a fascinating application of technology to helicopter that's been used for a long time on stationary gas turbines.

For anyone who knows anything about turbine engine performance, where cold air is better than hot air, it sounds strange at first to try to recapture the heat spewing out the exhaust and recycle it back into the engine. As with anything, a little knowledge is sometimes a dangerous thing. In this case, using the exhaust gas usefully makes a lot of sense when you understand what's being done.

The basic principle of a gas turbine is to extract heat energy from burning fuel. Air is compressed by the compressor section and sent to a combustion chamber where fuel is added. The fuel-air mixture burns and a portion of the energy is used to power the compressor. The rest of the exhaust gases are either used for propulsion (a pure jet) or have the energy extracted by turbine wheels. Pretty simple – but consider how much energy is heading out the exhaust in terms of hot gas. If some of that could be used fuel efficiency would increase. The problem is where to put that heat. Turns out that the ideal place for putting heat is into the air coming from the compressor before the combustion chamber. For stationary gas turbines (gas pipelines, ships, etc.) this is done through a complex series of heat exchangers and suitable tubing. Size and weight of the heat exchangers for ground based applications are of little significance. However, for aircraft, size and weight are critical issues and have prevented the use of recuperators.

Frontline Aerospace, Inc as part of their ummanned aerial system development found that the Rolls-Royce 250 series engines were an excellent fit for their MicroFire™ recuperator because the compressed discharge air tube crosses right by the exhaust duct, other gas turbines are considerably more complicated to retrofit.

All recuperators involve directing air from the compressor through the heat exchanger, where heat from the exhaust is extracted, and then re-directing the much hotter gas to the combustion chamber.

Why would you want to add heat to the air going to the combustion chamber? Several reasons spring to mind – better evaporation of the fuel mixture means better combustion with fewer particulates. Hotter air vaporizes the fuel better than cold air, yet the key reason for a recuperator is that with hotter air less fuel is needed to bring the combustion gases to temperature and create work. The end result is improved fuel economy – up to 40% savings in a steady state is being projected. Even if it means at the end of the day only 25% improvement in fuel economy – that' significant.

Now fuel economy may not be a big thing for some helicopter missions, but with the price of fuel being what it is and not likely to come down, for a lot of folks this can be a significant saving. For those involved in loiter missions, such as police operations, it means longer time on station between refueling (which might start to cause bladder pressure problems with the crew, but that's another issue).

But there's no such thing as a free lunch – the heat exchanger and associated plumbing will probably weigh about 40 to 50 pounds. And the effect on TOT is not yet clear – tests are just getting underway on the concept.

But at least someone is looking at ways to improve our fuel economy. And ways to keep me looking for new stuff at trade shows!

# CHAPTER 47 *Can You Trust Your Navigation Data?*

Not Previously Published

*Comment: A flight management system (FMS) resided only between the flight crew's ears. All procedures were visually described-analog in nature-and carried out in accordance with practiced procedures.*

*Problem was driven by very small memory in units. Remember wkem 30mn was a big drive?*

## *IN THE BEGINNING*

For many years, airlines flew instrument procedures using paper approach charts and maps, and with only ground- based navigation aids. Some major airlines still maintain such procedures.

Then along came the inertial navigation system (INS). Initially, only the 'big boys,' who took advantage of earth- bound navigation aids to keep the INS updated, operated them. The price of an INS was a major factor, along with its weight and size. INSs were used solely for high-altitude, en-route navigation, and only as a supplement to conventional navigation aids.

Then came two explosions in technology: growth in computer power and memory, and the arrival of Global Positioning System (GPS) navigation. Separately, their effect on aviation was significant. Combined, it became earth shaking.

In terms of flight planning and accuracy, what once was possible only in

transoceanic jets is now achievable in a Cessna 172. Virtually every aircraft type and operation have benefited from this incredible technology duo. With powerful computers, small business aircraft could adopt a complex FMS. With GPS, even small general aviation aircraft could enjoy very accurate navigation.

## *THE DOWN SIDE*

But technology can be a mixed blessing. In the past, computerized FMSs were used only for high altitude, en-route navigation by a small group of highly trained, regularly tested professional crews. Capabilities were limited, and the procedures were not used near the ground. Any instrument approaches were flown using ground-based navigation aids that were closely monitored and cross checked.

Now we have a wide cross section of pilots-some with no training on the equipment (let alone an ability to use the equipment during a flight test)- using an FMS that will fly a complete arrival and instrument approach. Instead of radio signals, today's pilots use only mythical points in space for guidance, with no ability to cross check, and with the potential for errors along the chain of events.

And technology is only as good as the data it uses. With the FMS, the problems commonly are due to inaccurate data. As always, the regulators have not quite caught up with the technology. Things are not as secure as you may think, and with inaccurate data, the problem will likely affect one of the most critical flight procedures: the instrument approach.

A leading avionics manufacturer currently conducting a comprehensive survey found errors in 95% of the instrument approach procedures due to inaccurate data, and 5% of the errors wer significant.'

It was once fashionable to say these problems were all and solely due to the databases. However, some sleuthing revealed that this answer can be superficial-and often proffered by avionics manufacturers to deflect criticism.

In fact, there exists an end-to-end problem with the data acquisition and processing procedure. It can start at the raw data used to develop the instrument procedures, range through the manipulation of that data into a manageable database, and finally come out of an FMS as something that bears little resemblance to what may be printed on an approach plate.

## *FROM THE BEGINNING*

Where do the errors come from?

Let's start with the raw data, most of which comes from national authorities under an International Civil Aviation Organization (ICAO) agreement. There is no guarantee that the data is all correct, or even that people in those countries care about their data.

Many countries do not have the correct geographic referencesystems, so if you want to use their data, you must first convert it all to the same format. An example is the WGS-84

standard used for GPS data; not all countries adhere to the standard, so conversion is required.

And you thought you had a problem with high school geometry.

If you have only an ILS, or even a VOR at a remote airfield, the VOR's or airfield's exact location matters little, so long as the two are correct relative to each other. But when you introduce the use of highly accurate GPS, any prior variance can cause confusion.

Today's computers can also cause confusion. For instance, most instrument approach procedures were designed to be flown using analog, ground-based equipment, with humans or, at best, analog computers making decisions on rate of turn, corrections to desired track, and so on. However, some procedures just cannot be coded into a format suitable for a digital computer. In other words, procedures that are not difficult for humans may be impossible for the airborne computer.

**Computers Force Compromise** Remember that when this computerization process started in navigation, computers were nowhere near as capable as they are now. In fact, only the very latest FMSs use an Intel 486 processor.

Memory is another matter. No FMS today has more than 4 megabytes of RAM, a major contributor to the data accuracy problem. If a certifiable Pentium II or 604PowerPC chip with 32 megabytes of RAM were possible in an airborne computer, most of these problems would shrink to more manageable proportions. Instead, many compromises are required to make the systems work.

One compromise, for example, was a requirement to code the analog procedures into something digital-what is known as the ARINC 424 standard. How much has this standard changed since its inception? It's now up to version 14. Each version of the software meant minor changes to the way data was coded, and as any software person will tell you, that's a recipe for disaster. Old data has to be completely reviewed.

This creates a slightly delicate problem. The certification standard for FMSs is such that the software and hardware never have been designed or tested to be the primary means of navigation. Check the flight manual supplement for your FMS; it should state: "not intended for primary means of navigation.'

This means you can use the FMS for navigation, but if anything goes wrong, it better be clear that you use the hard-wired normal navigation aids (VOR, ILS, ADF, DME) as the primary means of navigation, and you only use the FM'S as an assistant. Ditto if you plan to use the FMS for VNav-most systems were never certified or tested to be an ILS replacement.

## *A SCENARIO*

From the gathering of raw data, we move on to the database providers for today's nav systems. These are the folks who process the raw data.

To date, there are only three providers: Jeppesen (the largest), Swissair and Racal. To avoid embarrassment, and to use a fictional account of nav data development for an FMS, we'll create a fourth provider, DataNav.

Here is the scenario:

DataNav takes raw data, converts it to suitable geographic coordinates, and manipulates it in its own proprietary way. The company applies a very detailed quality control process, involving much double and triple checking. Information that changes on the normal ICAO cycle (28 days) for aviation data) must be included in each new update, and this requires a rapid turnaround of changes. At this stage, the data is still not in ARINC 424 format.

A typical customer, called Airline A, operates within a defined geographic area and does not need, nor wants to pay for, worldwide data. It chooses an FMS from, say, MegaAvionics and now needs the data for its defined area of operation.

MegaAvionics has a contract with DataNav, who, in turn, provides a worldwide data package. This transition from DataNav to MegaAvionics is the only time the data actually will exist in ARINC 424 format. Once in MegaAvionic's hands, the data is transformed to the company's own proprietary software, so that it can be used with the avionics equipment offered by MegaAvionics.

## NOT A PERFECT WORLD

MegaAvionics *should* (and the emphasis is on the should, as not every avionics manufacturer is vigilant in this area) apply its own quality control process to the software to eliminate problems as its engineers pack it into a form that can be loaded into their FMS and give Airline A only what it paid for. Finally, Airline A receives its data package a few days before the scheduled changeover date to make sure it can be loaded into the airline's fleet in time.

In a perfect world, no problems should emerge. But, as we allknow, the world is not perfect. Here are examples of what can go wrong:

Wrong runway-In a true experience, the crew of a twin-engine commercial jet is the first to fly a recently commissioned GPS approach to a remote island. They dutifully call up the GPS approach from their FMS database and follow the rock-solid guidance down to the missed approach point. The weather isn't that bad, and they should see the runway. But they can't find it. Finally, just before they decide to make a missed approach, they spot the runway out of the side window, nearly one-third mile to the left of where they thought it should be.

Despite the best efforts of the database manufacturer, this error appears to have slipped through. The moral here is to not fly an approach using an FMS that hasn't been flown during daylight, or at least flight checked in daylight.

Duplicate waypoints- Canada has quite a number of low-power non-directional beacons (NDBs) across the country that share the same single identifier. Loading an approach into Halifax, Nova Scotia, several years ago, the users of one brand of panel-mounted GPS found that the single-letter identifier, missed-approach holding point that the computer selected was 1,200 nautical miles away from the one it should be using.

The solution, in this case, is to double-check the route for 'reasonableness,' making sure distances and bearings look right, latitude and longitude are correct, etc. As it will be some time before the final release of ARINC 424 is made (if ever), this problem could re-occur.

ILS transitions-Several operators noticed that transitions from distant fixes to ILS approaches that had more than a 30° intercept angle featured a waypoint and turn that cut into unprotected airspace. This waypoint did not show on any approach plates.

At least one major avionics manufacturer is known to have scoured the data it received from the database provider and eliminated all the offending transitions. But others have left them in.

'Routine' update-Pilots of a light business jet were quite surprised to find that, following a routine database update, the procedures that worked perfectly before the update, sudden! would not work at all and caused th FMS to lock up.

Miscoded waypoint-A crew in a light business jet attempted to enter a waypoint named 'xxxx1' and discovered it was about 2,000 nm from the one they wanted. Eventually, they discovered someone had put the desired waypoint into the database as'xxxxl.'

## SOLUTIONS EMERGE

What's being done about the situation? RTCA has set up Special Committee 181 (SC 181) to develop an end-to-end data integrity process. The final document, DO 200A, was published in November

1998. It contains the necessary steps to ensure that a quality assurance process exists at every stage.

However, DO 200A is not a mandatory document. ICAO has recommended it be used, but this has little legal clout.

Major airlines that use FMSs have developed special sections to handle the data, verify it, ensure it is loaded promptly and properly, and liaise with the avionics manufacturers and, indirectly, with the database suppliers.

Where does this leave the smaller airlines with panel-mounted GPS receivers, or the corporate flight department? They must determine whom to call when a problem arises: the avionics manufacturer or the database supplier.

They should not wait for a report from the manufacturers. Many have no way of contacting users in a quick manner, and to date, none have had an Airworthiness Directive (AD) issued against them for inaccurate data, despite some pretty bad problems that have cropped up.

The smaller airlines and corporate flight departments also must determine if the regulatory authorities should be informed, and if so, by what means? Interestingly, Transport Canada has requested all database-related problems be reported through the Service Difficulty Reporting System. As this is a multinational system, perhaps other countries might consider this as a way to ensure problems are at least tracked.

## *TAWS, Too*

So far, we've only talked about FMSs. But the problem is equally relevant to the databases and processes used in the terrain avoidance warning systems (TAWS).

In the United States, there is no requirement to monitor the underlying navigation aids when making a GPS approach, though many other countries prudently require the underlying nav aids to be used as a cross check.

Remember also that the software in airborne marvels such as FMS and TAWS need not be written to a high level of stringency, as the industry-wide view describes these devices as no more than supplementary means of navigation. However, a groundswell within the regulatory agencies is emerging, and this level of software rigor may no longer be sufficient.

What can an operator do? If you're in a major airline, get to know the database section and how to report problems. Make sure the problems are tracked to a solution.

If you're a smaller operator, ask your avionics supplier about its quality control process and how it intends to implement D0200A. Ask the same thing of the database supplier if you get the data directly from it. Make sure you know how to report problems, to both the avionics and database supplier, and ask your local regulatory agency representative how he should receive problems.

# CHAPTER 48 *Differential GPS Approach*

Not Previously Published

*Comment: One of the nice things about being in flight testing is that you get to see lots of new ideas and technology – some very promising, others more 'flight of fancy'. Some have immediate potential to improve aviation, and some appears to be solutions looking for problems.*

In the helicopter world, we don't see a lot of this new technology put into practice. In comparison to our fixed wing brethren we lag far behind in the practical application of technology. Why this is our lot in life may be the subject for another discussion.

In the commercial fixed wing business jet world two of the ideas that have gone from 'good idea' to installed, operating hardware include synthetic vision of the outside world and head-up displays with velocity vectors (or flight path markers) and combinations of the two. The path from concept to execution was not an easy one, but it was accomplished. And it wasn't cheap, but at upwards of $20 million for the airframe, another half-million doesn't seem like much. When it helps guarantee that the boss will arrive, it seems a small price to pay.

Where are we in the helicopter world? If you accept that the reason for the new equipment is to guarantee a safe landing at the destination, then the helicopter equivalent would be equipment to guarantee a safe arrival at a hover to a helipad regardless of the wind or weather. What or how it's done is almost immaterial, as long as it can be done safely (which means meeting some standards of reliability, integrity, and so on).

The thing that is really irksome is that it has been done, and not just once, but several times in several different areas. It was 7 years ago that I flew such approaches as part of a demonstration program, and I've sat through presentations at professional forums where others talked about their successes. One of them was an IFR approach to hovering 40' above the water alongside a ship that was underway.

(Those who know a lot about GPS should skip the next part, as it's a very rough description.) 'Normal' GPS won't work because the height signal is not accurate enough to provide accurate height above ground or precise enough position.

One system used a real-time Differential GPS (DGPS) ground station with a datalink to the helicopter. The DGPS basically says 'I don't care what the satellites say, I know exactly where I am, so I'll correct the satellite data and send the corrections to the helicopter. (The accuracy can be literally inches).

Another system used a combination of DGPS and millimeter wave radar to provide redundancy, again with a datalink between ground and air.

With an accurate height and position signal, we can fly to the hover – but how?

If you've ever tried to fly a decelerating approach in IMC from 90 to even 60 KIAS, it is not easy. When the speeds go slower than 60KIAS, the task approaches (no pun intended) impossibility for several reasons. First the airspeed indicator stops indicating anything useful below 40 KIAS, and ground speed has to come from the GPS. Secondly, heading control becomes extremely difficult – there is not enough inherent directional stability or slip ball cues below 60 KIAS to maintain track and heading if you're doing it manually, and finally, being below minimum power speed (in the region of reversed command in fixed wing terms), means that a sharp cross-check is needed to maintain speed and height control, let alone track. All the approaches to a hover have been flown using 4 axis (pitch, roll, yaw and collective) flight director cues as a minimum and most use a 4 axis autopilot.

The effect was nothing short of magic- follow the FD cues and watch the airspeed needle slink to zero while still several hundred feet up, (or better yet, punch the right buttons at the correct time and watch the system do it's thing), and arrive at a 50' hover over the desired spot. When the 'end of approach' light comes on, look up and land. Even with a 10 knot tailwind.

Further reflection on the potential made me realize that, just like fixed wing airplanes with Category IIIB capability, guidance right to touchdown was going to be necessary.

The reasons for suggesting this comes from basic performance - these approaches are not going to be flown in single engine helicopters (they don't have the necessary redundancies and systems, particularly the 4 axis AFCS). So, at some point on the approach, nearly any twin engine helicopter is going to be committed to land if it has an engine failure. That point is well above the DH of 50' AGL for nearly any helicopter I know, based on Category A performance.

But be of good cheer – if the system can give guidance to a 50' hover, it certainly can give it to touchdown. And who has ever heard of not being able to see the ground from 50' in even the most dense fog?

But the problem remains – Why is this not being brought into to everyday service?

Perhaps it's a problem of size of the market compared to the cost. Perhaps it's a problem of no real need. Where and when could you use such a system? Getting the patient to the hospital regardless of the weather? Getting the boss to his destination every time?

But I personally think it's because we're happy with what we have – an affliction of the rotary wing world.

# CHAPTER 49 *Dealing With Crowded Airspace*

**Vertical** Not sure

*Comment: Ensuring safety when flying in a crowded airspace takes much more than just technology or ATC oversight.*

Helicopters have some unique characteristics that gets them employed in some unique situations. these are situations our fixed-wing brethren never see, or, if they did, would have changed long ago.

I'm referring specifically to the highly crowded airspace that happens around catastrophes or major medical emergencies; situations often known to the rest of the world as news events.

## *At the Scene*

Most of the time, when emergencies happen in North America, you can be certain of finding helicopters all over the airspace above it. Some helicopters are the actual first-responder or aid ships, lining up to pick up or deliver people or cargo. Mostly, though, it's the news helicopters buzzing around for a good camera angle.

These situations develop in a matter of minutes, last, at most, a few hours, and then are done. They can develop virtually anywhere, not just at airports or close to air traffic facilities. Put another way, they're unpredictable.

Let's analyze a typical helicopter swarming. A newsworthy event will do in this case, since they are the most common. A major vehicle accident occurs, and both emergency medical service (EMS) helicopters and police or fire aircraft are required.

In addition to the para-public assets, various local electronic news gathering (ENG) helicopters are launched as well, to cover the "breaking" news story. Competition between news stations can mean pressure to get there first, and egos can get in the picture as well — whether on the ground back at the news station or in the aircraft itself.

Both the parapublic helicopters (police, fire, EMS) on scene and the commercial operators (ENG) have their own sets of procedures and rules. On scene, there will be jockeying for position. Law enforcement helicopters have requirements that will be different from ENG, which, in turn, will be different from the EMS operators. Ideally, everyone stays in their own zones and co-ordination and communication between helicopters ensures safety prevails.

For illustrative purposes, though, let's say a mid-air happens between one of the EMS helicopters and an ENG ship. In the aftermath, there are immediate cries for: more air traffic control (ATC) oversight; to make scenes like a restricted area; or to impose a control zone at this type of scene. This understandable knee-jerk response unfortunately ignores the inherent physical realities.

## *Why Obvious Solutions Don't Work*

One of the big reasons more ATC oversight or control zones/restricted areas wouldn't work at emergency scenes is that many are not be covered by radar and most are probably outside controlled airspace. Additionally, the speed with which the response to an emergency develops would require the closest ATC unit to have people on standby all the time. Equipment and training of the ATC folks would also be needed for these unique situations. All of this is expensive and difficult to justify.

We have to accept that it is impossible for ATC to even consider a smidgen of control. This means we helicopter folk are left to our own devices at emergency scenes. You see, fixed-wing aircraft can be regimented by ATC and under radar coverage for the most part, with separation distances and altitudes, because all their facilities are set up for firm, fixed runways. The emergencies we deal with happen anywhere.

If there is an event of sufficient magnitude and duration (e.g., a forest fire) to justify it, then ATC can wall off the airspace with a temporary flight restriction to let the working machines fly in relative isolation. In these cases, it is extremely likely the operators themselves establish de-facto control of traffic anyways.

So, what can we do about other emergency situations? I hear some of you shouting out "TCAS, just like the airliners have." But TCAS requires a signal to interrogate the transponders on other aircraft. Meaning that all the aircraft have to have serviceable, operating transponders.

Also, like enhance enhanced ground proximity warning systems, too many false alerts will result in the system being ignored. When TCAS is shouting out audio alerts every few seconds, it's going to get turned off pretty quickly — especially in an environment that requires a lot of internal and external communication monitoring. At least one of the helicopters involved in the mid-air collision in Phoenix last year had TCAS and that didn't prevent the accident. This points to an example of the limitations of the current TCAS units available: most will only show conflicts with a vertical closure of more than 500 feet per minute.

Even if TCAS were available on all the ships on scene, the TCAS units I'm aware of are set up for high-flying, fast-moving airplanes. The minimum scale on the display is typically two nautical miles — which means everyone at the swarm will be shown, with lots of conflicts and not much useful data to help the pilot. Is a helicopter-specific TCAS possible? Certainly! Will we ever get it? Depends on how much we're willing to pay, how much noise we're going to make, and how much attention the avionics people pay to an unstated, but real, requirement.

## *What We Can Do*

In the meantime, we have to rely on infinitely adaptable humans to keep things straight. And, so far, (he said knocking furiously on the nearest piece of wood), it's worked pretty well. We've only had two major accidents I'm aware of in the recent past. I'm sure there have been a slew of close calls. Unfortunately, the NASA Aviation Safety Reporting System, which is normally a gold mine of information, can't do a generic helicopter-close-encounter-with-other-aircraft search very easily. Experience, though, says that when there's an accident, there have been a fair number of close calls, too. The question we have to ask is what was done about them to make sure they didn't happen again?

Close calls are often just filed under the experience column. We like to think we can be all things to all people — after all, we're helicopter pilots aren't we — and what could be more complicated than flying a helicopter? We can do anything! ****Not so fast, moose-breath.**** Life is way more complicated than we know, and to make us better, we either need training or experience. Sadly, experience gives the test first and the training later. It's better to get the training first.

Training is always an issue with any operation. Cost is part of the issue, but so is the mindset. What can be difficult about being a news helicopter pilot, or a crewman on a news helicopter?

Let's assume we are a helicopter pilot and have had the benefit of mentoring by a grizzled veteran of ENG. We probably have to work in an environment with others in the same business. Do we have regular meetings to discuss and sort out potential problems? Do we join organizations like the National Broadcast Pilots Association or Helicopter Association International's ENG group?

Do we have any letters of agreement with ATC? A surprising number of major cities are not covered by controlled airspace at low altitudes, so it's not uncommon to be operating without ATC coverage. But even an unofficial letter of agreement would be a good place to start.

How about the local and regional police agencies? Do they have any procedures or agreements that they'd like you to use? It would be worthwhile to keep on their good side. After all, within a short while, you'll likely know their call signs and probably their voices on the radio. Are they part of your unofficial group that meets to discuss issues related to flying in close proximity? Better yet, are you part of their group?

As this is a parapublic-focused magazine, let me also remind each first-responder sector to keep in touch with the local units in your area, and be aware and meet/communicate with any civilian operators you might normally expect to come into contact with. It's just that little bit extra that will help ensure a higher level of safety when you're on scene.

A good example of the opposite of this came from one of my colleagues, who told me of his experience in ENG. When he met with the local constabulary, he found out they had been using their own frequency for many years. It was not a common frequency, and was not known to those outside their unit. When he asked why they weren't using the common frequency listed in the Aeronautical Information Manual (123.025), their response was "Because that's the way we've always done it." Which, of course, was not particularly helpful to keeping everyone in the picture.

This brings up another common sense question: why don't we have two aviation comms radios in all helicopters? While only one is strictly required, if you have to operate in an area where ATC is required, how will you communicate with the other helicopters about your intentions and position? ATC certainly won't like you cluttering up the airwaves with what they'll consider non-essential verbiage. If you're operating where there is no ATC, having the second radio means you can use another air-to-air frequency if other operators are set on using something different from the agreed mutual frequency.

Is there an agreed-upon set of phrases that mean the same thing to everybody? Communication is more than just talking on the radio — it implies clear, unambiguous words with the same meaning to everyone.

It's far better to have unofficial rules amongst the locals than mandates from a distant and disconnected agency like the Federal Aviation Administration. Not that I have anything against the FAA, it's full of folks who are usually extremely interested and concerned about aviation safety. But, lawyers often get in the way of common sense.

I guess the central point of my message is that, like anything else, it's best when you get involved. If you don't like what's happening, you have a chance to affect things if you get involved. If you don't, you likely deserve whatever happens to you! In the meantime, keep your eyes peeled!.

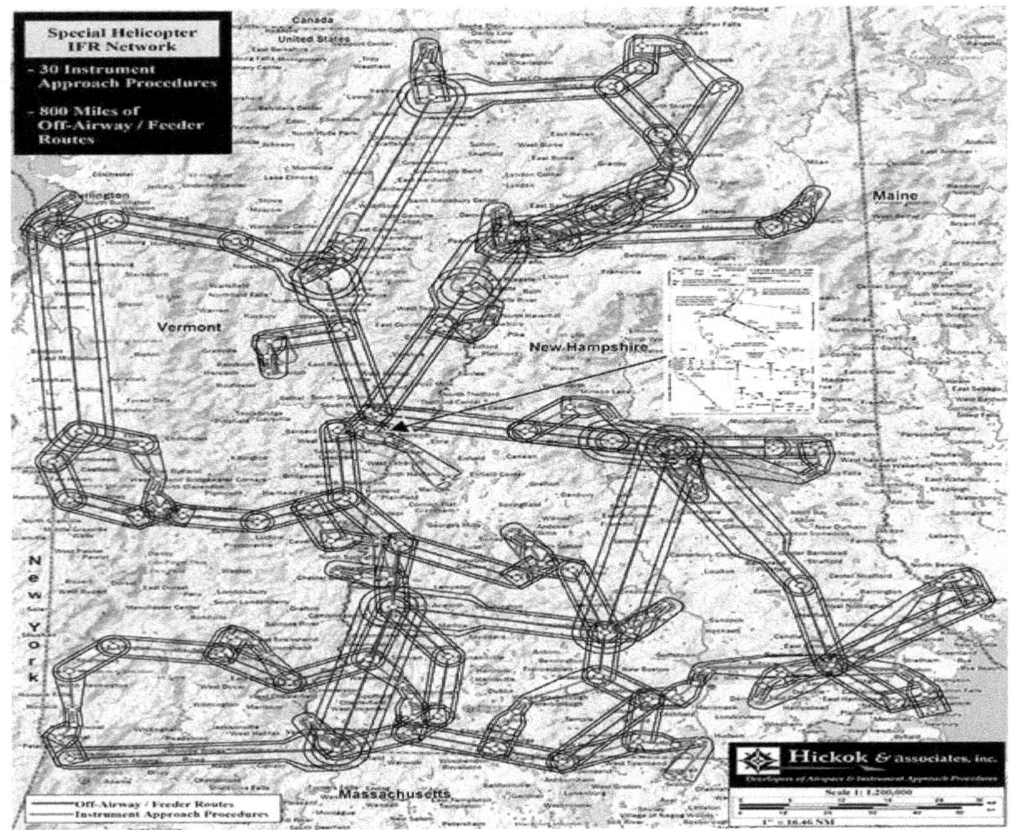


Figure 49-1 **Typical old style Instrument panel**

# CHAPTER 50 *Fly Toward the Light*

Vertical911 AMTC Issue 2009

*Comment: Can we develop a simplified version of an IFR route structure that improves the safety and efficiency of HEMS operations?*

We certainly have the technology. We certainly have the need. But, do we have the political will?

## *Fundamental Re-Shaping Of the System*

I'm talking about fundamentally re-shaping a troubled portion of the helicopter industry. I'd like to say the whole rotary-wing aviation world would benefit, but it would be nice if it just helped the most currently visible portion of it — the helicopter emergency medical services (HEMS) sector.

What am I talking about? As with anything, it's important to have a name that fits, so the issue can be easily handled and understood. The main premise of what I'm talking about is bringing over an important safety element from the airline world — flying instrument flight rules, IFR, all the time — and combining it with helicopter-specific requirements to make it simple. So, I'm going to call it "IFR Lite."

## *IFR Lite*

The airline world has used the IFR Lite concept success- fully. In Alaska, one airline combined global-positioning system technology with other equipment and procedures to solve the problem of transitioning over mountains and fjords from the high-altitude airways structure to the instrument landing system (ILS) approach beam. It wasn't simple, but the end result is that the airline is now safely flying procedures with previously unheard-of closeness to the terrain — as little as 500 feet from wingtips to rocks. The "how" of this development is very complex and beyond the scope of this article, but the "why" is as relevant to the rotary-wing world as it was to that airline.

When scene calls are unpredictable, there are general areas for these scene calls, so they can be lumped together by region.

## *The Technology*

Let's look at how we could apply the principles of IFR Lite to a HEMS environment. We'll discuss the technology first. To make things easy, we're not going to talk about VOR/ DME (very high frequency [VHF] omni-directional radio range/distance measuring equipment) or ILS. These systems don't work reliably at the heights which helicopters fly, and VOR/DME doesn't have the required accuracy.

Instead, we're going to talk about GPS, and not just GPS, but Wide Area Augmentation System (WAAS) enabled GPS. More specifically: Required Navigation Performance (RNP) WAAS GPS.

Coupled with this, to go IFR Lite, we'll need a GPS receiver capable of three-dimensional flight plans. All of this technology exists, and, indeed, many helicopters in EMS already have such equipment. However, we also need a helicopter that is not just equipped for IFR, but is approved (certified) for it.

RNP means you can specify the accuracy needed. For example, if you decide that you need to have an "airway" that is only 0.1 nautical miles from center to outside edge, you can tell the RNP system that 0.1 nautical miles is the required performance. The equipment will warn you if the GPS satellite geometry or some other problem is degrading the accuracy of the signal so that it can no longer guarantee the accuracy requested.

## *Route Planning*

The next step in developing an IFR Lite model is laying out our routes. This is not as difficult as you might imagine, but it is a process that requires attention and discipline, and some knowledge of how these things are done. What seems like a simple process, as explained in this article, actually requires knowledge of one of those

arcane (there's a word to look up in the dictionary) bits of aviation: how to approve an instrument procedure airway. Folks who understand and do this do exist for the helicopter world — you can look them up, too. (They tell me I'll get a small percentage of their fees for mentioning them, but I don't believe 'em).

If you think about a HEMS operation, aside from the predictable places like hospitals where most patients end up, there are a finite number of areas where pilots generally fly. While scene calls are unpredictable, there are general areas for these scene calls, so they can be lumped together by region. For ease of discussion, let's say that, in our model HEMS operation, we identify six different major areas where we fly. Next, we pick a central location within each of those areas — I would use a prominent landmark, something that is easily identifiable from the air.

Once identified, we're going to construct a low-altitude IFR Lite route from our base to each of those landmarks. The route may be a straight line, or it may follow s

ally occurring feature such as a major high- way, river or ridgeline. For obstacle clearance, we're not going to apply the "normal" IFR obstacle clearance heights for obstacles within five miles of our track, but a more modest height above obstacles that are within 0.3 miles (or whatever RNP value we think is appropriate). As an example, let's say we choose 500 feet above obstacles that are within 0.2 nautical miles of our track. If we choose our route carefully, we can get down to some pretty low heights above the ground.

## *Separation From The Fixed Wing World*

In this process, it's worthwhile to note other things — like instrument approach and takeoff paths from airports — that may be close to the route, because we don't want to start mixing it up with the normal IFR world. We need to take care of turns on the route and ensure we have clearance when turning... and here's where we can nominate waypoints as either fly over (I must pass overhead) or fly-by (I can cut the corner).

Pretty soon, though, we'll have a little jewel of a route marked out. Next, we fly it in good weather, make sure we've seen all the obstacles, and that it is a safe and reasonable route. Once that's done, we fly this route all the time to the end point and then carve off to the change- able landing zone for the scene call. It probably won't add more than a couple of minutes to our flight time — and we probably always get to the scene before they're ready for us to take the patient anyway — so little or no damage is done to our reputations.

## *A Cornerstone of Safety*

I'll say that again: we fly this set IFR Lite route all the time, at the altitude we've cleared. And, we watch out for new obstacles (those pesky cell-phone towers are being planted by Johnny Cellphoneseed, I swear).

When we've done this, what we've first accomplished is a measure of repeatability and sameness. Boring as it may be, it's just one of the cornerstones of safety. When the weather's marginal, we've got a safe route to fly. And, if we can't maintain the altitude we've deemed to be safe, we've made the decision process that much easier.

If the visibility starts to really go down, we won't be tempted to slow down and go down, because we're already at the minimum we know is safe. When the weather's really bad, we'll know it much earlier than if we were worried about navigating and avoiding obstacles at the same time as watching the weather. (Think about one thing for a minute here: do airline crews ever worry about running into obstacles on their IFR-approved routes or instrument approaches? Of course not! Neither should we in our normal course of navigation.)

And, if the whole world turns to corn flakes (or your breakfast cereal of choice), and we have no choice but to fly IFR, we know where we are and what to do next. If we know the weather is fine at the other end of the route, we can carry on with a greater degree of confidence than that which previously existed. If we get to the jumping-off point and the weather isn't very good, we already know it and can make our decision easily. (We should make sure we have an escape or turnaround place nominated so we can get out of a bad situation with some grace and aplomb.)

While IFR Lite means we'll have to work with our local air traffic control folks, I'm sure they'll be delighted to know where we are nearly all the time, and that we can fly this route when the weather is bad without mixing it up with their faster-moving traffic.

The purists among you will be screaming, "Heretic! Burn him at the stake! We're not allowed to do that!"

Neither was the aforementioned Alaskan airline, until they worked it out in conjunction with the Federal Aviation Administration and proved it was safe.

IFR Lite isn't going to happen overnight, and it may not be as simple a process as what I've described here. But, some version of this will work — and just happens to be working at Dartmouth-Hitchcock Medical Center in Lebanon,

N.H. *(see the sidebar on p.82)*. As such, the issue may be evolving a lot more quickly than you think.

So ends the heresy lesson for this issue.

## *Proving the Concept*

The low-altitude route concept described here is just that — a concept. However, one air medical program, Dartmouth-Hitchcock Advanced Response Team (DHART), has already developed and implemented a complete, low-level IFR route structure based on GPS technology. Dartmouth-Hitchcock Medical Center and its DHART pro- gram teamed up with GPS-approach developer Hickok & Associates to create the first fully integrated, private, low-level IFR helicopter GPS route structure in the world.

The "how" of this development is very complex and beyond the scope of this article, but the "why" is as relevant to the rotary-wing world as it was to that airline

While scene calls are unpredictable, there are general areas for these scene calls, so they can be lumped together by region. .

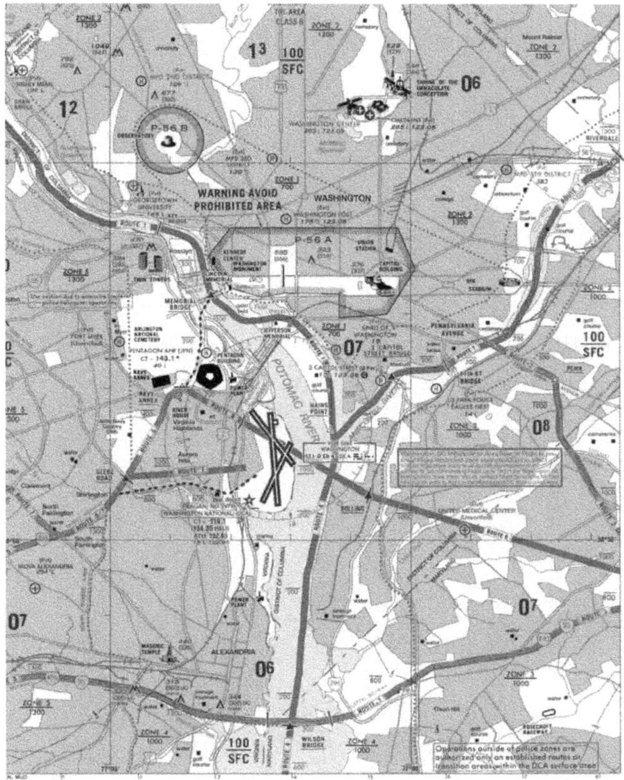


**Figure 50-1** **Helo ropute around Washington DC Center**

# CHAPTER 51 *Flying IFR With a Slung Load and Without Navaids*

Royal Canadian Air Force's
Flight Safety Magazine

*Comment: There I was, Resolute Bay, N.W.T., in late winter, with a military operation supporting scientists out on the ice.*

It was time to bring in the camps and there was one last load to take. The day was not great — 500 foot overcast, two miles in light snow — but it wasn't forecast to get much worse.

I was the captain of a four-man crew flying a UH- 1N. For this mission, our magnetic compass was useless, and the directional gyro was set by flying down the runway at Resolute and then setting the heading bug on shutdown for re-alignment. Navigation was by cross-bearing on two automatic direction finders (ADFs) — one at Resolute and one at another ice camp. As a backup, we had sun tables, where you look up the time of day, turn toward the sun and align the gyro... if there was sun that is.

At our destination, there was snowfall and low cloud, with a light wind coming directly from Resolute. After we packed up the interior and the cargo net for the underslung load, we re- started with me in the left/co-pilot seat. We lifted off to hover and climb, accelerating to find the maximum safe speed for the load. The ship was well behaved up to 70 knots indicated airspeed (KIAS)... and that was good, because the world had basically become instrument flight rules (IFR). At 70 KIAS, things were comfortable, and there was some margin to maximum speed: 80 KIAS with an underslung load. We climbed a couple of hundred feet and saw no discernible horizon. The trip back home was going to be more or less IFR, but we'd done night slinging before so this wasn't that different.

This is where that old axiom of things forgotten being remembered at inconvenient times came up. I suddenly realized I'd forgotten to reset the compass. We had taken off into the wind, which meant we were heading more or less toward Resolute. No worries, I thought, I'll have the co-pilot tune in the ADF at Resolute and since we're not far from a known bearing, we'll sort things out quickly. Our only other navaid was a TACAN (tactical air navigation) which could pick up the DME (distance measuring equipment) from the VORTAC (very high frequency omni-directional radio range tactical air navigation aid), but not the bearing. We did have a good DF system for both UHF and VHF, though, which meant we could home in on the Resolute Flight Service Station. After telling our co-pilot my plan, I congratulated myself on my quick thinking.

After a few moments of watching the co-pilot fumble with the ADF and getting no meaningful response, I told him to "try the ADF at the other end of the runway." Still no solid bearing. "Call Resolute and ask them for a long count," I said, "and we'll DF them."

Repeated calls on all known Resolute frequencies proved equally fruitless. Now, not only did we not know what our heading was, we had no idea of our actual location.

Thinking this was time to show captaincy rather than stick and rudder skills, I turned the controls over to the co-pilot. Unfortunately, I had no greater luck. No navaids worked, except a DME that showed us closing on Resolute. About this time, two other airplanes came up on 121.5 asking where we all were and where was Resolute's Flight Service Station? After determining none of us could get Resolute on any radio, and that we weren't going to be a factor for anyone, we agreed to listen out.

Between our ice-pack takeoff point and Resolute, a small island stood about 500 feet above sea level. Worried that we might not see it, and now not certain of our position, I asked the co-pilot to climb to 1,000 feet. Shortly after the climb, I noticed the airspeed decrease slightly and the nose come up, then drop, and then the airspeed increase again. Just before I could ask the co-pilot what was going on, he yelled, "I've got vertigo — you have control."

I took the controls and re-stabilized the load, then noticed we were no longer getting closer to Resolute. The DME had stopped decreasing at about 15 miles. Taking a chance, I turned left and was met by the worst case of the leans I'd ever had. Giving control back to the co-pilot wasn't an option, so I struggled my way through the turn and was rewarded by the DME decreasing again. At this point, we could see from the radar altimeter that we'd passed the small island, and, backed up by the DME, decided to descend. Just then, Resolute Flight Services came back on the radio. I told our co-pilot to have them do a DF on us and we would do one on them. This was not something Resolute's radio operators were familiar with, so it took them a minute to figure it out. They eventually gave us a bearing that seemed reasonable (we still had no ADF on the air) and I told our co-pilot to put the tail of the needle on that number.

By now, we were a couple of miles from Resolute and only a few hundred feet above the ice. Flight Services then greeted us with the weather: 200 feet and half a mile in snow and blowing snow. We knew we'd crossed the shoreline, though, when the radar altimeter and barometric altimeter disagreed and we were greeted by the cultural trappings of Resolute: telephone poles, huts and so on sticking blackly out of the snow. Now visual, we hovered to the drop-off spot and let down our load. Landing and shutdown followed quickly after that.

Elapsed time was only 45 minutes, but almost seemed an eternity. Even though I knew we could have landed out on the ice if need be, it was strange how all the options we had for figuring out where we were, and where we were heading, all ran out at the same time.

**Figure 51-1 How did the artist know I had moustache?**

# CHAPTER 52 *Risk Assessment is Just Decision Making*

**Vertical** October / November 2010

*Comment: Recently, risk assessment has risen as a 'must-have' tool in helicopter operations. Is it really that new an idea? And does it improve safety as much as some would like us to think?*

Flying is complicated, helicopter flying even more so – there are many variables. EMS helicopter flying is incredibly complicated because of the very long list of unknowns. And the decisions necessary to handle those unknowns are not simple.

As an aside, I was involved in a labor dispute involving EMS pilots who were claiming they didn't have to make decisions on their job (and hence could be put in a different pay category and claim overtime). A cursory analysis showed that not only were decisions being made, but complex decisions were being made at a very high rate.

Risk assessment was being done, but not in a classical, structured sense.

It appears that sometimes too many poor decisions have been made in the EMS helicopter business, so it's natural to think that something as close to motherhood and apple pie as risk assessment would be a good thing.

Since we're still having crashes despite this, it's worthwhile to stand back and look at what risk assessment is really all about.

Basically, the process is an attempt to put some structure to decision making. In an pervasive effort to reduce everything to a very simple level, risk assessment methods have been imposed to help make pilots make decisions better (or perhaps push the decisions to a higher, more detached level) – away from the immediacy of the situation.

The risk assessment method appears to try to reduce the variability of decision making in EMS. A brave attempt, but like any solution must be viewed with some caution. And like any process, needs extensive training.

I teach experimental test pilots and engineers how to use a qualitative assessment tool called the Cooper-Harper Rating scale. In over 10 years of teaching it, it's obvious that many of those who had been using it without dedicated training were using it incorrectly. Often they were significantly misusing it. With training and mentoring, the Cooper Harper Rating Scale can be a very effective tool – but it needs training. It's the same thing with risk assessment.

## *SO– WHAT IS A RISK?*

A risk is the total of the hazards that contribute to it and a measure of the likelihood of the hazard happening.

In other words – what can go wrong? And then how likely is that thing to happen and how bad it would be if it happened? Unstated is the options available.

Risk assessment can take only the known risks and assessing the possibility of that event happening based on prior experience and known consequences if it did happen. The first thing to note is that only known risks can be assessed. And often it's the things we don't know that can reach out and grab us. And what if our probability / possibility is based on incorrect data?

To do a thorough and correct job of risk assessment means that we have to look at all the risks. That in itself is a huge task. If we knew what all the risks are.

For example, there is a risk of an engine failing. It's made by men of earthly materials.

Operating in the HV curve for most light, single engine helicopters is more of a risk than operating outside the HV, but only if the engine fails. But how much more of a risk if the countryside underneath is very inhospitable for landing if the engine fails? Being outside the HV curve won't make a really significant difference to the outcome. Training and knowledge of what the symptoms are of an engine failure, and pre-planning your actions for that eventuality reduce the risk. Having a superbly maintained engine with monitoring systems would also reduce the risk. And so on.

We 'know' the probability of a turbine engine failing is supposed to be once in every 10,000 hours. This assumes everything else such as fuel and maintenance is fine. But what are the risks of bad fuel? What if the engine is very old or near to overhaul or has some hidden flaw that increased the probability for failure on this flight significantly?

But most of the issue is – what can be done with the information? How can we reduce the risks associated with an operation?

If there are several risks that can happen at once, will the risk assessment method allow us to identify the worst one (in terms of both the hazard and the consequence) and fix it before we fix something that's easier to fix, but a lower risk?

Like a flight schedule is a place to make changes from, a risk assessment matrix is a place to start deciding if the assessment was right.

Transport Canada runs an internal risk assessment training course, and my colleagues tell me that even after that training, two groups looking separately at the same scenario will come up with widely different assessments of the risk. Only after discussing the assumptions each group used are they able to resolve the differences.

A risk assessment matrix showed that the combination of something happening that was improbable which had catastrophic results was a medium risk. Let's say that event was loss of transmission oil from a transmission that has a very short run dry time. The consequences of this are not all the same – it depends on where you are when the loss of oil happens – on the ground with the engine stopped is of no consequence (assuming you notice the loss of oil prior to going flying). In flight, the consequences are also not all the same – are you over open farmland during the day or the middle of the ocean with high winds and large waves? Is it at night? Or IFR? Are you at low altitude so you can land immediately without or high enough above the ground you need binoculars to make out people? Do you have clear and unambiguous warnings or a confusion of indications?

Weather is always a risk What is the chance it will get better compared to the chance it will get worse? How much worse before it becomes an issue for completion of the flight? Do we have a decision point that will help us know when to say know?

Which brings us to the most important part about risks -making a decision. More often than we may realize, the real issue is that no decision is made. This was found to be an issue in several fighter accidents, where the pilot didn't eject until his wingman told him to – the pilot didn't have a pre-set point where he had decided he was going to eject. It took several close calls before someone recognized the problem for what it was, and the problem was resolved by specific training.

How often do people continue to fly in bad weather instead of turning around or landing in a field? Not out of a conscious decision to continue, but because no decision was made. In my limited experience when faced with bad weather, I knew when I was going to make the decision – perhaps because I had been well mentored.

Were you ever permitted to make a decision about the weather during your flying training? My informal survey of both civil and military pilots was that someone else always made that decision. The first time most pilots had to make a decision about the weather was when they were on their own, and most felt ill-prepared for the decision.

If you don't make a decision, someone else will. You may not like the consequences of their decision or the erosion of your ability to decide on your own. So learn to make decisions – good decisions.

Risk assessment is really nothing more than an attempt to put a formal discipline into decision making. Why don't we train pilots on how make those important decisions instead? And how can we do that? Simulators help....

# CHAPTER 53 *Learn From The Mistakes of Others*

**Vertical** January 2008

*Comment: Over the past couple of years, I've become far more acquainted with accident reports than I'd like to be.*

I know no one ever sets out to have an accident, but a lot of us certainly do end up having them. Some people have asked me if flight time makes a difference to the likelihood of having an accident? Insurance companies, customers, operators and chief pilots certainly think so. But, is flight time the only guarantee of experience?

Experience is not what happens to a person, but what they learn from an event. I've seen pilots with 800 hours who had judgment and maturity far beyond their flight time. Likewise, I've seen old pilots with 7,000 hours who seemed to have only had one experience, repeated 7,000 times, and didn't possess much maturity.

What makes the difference in an individual pilot? Attitude has a lot to do with it. Good pilots are always learning.

This, of course, begs the question, what are they learning? Lessons, good or bad, learned early in a career are the basis for future lessons. It is also correct to say that those of us who are still alive are the ones who survived our mistakes. We either learned to avoid the situations that got us into trouble or were lucky enough to not have things line up the same way again, or a bit of both.

## *Headware Skills*

Since we all started out as rookies at some point, let's look at what a pilot is equipped with (or not equipped with) upon graduation. The practical test standards dictate that a certain level of motor skills and judgment must be displayed. As we all know, though, there is much more to flying than demonstrating you can do a quick stop, or a power recovery autorotation. "Headware" skills are the real key. Accidents are generally not caused by stick and rudder skills, but the ability to have good judgment and make good decisions — something for which we don't seem to train pilots very well.

I recently asked a senior pilot from a manufacturer what levels of competency, judgment/decision making and technical knowledge they encountered with pilots who attend the company training school. He said they normally had to administer some tests on technical knowledge and competency before starting training, but, often, there was quite a bit of judgment/decision-making training which the company had to do that should not have been required.

For experienced pilots to not be able to display good judgment skills is quite revealing. It's likely they didn't suddenly forget them, but never had a chance to learn what they needed to as a young pilot, or simply got away with a mistake early on and kept thinking in this manner.

## *Reinforcing Bad Decisions*

Consider that most student pilots are not required or allowed to make decisions about the weather — the instructor, operations or someone else decides when the conditions are not good enough. Now, how many instructors will take a student pilot out in less than ideal, but still safe and legal, conditions and let the student see what the practical problems of flying with reduced visibility are? (One problem is scheduling bad weather so the lesson comes at the ideal time in the student's learning process.)

Even the Canadians, who have a low-visibility endorsement for helicopter pilots, only require a discussion — not a demonstration in flight — before being approved. Even a minimally certified simulator or flight training device would be a better learning experience.

So, now we have a junior pilot, with little in the way of preparation for flying in less than ideal conditions. He or she encounters deteriorating weather on a solo trip, but presses on, and is successful in flying low and slow, dodging the towers and trees, and arrives safely at "home plate." No one else knows the weather this pilot flew in because the cloud base and visibility were fine at both ends of the trip, just bad in the middle. What lesson does he or she learn? They can hack bad weather. "It's not a real problem," they say to themselves. "What were the feds concerned about with the visibility requirements?"

The next time the pilot encounters these conditions, they press a bit more, slower and lower to the ground. Again, he or she makes it, this time pressing because of a commercial pressure to finish the trip or get the machine back for tomorrow's flight. The wrong lesson is reinforced. You all know the final result here. Sometimes it hits home much later, when the pilot has lots of flying time, but its that wrong lesson learned a long, long way back during their low-time days that is the key not mentioned in the accident report.

## *Lessons From the Fixed-Wing Side*

Both of my long-time readers know I often use the fixed-wing world for comparison, so lets head there now. The fixed-wing world has a long head start on us in terms of making mistakes and learning from them. Their safety record is significantly better than ours as an industry, so maybe some things can be gleaned from their methods.

In the airlines, pilots are not sent off to be solo, ever. Airline pilots undergo a long period of mentoring before they become captains. This may be one year, but is often much more. Regardless, there is always a period spent as a co-pilot. During this time, there will be both official observations and unofficial mentoring. Mistakes will be prevented by the senior pilot, and, perhaps, the co-pilot will also prevent a mistake by a senior pilot and learn from that. For those who even spent time as a second officer (a concept now dead in fixed-wing circles, but never in existence in the helicopter world), this was a perfect time to observe and take notes of good and bad captains. One of my airline friends said this was instrumental in helping him become a better captain when his time finally arrived.

It's not just the airlines, though, as most militaries put junior pilots in positions where they are watched and mentored for several years as well. Even single-seat fighter pilots fly as wingman for quite a while before being allowed to lead missions.

## *A Lack of Real World Training*

Compare the fixed-wing situation to the helicopter world, where nearly every entry level job is single pilot. Junior pilots are sent to work solo, often with little direct supervision.

Even the typical route of flight instructing to obtain the flying time needed, can be pretty much be considered as solo flying. Although, with this situation, at least in good schools, there is regular supervision, so, ironically, there is actually some of that mentoring we're looking for.

The problem with training situations is that flying a helicopter with a limited capability to change weight and center of gravity, or where little flying is done at the real limits of performance and in a very tightly controlled environment, does not prepare one well for the real world.

In the real world, the payload can be 50 per cent of the empty weight of the machine, where every legal ounce of performance has to be squeezed from the machine to make money. Where is the mentoring to ensure that this transition is not just shown once, but reinforced over a period of years?

To be sure, mentoring is difficult given the small fleets (less than five machines) that make up about 80 per cent of the helicopter world. Perhaps the advent of low-cost flight recorders will improve the situation ****(see p.xx, this issue)****. Getting a chance to review one's good and bad decisions after the fact can have significant benefits.

The few helicopter fleets with a mix of two-crew and single-pilot operations that have practiced mentoring of low-time pilots have felt it sufficiently worthwhile to continue the practice. Making the transition from that two-crew aircraft to a single-pilot ship has proven, for the most part, to be easy.

Given that helicopters have many more variables to contend with than any fixed-wing aircraft, maybe it's time we consider mentoring as well — even if it's just to sit down and review a pilot's day of flying.

In the mean time, we need to starting thinking about a good process for ensuring our junior pilots are well prepared for their careers so we can prevent them learning the wrong lessons at an early stage.

Author's Note: I wanted to pass along a revision to an earlier article about autorotations to the grass, in response to that other loyal reader of mine. It is safe to do hovering autorotations to grass.

# CHAPTER 54 *Helicopter to Fixed Wing Comparison - Simulators*

Vertical June / July 2009

*Comment: The fixed wing world has already served as a great point of comparison for the helicopter world.*

It has shown us how we unrestricted aviators, while enjoying more freedom of action, and being nicer folks in general, have not paid attention to what could be done to better our circumstances. This issue's column is going to concentrate on simulators and training in them as an example of where we could certainly do a lot better. By using this increasingly available technology, we could help ourselves in the same way the fixed-wing world already has.

## *Inherent Complexities*

If you didn't know it already, one of the major differences between rotary- and fixed-wing is that helicopters are much more complex than airplanes — which means it's a lot more difficult to get a good helicopter simulator. I can certainly confirm that notion. Having had some experience in teaching pilots how to flight test helicopters, I quickly saw that the complexities in comparison to seized-wing aircraft are significant. Trying to mathematically model those complexities correctly takes people who know all the upper and lower case Greek letters, and how to use them in various formula. But, it can be done, and with modern computing, it can be done at reasonable cost. Adding to the difficulty of modeling helicopters is the requirement to accurately model the visual cues we need and the atmosphere we fly in. These are problems, however, that can be overcome if there is sufficient will to make things happen.

Of course, the problem is not just one of technical complexity, it's financial as well. Boeing 747 pilots get their first real flight in the aircraft when it's in revenue service — they do not fly the real ship in training. They have been doing this since very early on in the model's program. Think about that for a moment. This means the performance and handing of the 747's simulator is so close to the real thing that all the flying, both normal and emergency procedures, can be taught in it, safe in the knowledge that the real aircraft is exactly the same. A $25-million simulator for a 747 is not difficult to justify when the real thing costs several times that amount, and the revenue lost when an airframe has to be used for training is substantial. But, when a helicopter costs $4 million, while the simulator costs $25 million, and the per hour cost of the sim is $2,000, while the real helicopter's direct operating costs are $800, the equations start to look — at first glance — somewhat backward.

The comparison of purchase and operating costs alone, though, leaves out several very important benefits of the simulator. These benefits include, but are not limited to, being able to:

- Realistically train one's crew;
- Do things you can't do in the real helicopter;
- Do things you could do in the real helicopter, but if done in the real ship it wouldn't be done in a safe way;
- Do things you could do in the real helicopter, but if done in the real ship it couldn't be done in an economical way.

There are lots more, but let's leave filling out this simulator-over-real-helicopter benefits list to a future column.

## *Development Differences*

What we need to concentrate on for this discussion is the differences between helicopters and fixed wing not just in the use of simulators, but in the acceptance of simulators. For most new fixed-wing ships, the delivery of the first aircraft coincides with the delivery of the first simulator. Simulator development parallels the real aircraft so that flight test and certification crews can actually be using the simulator as part of the certification effort. That means customers can begin training prior to delivery of the first aircraft. In the helicopter world, this is not the case — in fact, there are several complex, twin-engine, instrument-flight-rules-approved helicopters that have been on the market for more than 10 years that are only now just getting simulators approved. For some upcoming helicopters, the simulator will not be in service until well after the real machine enters service. Why are helicopter simulators not naturally introduced at the same time as the real machine?

Part of the problem is that getting the data to model a simulator is different than the data needed to obtain certification of the real helicopter. Getting data of any sort requires careful planning and takes time, which in turn costs money. Fixed-wing aircraft are relatively simple when it comes to gathering the data needed to model their aerodynamics and performance, but helicopters are much more complex. So, unless data was obtained during specific tests at the same time as certification, it's going to be awhile before the simulator gets developed. The amount of data required depends on the level of fidelity of the simulator. A generic simulator (one that flies like a single-engine turbine helicopter for example) doesn't need to fly exactly like any particular helicopter. But, you don't get a lot of training credit for this, and it would not be able to provide you with a type rating on the real machine (assuming these even existed for small helicopters in the Federal Aviation Administration [FAA] world, but that's another story).

For a simulator that's going to do all the training necessary for a type rating (with no flying in the real helicopter), it had better fly exactly like the real thing — and something like that takes a considerable amount of data to create.

Consider, for example, that there is no requirement during certification for the roll rate to be measured; but there is a requirement for this for the simulator to be able to duplicate the amount of roll rate you get for a given amount of lateral cyclic movement. Then, there's everything else that accompanies the lateral cyclic movement, such as changes in torque, adverse or proverse yaw, and change in pitch attitude, all of which must be correct to within very tight tolerances. How about if the real ship has an automatic flight control system? It would mean failures must be duplicated accurately. As complex as it can be, it has been done: the Sikorsky S-76 has several Level D simulators available. The real question is why hasn't it been done for all the helicopters that have sprung up since the S-76 simulator came into service?

## *Usage and Acceptance*

A recent presentation by a major fixed-wing airframe manufacturer highlighted the importance of simulation in that company's development process. For this company, every stage of development on its new aircraft was done first in a simulator of some description. A very realistic flight simulator was available very early on in the program and was used by the flight test and FAA crews to fly each test point before it was attempted in the real thing. (Obviously, it would only be "close" to the real aircraft at the beginning, but it would be continuously fine-tuned as the test program provided real-world data). I've never heard of this or anything close to this happening at any helicopter manufacturer, anywhere, in any model's development program.

So, what does this mean to us unrestricted aviators? It's likely going to be at least a year or two after the real aircraft hits the market before you'll get any training in a helicopter simulator. I'd be surprised if it occurred in a shorter amount of time, and very surprised if any new helicopter certified in the next five years has a simulator delivered at the same time. Now comes the real rub: how many pilots who fly a helicopter type that has a simulator will actually get to use the simulator for training? Compared to our fixed-wing brethren, it will be a paltry percentage.

Nearly all those who fly business jets spend at least two weeks per year at a major simulator training center. A Gulfstream pilot will typically get over 30 hours of simulator time per year, all as part of the cost of doing business. One of the reasons that this much training is done is because the insurance companies dictate it. If you don't do this much training, you face either not flying in the airplane or having an insurance premium that is sky high.

### *3 Hours of Simulator Training...*

In the helicopter industry, where more than three hours of simulator "training" per year is a lot, it will be a long time before we budget for the travel, replacement crew and training costs to be an equal to the fixed-wing world. For too long, the regulatory authorities have allowed flight tests and checks to be done in the real helicopter because no suitable simulators existed. Given the small explosion of simulators in the Gulf of Mexico alone, we could see a lot more check rides being done in the simulator; partly because it's certainly easier to predictably schedule and control the check-ride cycle!

Just think of the changes that might happen if simulators were mandated by either the insurance companies or the regulatory authorities. We'd see more people getting better training on the systems and the operation of helicopters. Perhaps that 25 percent of pilots who don't use the autopilots that they have installed in their ships would be reduced to near zero. Perhaps helicopter pilots would really start to learn why they shouldn't fly in reduced visibility at night. Perhaps there are so many things we could discuss, this column would never end. In the meantime, let's hope and pray we get more helicopter simulators for smaller helicopters, as it can only help the health and safety of our community.

# CHAPTER 55 *Why aren't Helicopter Operations as Safe as Airlines?*

Not Previously Published as Single article

*Comment: Why aren't helicopters as safe as Airliners???*

There's been quite a bit of discussion about raising the level of safety in helicopter operations to something approaching that of airliners. An admirable aim. Any way that we can reduce the number of accidents and incidents will help us in many ways – fiscal (accidents are expensive), physical (people get hurt and / or killed in accidents), and most importantly, moral (accidents and incidents give us a bad reputation). And then there is the human cost, which cannot be measured in any way. Too many people I've known have gone west in helicopter accidents.

The next several columns are going to look at the differences between helicopters and fixed wing, and point out ways that perhaps we can improve the situation. I'm sure both of the readers of this column can contribute other insights and suggest ways we can improve. I look forward to hearing from you!

## *AIRLINERS VS. HELICOPTERS*

Some things that are very relevant to airliners are not relevant to helicopters, yet we are expected to use the same systems. From this, several helicopter-unique observations and answers can arise. Some of those observations might appear, at first glance, to be, "Duh, that's so obvious," but their implications are huge. The very first observation, and one that will have an effect throughout is that airliners operate from airports. ***The devil, you say.***

Helicopters, of course, often never see an airport. So, what's the effect of this? Consider any airport that an airline operates to and from. It contains, at a minimum, radio communication. It also has navigation equipment, normally an instrument landing system, along with runways that have a glide-path-angle indicating system and lead-in approach lights and edge lights. Wind information is available in the form of windsocks (lighted), and often the actual direction and strength in the form of numbers provided by air traffic control (ATC). And, of course, there is weather information. The airliners themselves all have dual navigation equipment, dual radios and probably weather radar. The aircraft and crew 114 verticalmag.com are certified for instrument flight rules (IFR), while the aircraft is certified for flight in icing conditions and has autopilot. Specific procedures for single-engine failure are defined, and detailed relevant performance charts for the ship are available.

Some things that are very relevant to fixed wing are not relevant to helicopters, yet we are expected to use the same airspace and operations. Several helicopter-unique answers might arise from this.

Some of the observations might appear at first glance to be – DUH – that's so obvious. But the implications of some of these observations is huge. The very first observation, and one that will have an effect throughout is;

*Airliners operate from airports. Helicopters often never see an airport.*

Consider what any airport that an airline operates to contains:

‰Radio communication
‰Navigation equipment, normally an ILS
‰Runways with glidepath angle indicating system and lights at night
‰Wind information in the form of windsocks (lit) if not actual direction and strength as numbers from air traffic control
‰Weather information

Now consider what every airliner has:

‰Dual navigation equipment
‰Dual radios

‰Probably weather radar
‰Aircraft and crew are certified for IFR
‰Aircraft certified for flight in icing
‰Autopilot
‰Specific procedures for single engine failure
‰Detailed relevant performance charts
‰Consider the crew:
‰Two pilots, both with multi-engine and instrument ratings, with regular training in simulators
‰Both pilots will have been trained in crew environment
‰Significant experience before becoming captain
‰Type rated on aircraft
‰Probably has significant experience in other airplane types

Consider the flying:

‰Scheduled
‰Controlled by Air Traffic Control
‰Dispatch takes care of weight and balance, flight plans
‰Known departure and arrival places and procedures
‰Routine nature of operations
‰Legs of flight are of significant duration
‰Fuel reserves for IFR flight are not a major penalty
‰All flights are IFR

## *ARE YOU STARTING TO GET THE PICTURE?*

Let's look at each of these features (and many others) and compare fixed wing and helicopter operations, and see what could be done to the helicopter side of things to improve our safety record. In an ideal world, everyone would instantly agree and sign up for these improvements. In a real world, - well, we'll probably be retired before the authorities get around to acting on them.

## WEATHER

Although helicopter operations are mostly VFR, it appears that helicopters have more than their fair share of weather related accidents.

| Airline Situation | Helicopter Situation | Areas for Improvement |
|---|---|---|
| Detailed weather reporting is available at all airports through trained observers or automated data. | Operate a long way away from weather reporting stations. Pilots must observe weather and try to predict what will happen. | Need a suitable way to observe the weather and make predictions based on what we see.<br>Need good instruction on how to do micro-climate weather observations and short-term predictions.<br>Lots of mini-weather stations are now available and connected to the Internet. We need to find a way to use that information for helicopters. |
| Weather reports for departure and destination and alternate routes are provided. | Weather en route, rather than at takeoff and landing sites is the major concern. | Need better en route local weather reporting. |
| Weather radar is available at each airport. | Very seldom is weather radar coverage available in most areas where helicopters operate. | XM Satellite weather is nearly instantaneously available anywhere in North America. |
| Wx weather radar is available on airplanes. | Wx weather radar is seldom installed on helicopters. | Not a major factor for most helicopter accidents. |
| Wind direction always reliably known prior to landing and takeoff. | There is no way to accurately know the wind's direction in unprepared landing sites. (The situation is even worse at night.) | Need accurate low-airspeed sensor for speeds below 40 knots indicated airspeed (discussed later). |
| Airlines have relatively few accidents caused by weather. | There have been quite a few accidents where helicopter pilots didn't understand implications of flying in less than desirable conditions. | Need to institute training scenarios in simulator for: night encounters with bad weather, and whiteout/flat-light conditions |

Table 1 – Weather issue differences between helicopters and airlines, and how helicopters handle weather can be improved.

| Airline Situation | Helicopter Situation | Possible Method to Improve |
|---|---|---|
| Excellent weather reporting at all airports they use. | Operate long way away from weather reporting stations. Pilots must observe weather and try to predict what will happen. | Need to be able to observe the weather and make predictions based on what we see.<br>Need good instruction on how to do micro-climate weather observations and short-term predictions.<br>Lots of mini-weather stations now available and connected to internet. Find a way to use that information for helicopters. |
| Weather radar at airport. | Very seldom is there weather radar coverage in most areas where helicopters operate. | XM weather is nearly instantaneously available anywhere in North America. |
| Wx Radar on airplane | Seldom installed | Not a major factor for most helicopter accidents |
| RVR for low visibility measurements | | Not relevant |
| Wind direction always reliably known prior to landing | No way to know wind in unprepared landing site (even worse at night). | Need low airspeed sensor below 40 KIAS (see performance discussion later). |
| Airlines have relatively few accidents caused by weather. | Quite a few where pilots didn't understand implications of flying in less than desirable conditions | Institute training scenarios in simulator for:<br>Night encounters with bad weather<br>Whiteout / flat light conditions |

## WEATHER REPORTING

Although helicopter operations are mostly visual flight rules, it appears we have more than our fair share of weather-related accidents. Weather is seldom an issue for fixed-wing on their route of flight, except for thunderstorms. It's just something they have to fly through or over. They're on instruments from takeoff to touchdown. Weather at destination is pretty important, but, even then, aside from thunderstorms, it's merely a hindrance to getting to a position to land the airplane, or it means the rapidly vanishing in-flight service may be interrupted. We, on the other hand, worry about weather en route... and have little to help us. We fly relatively low to the ground in comparison to the fixed-wing world, so even small changes in terrain affect our flight conditions significantly. What we need is more training in micro-climate and micro-weather. This includes training on how to predict the really local weather, how to judge when conditions will deteriorate, and knowledge things like upslope flow and winter or summer effects. remember at least a couple of places where we knew the local weather was going to be bad if there was an east wind. In my military days, at one base, if we could smell the local pulp and paper mill, we knew it was probably not a day we would be flying.

**Predicting the Weather**

Helicopter accidents are seldom related to thunderstorms, but there are far too many accidents due to fog and low ceilings. Both fog and low ceilings are closely related to a very simple, but often-neglected concept — the temperature/dew-point spread. Sadly, all too often I've read accident reports of emergency medical service (EMS) missions where the temperature/dew-point spread was either zero or a very small number. When there's less than 2 degrees C (3.6 F) difference between the two numbers, you know the ceiling is going to be less than 1,000 feet above ground. If you're flying toward higher ground, you're going to rapidly run out of visibility and flying room. Fog and low ceilings could more easily be predicted if there were more places reporting just air temperature and dew point.

Given that you can buy a good system that shows both temperature and dew point, as well as relative humidity, for less than $100 at a big box store, I have to ask why we haven't got this equipment at every police and fire station, and have it integrated into the weather system? It shouldn't be that difficult or expensive to do. Every fire engine could have a system like this. Most of the time there are fire engines at EMS scene calls, and the resulting data provided would be useful information to know when you're heading into a relatively unknown area at night in less than ideal conditions. That way, the lapse rate and temperature/dew-point spread could be used to calculate where a cloud base should be for all those places. For areas with mountain passes, this would be a good way to check to see if the passes are clear of cloud and fog. We get the same basic weather training as airline pilots, with lots of emphasis on upper-level stuff helicopter pilots seldom, if ever, encounter. What we need is a little more emphasis on weather predictions in training, and operational procedures that help educate pilots on what to expect.

## *Navigation*

Significant number of helicopter accidents are as a result of poor navigation (CFIT)

| Airline Situation | Helicopter Situation | Possible Method to Improve |
|---|---|---|
| Full suite of Navigation Aids (VOR, ADF, ILS, DME, GPS) | Mostly by VFR sectional (GPS is also heavily used for VFR, but not IFR approach approved equipment) | Better training on use of GPS for low level VFR operations.<br>Better use of technology to improve obstacle avoidance.<br>(Car GPS systems are much more sophisticated than most aircraft GPS) |
| Navigation aids at all airports<br>(mostly ILS) | Most helicopter operations do not have radio navigation aids nearby. | Helicopter-specific instrument approaches using GPS would help make flights more deliberate. |
| Purpose of navigation systems is to allow airplane to be position with runway at end of IFR approach. | Any helicopter instrument approaches don't have repeatable references at breakout (see runway environment later) | Make better approach lighting system, specifically for helicopters. |

# INSTRUMENT FLIGHT

### Aircraft IFR Capability

| Airline Situation | Helicopter Situation | Possible Method to Improve |
|---|---|---|
| All fully IFR capable | Most light helicopters are not IFR approved or approvable | Reduce requirements for IFR to minimum necessary – in terms of equipment and stability and control / handling.<br>Develop low-cost AFCS to improve handling. |
| Fully coupled autopilot | Few have autopilot. 75% of those that have autopilot use it. | Ensure autopilots are used by all. Training on use and testing on use as part of check ride must be mandated.<br>May be more cost effective to permit IFR on single engine helicopters with suitable low-cost stabilization than to keep having crashes. Ensure pilots are properly trained (see below). |

### Pilot IFR Capability

| Airline Situation | Helicopter Situation | Possible Method to Improve |
|---|---|---|
| All pilots are instrument rated as requirement for FW commercial license | Most are not instrument rated. | Make it a requirement to obtain an instrument rating for a commercial helicopter rating |
| All pilots maintain instrument currency. Every flight is an instrument flight. | For those who are instrument rated, most do not maintain currency | Provide low-cost simulators to allow pilots to maintain currency |
| All fitted with TCAS | Most not fitted with TCAS | Fit with TCAS. |

### IFR Infrastructure

| Airline Situation | Helicopter Situation | Possible Method to Improve |
|---|---|---|
| Airways are set for mid-to-high level operations. | Not suitable for helicopters to fly IFR due to icing, or time to climb to altitude, etc. | Low level (<2,000' AGL) helo IFR routes with very tight RNP values. Make good use of GPS and WAAS. |
| Runways well lit with VASI / PAPI system | Often landing sites are in the middle of brightly lit urban areas or not lit at all | Get low-cost helicopter appropriate approach lighting system for those bases that have enough traffic. |
| Fuel Reserves required are minor penalty for most FW aircraft. Lower fuel consumption as fraction of weight than helicopters. | Fuel reserves are a major burden for a helicopter to plan to fly IFR. | Reduce fuel reserves to 15 minutes.<br>Reasons for IFR reserves are FW based, and helicopters have much more flexibility. May need to increase GPS approaches in some areas. Or ensure zero/zero approach capability so there is no need for alternate airports. |
| Fuel reserves based on need to have alternate airport for weather and runway closure reasons. | No need for runway closure reasons unless it's a helipad that can only take one helicopter at a time. | Develop appropriate alternate requirements – including no alternate required for large heliports, certainly for airports. |
| Most IFR flight plans filed by dispatch with scheduled time of departure. Time to obtain clearance is short when airline is ready. | Most helicopter operations not scheduled. Difficult to obtain clearance on short notice, especially when necessary to share FW IFR airspace. | If it took 5 minutes to get a clearance for a low-level, not to interfere with other FW traffic for IFR, this might give more impetus to use IFR system |

**Runway and Landing Environment**

| Airline Situation | Helicopter Situation | Possible Method to Improve |
|---|---|---|
| On breakout from IFR approach, airplane will have 'standard' environment: | IFR approach techniques not often used, even in night conditions that should be classified as IFR. | Insist on standard approach techniques, particularly at night or in marginal VFR conditions. |
| Directly in front of both pilots | For oil rigs, sometimes one pilot cannot see landing area when high drift angles necessary due to winds | Ensure multiplicity of approach paths possible so that both pilots can see landing area. |
| Closure rate with lights at 'standard' rate due to approach airspeed. Gives good depth perception. | Different approach gradients and speeds used on approach result in every approach being different. Some approaches conducted downwind. No standard way of judging closure or descent rates visually or using flight instruments or navigation equipment. | Develop method of showing closure rates visually and using navigation systems. |
| 'standard' approach gradient set at 3° (or very close) | No standard approach gradient | Determine suitable approach gradient for each type, and have glidepath angle remotely adjustable from cockpit for glidepath. |
| Instrument approach guidance consistent with runway environment | No instrument approach procedure | Develop VFR short range approach procedure for helipads and heliports to permit 'standard' approach paths to be flown. |
| Runway lights designed to provide good references | Often poor lighting on helipad | Develop better helipad lighting configurations |
| VASI / PAPI lights aligned with direction of landing | VASI / PAPI lights may not be used and probably not aligned with direction of landing | Get VASI / PAPI lights that can be adjustable for both azimuth and elevation for helipads and heliports. |
| Landing direction dictated by runway, crosswind accepted as part of landing task | Landings made into wind, crosswind not accepted / favored over landing into wind | Accept approach with crosswind in order to have good approach lighting. |

**Maps and Charts**

| Airline Situation | Helicopter Situation | Possible Method to Improve |
|---|---|---|
| IFR charts and approach plates updated every 56 days. Provide exactly the information needed for operation. | 1:500,000 scale maps, (some urban areas have 1:250,000 charts) Maps updated every 2 years(?). Sectionals contain lots of ATC information not used by helicopter pilots. | Provide 1:250,000 scale maps with only low-level (<500- 1,000' AGL) ATC information, Update every 6 months. |
| Airport diagrams as part of data provided. | When operating from airports, must obtain airport diagrams from IFR charts. Not normally provided on VFR charts. | Provide airport diagrams as part of VFR charting. |
| | | Provide geographical data so that customized maps can be printed / used by helicopter pilots for their own area. |
| Towers and low level obstacles not a problem en route. | Towers and low level obstacles a problem en route | Provide easy way to update VFR charts and distribute information. |
| Cockpits not cluttered with maps and books | Housekeeping of maps and charts not easy in most helicopters, especially single pilot operations | Make map sizes more appropriate. Integrate GPS information to make operation better.44 |

Sectional maps have way too much high-level information that is irrelevant to helicopter operations. If you're going to be up that high, you'll probably be IFR anyway. Why not provide information that can be printed with only the information wanted at the scale that we want?

## *Scheduled Operation*

| Airline Situation | Helicopter Situation | Possible Method to Improve |
|---|---|---|
| Scheduled well in advance | EMS flights closer to military Air Defense Scramble plus for added adventure - you don't know where you're going to land when you take off. | Not possible to improve on EMS operations |
| IFR Flight plans submitted in advance | | Be able to submit low-level, local IFR flight plans with few minutes notice. |

## *Support Personnel*

### Dispatchers

| Airline Situation | Helicopter Situation | Possible Method to Improve |
|---|---|---|
| Dispatchers provide most information needed to flight crews. Dispatchers trained and certified by FAA. | Pilots have to find all the information about routes, landing zones, weather, ATC in a piece-meal fashion.<br>Any 'dispatch' function is only like a taxi-cab dispatcher. | Provide training and certification to dispatchers and other operations personnel. |

### Others

| Airline Situation | Helicopter Situation | Possible Method to Improve |
|---|---|---|
| Lots of specialized workers – baggage handlers, refueling, push-back, cleaners, security | Mostly all handled by pilot.<br>No training required by regulation. | Have specific training on each of the appropriate responsibilities – refueling, for example. |

## *CFIT and Other Safety Issues*

### Equipment

| Airline Situation | Helicopter Situation | Possible Method to Improve |
|---|---|---|
| Have EPWS, TAWS by law. | No such requirements and no such equipment | For any helicopter flying at night outside a built up area, mandate EGPWS and TAWS appropriate for a helicopter. |
| GPS equipment built in to flight management system / cockpit | Hand held GPS attached somewhere in cockpit | Built-in GPS as standard. |
| | TAWS typically hold-over from FW, not relevant to helos, considered to be a nuisance by most pilots. | Develop helicopter specific TAWS. |
| All FW flights are IFR | Nearly all helicopter flights at night are VFR. And there is no such thing as night VFR. | Make all helicopter flights at night follow IFR-like rules and procedures – Minimum En route altitudes, etc. |

## Performance Data

| Airline Situation | Helicopter Situation | Possible Method to Improve |
|---|---|---|
| All scheduled airlines have significant performance data, planning and capability | Helicopter performance does not meet needs of operators. Does not provide full picture of performance. | Helicopter performance charts need to be changed to meet real requirements – power required to hover as function of weight, density altitude, height above ground and wind.<br>Engine power available as a function of pressure altitude and air temperature. |
| Single engine failure not an issue at any stage of flight | Many twin engine helicopters do not have single engine performance for significant parts of takeoff and landing profiles. | Develop profiles that compromise performance vs. risk |
| Highly reliable engines | FW engines have significantly lower failure rates than RW. | Monitor RW engine failure rates and make manufacturers accountable for failure rates |
| | | Mandate monitoring systems for all RW turbine engines. |

## Performance Information

| Airline Situation | Helicopter Situation | Possible Method to Improve |
|---|---|---|
| Accelerate stop distance | Hover performance not possible to calculate in terms of power required to hover and compare to power available, especially for above specification engines. | Provide power required to hover as function of hover height, wind speed, weight and pressure altitude and temperature. |
| Takeoff distance to clear 50' obstacle | 'Maximum performance takeoff' persists as a myth. No charts, no set procedures, no consistent methods for operational use of this technique | Provide better low airspeed sensing system and climb gradient charts |
| Engine Performance checked regularly | No need in most operations to ensure that engines are meeting 'minimum specification' power outputs | Mandate regular checks of engine output in order to ensure performance is obtainable. |

Accelerate stop distances, landing distances etc. – the things the FW world needs for safety are pretty well established. We don't even have way to determine the power required to hover – an essential bit of safety information.

## CREW

### Number of Pilots

| Airline Situation | Helicopter Situation | Possible Method to Improve |
|---|---|---|
| Two pilots, even the small commuter aircraft | Single pilot for nearly all operations | Two pilot operation for night flights. |
| Mentoring of junior pilots is standard | | Provide mentoring opportunities for junior pilots in larger helicopters. |
| Training is extensive | Minimal training on type | Mandate minimum of 10 hours on type, |
| Type rating on aircraft used in passenger service | No type ratings until larger helicopters. | Type ratings for piston, turbine and twin engine helicopters. |

### Training / Ratings

| Airline Situation | Helicopter Situation | Possible Method to Improve |
|---|---|---|
| Instrument rating standard | Instrument rating not required | Make instrument rating requirement for commercial helicopter pilots |
| Multi-Engine rating standard | No multi-engine ratings | Make multi-engine rating mandatory for commercial helicopter pilots. |
| Simulator training is norm | Few if any simulators for helicopters | Increase simulators for all helicopter pilots. |
| Hours requirement for commercial license is xxx hours | Only xxx hours necessary for commercial rating | Increase hour requirement for commercial helicopter rating |

## OPERATIONS

### Checklists and Standard Operating Procedures

| Airline Situation | Helicopter Situation | Possible Method to Improve |
|---|---|---|
| Standard operating procedures | Many situations could not be covered by standard operating procedures | Ensure simple procedures set up for most operations. |

## TRAINING

### Simulators

| Airline Situation | Helicopter Situation | Possible Method to Improve |
|---|---|---|
| All training and check rides completed in simulators | Very few simulators available for low-end helicopters | Make more simulators available for helicopters |
| No check rides given in real airplanes | Most check rides given in real helicopters | Make simulators available for check rides for helicopters. |
| Scenarios that are impossible to duplicate in real aircraft can be duplicated in simulator | Many scenarios cannot be trained for in real helicopters | More simulators realistic, and perform all training and check rides in simulator. |
| Scenarios that are dangerous to attempt in the real aircraft can be safely trained in simulator | Dangerous scenarios that are attempted in real helicopter often result in incidents or accidents | Make simulators realistic and perform all training and check rides in simulator. |

## HOW ABOUT THE CREW?

Well, there are normally two pilots, both of whom have multi-engine and instrument ratings, and have had regular training in simulators. Both are also trained in crew environment and have not only had significant experience before becoming captain, but are type rated on the aircraft they're flying and probably have significant experience in other airplane types as well. Finally, there is the actually flying. That has, more or less, been scheduled and is ATC controlled. Dispatch has taken care of weight and balance issues and devised flight plans. The flight has known departure and arrival places and procedures, a routine nature of operations and legs of flight that are of significant duration. The fuel reserves for IFR flight are not a major penalty, and all flights are conducted as IFR. Are you starting to get the picture?

We'll look at each of these features (and many others) and compare fixed-wing and helicopter operations to see what could be done on the helicopter side to improve our safety record. In an ideal world, everyone would instantly agree and sign up for these improvements. In the real world, well, we'll probably be retired before the authorities get around to actually acting on them. ***Does my cynicism show?***

# *Facilities*

## Landing Area Lighting

| Airline Situation | Helicopter Situation | Possible Method to Improve |
|---|---|---|
| Runways regularly checked for contamination, proper lighting | Helipads often are not checked for lighting, stray objects, security | Require helipads to be regularly checked in order to be 'approved'. |
| Lighting is standardized | Heliport lighting is supposedly standardized. | Ensure there is a standardized lighting pattern for helipads. |
| No distracting lighting around runway area | Often there is significant extraneous lighting near helipads and heliports | Make helipad lighting unique in color or pattern or some other unique method. |
| Standardized approach lighting | No approach lighting for most helipads | Develop some method of presenting approach lights for helipads |
| | Remote sites have absolutely no lighting | Set up reflective lighting patterns for areas that might be used infrequently. |
| Windsocks are checked for lighting | No method of even reporting if windsocks are lit or not | Ensure FAA has method for taking note of reports and following up on lighting for all towers over 200' AGL. |

## Emergency Crews

| Airline Situation | Helicopter Situation | Possible Method to Improve |
|---|---|---|
| Fire crews at all major airports | No fire crews, often not even any fire fighting equipment | Not many helicopter accidents result in fires, but training likely personnel on fire fighting might be worthwhile for heliports that have more than xxx number of movements per year. |

## Obstacles Near Facility

| Airline Situation | Helicopter Situation | Possible Method to Improve |
|---|---|---|
| Good procedures set out for things that are above a certain obstacle criteria | Even marked helipads don't have a set method of getting obstacles marked. | Check on this. How do you report obstacles? |
| Method to report obstacles – dispatch and flight planning / operations rooms have methods to gather and disseminate info on obstacles | Many helicopter operations are small and remote from sources of information. | Customize via internet to be able to disseminate information to small operators easily. |

## Unions

| Airline Situation | Helicopter Situation | Possible Method to Improve |
|---|---|---|
| Nearly all airlines are unionized | Hardly any helicopter operations are unionized. | Unions are double edged swords. Better working conditions are possible if done right. |

Nearly all airline pilots belong to a union - a union that believes in active participation in safety (ALPA's largest expense is putting pilots on all the various committees that regulate things like approaches, displays, etc., as well as having a rep on every accident that involves one of their members) (and I'm not slamming PHPA here - I think they're an important first step)

Hard to get enough helicopter pilots together in one room to form a union. Independence of operations also means less tendency to want to form a union. Bad examples of unions also don't help.

## *A Recent Question*

Recently, I had a question from this column's other reader (now I know who both of you are), asking whether a a guideline for using carburetor heat on a piston-engine helicopter that relied on an air temperature/dew-point spread of less than $5°C$ ($9°F$) might be useful. I was impressed that someone might have thought of that in the first place. Then, this same reader brought up the issue of local variations in weather that were human made. It was pointed out that if you fly downwind of a large cooling tower, you'll encounter very high humidity levels, even if you don't see any clouds of steam where you are. Not only high humidity levels, but also higher than normal temperatures. After all, they are cooling something by exchanging heat. Why is this important? It reiterates that helicopters constantly encounter micro-climate issues and issues of weather that fixed wing (especially airline) pilots never do. If we want to be as safe as they are, we must be vigilant and knowledgeable in how to recognize and predict these instances of weather change. In the next issue, we look at how the concept standardized procedures might help make our lives a little more boring... but safer.

# CHAPTER 56 *Fatigue in Helicopter Operations*

**Vertical** October /November 2007

*Comment: Fatigue is a well known issue in the fixed-wing world, but, oddly, doesn't surface often in discussions of helicopter operations. To be sure, there aren't many helicopter flights that cross time zones, or, aside from EMS and police, fly deep into the night. There also aren't many scheduled helicopter airlines. So, at first glance, one might think the issues that drive fatigue would be absent, and the subject limited to those who don't pay as much attention to their lifestyle as they should.*

Helicopter pilots, though, know it's much more subtle than that. Fatigue is, by definition, a 'decreased ability to maintain function or workload due to mental or physical stress.' One of the insidious things about fatigue is you're often the last one to notice it, and you're not in a good position to judge whether you are fatigued. Therein, as Shakespeare would say, lies the rub.

Most fixed-wing operations that deal with fatigue issues are multi-crew, which provides a chance for others to suggest when pilots are not at the top of their game. On the other hand, many helicopter operations are not just single pilot, but single-person operations. No one is around to see how you're doing, and, perhaps better stated, no one is in a position to judge if you're really as sharp as you should be.

What can cause fatigue? Well, there are a variety of things, including a lack of quality sleep, poor food, outdoor conditions that are extreme (too hot or too cold), lots of physical activity and stressful mental activity. Surprising, mental activity can be much more stressful than moderate physical activity. If you're overworked physically, it's much easier to spot than being overworked mentally.

## *Helicopter Operations Are Different*

That helicopter operations are different from fixed-wing flying is obvious, but what are the fatigue-inducing aspects of helicopter flying we may not have considered?

Seating is one - most helicopter seats are terrible, and sitting in one for hours on end is fatiguing. Add the vibration that is characteristic of a helicopter, and the effect compounds.

This is without having to adopt a strange posture for something like long-lining. A long-line pilot is a chiropractor's dream patient, as they face hours of twisting in the seat and being vibrated at the same time!

Wearing a helmet for hours on end also adds to fatigue, as does the constant noise. Both of these are almost non-existent in the fixed-wing world (outside of the military, that is).

The intensity of concentration is another difference found in helicopter flying. There is little actual physical work needed to manipulate the controls of most commercial helicopters. The forces are low and the movements normally small. However, this in itself causes a problem. The pilot has to provide the necessary mechanical characteristics and be very aware of the size and nature of the control inputs. This takes concentration, whether you know it or not. It may become second nature after a while, but it still takes mental effort.

Then, there is the intensity and frequency of that mental effort. Helicopters are unstable, so there is a continuous low level effort just to stay upright. But, there are also short periods of high level concentration. Helicopters typically make several times more takeoffs and landings than airplanes do. Since accidents are most likely to happen during a takeoff or landing, that's when our whiskers have heightened sensitivity and are out extra far, making sure everyone is kept safe. This means there are significantly more events to stress us per hour than for a fixed-wing pilot.

In most turbine engine helicopters we have even more variables to worry about, as far as limitations (which can easily be exceeded, normally at some cost to ourselves) and flight parameters are concerned. For example, there's typically only one way to takeoff in a fixed-wing ship. At the end of the runway, add takeoff power, ensure that no limits are being exceeded, and then hurtle down the runway until rotation speed, at which point you pull back and climb at the appropriate airspeed. In a helicopter, you need to determine your own direction of takeoff, ensuring there are no obstacles, then see if any limitations are being exceeded when you lift to the hover. Then, you have to decide what type of takeoff you want to do, and what airspeed you're going to accelerate to for climb out. You also have twice as many limitations to worry about compared to a fixed wing pilot.

Landing is pretty much the same situation, you have a lot more variables and a lot more limitations to observe and respect. Add to this that the performance charts don't really help, and the stress level, whether you know it or not, starts to ratchet up.

Precise hovering, if your job calls for it, is quite intense in terms of the concentration and mental effort needed. It can't be done precisely for long periods of time without exacting it's toll.

What does all this boil down to? The nature of the job in the helicopter world introduces a completely different level of fatigue than in the fixed-wing world. This is even before we take into account where we operate.

## *Living Accommodation*

Let's face it, most places in which helicopters operate are remote. This means the normal support structure that comes with civilization may not be as rich in or near a big city. Bush operations have few luxuries. Even if the food is good, living in a crowded trailer (or tent) doesn't make for a restful night's sleep.

In my air force days, we used to make fun of the transport pilots because they stayed in hotels, while we real men stayed in tents. When we talked about it over a beer, we realized they had a completely different set of problems than we did, and they had justified their sleeping requirements on the basis of their job. We won't even talk about the food situation...

EMS Operations

Most EMS operations that are around-the-clock provide decent living accommodations for the crews, and schedule according to crew duty time requirements. Changing shifts from day to night and back is not the easiest thing in the world, but, with careful attention, it can be managed. The stress that this can cause on home life is unmeasurable, but needs to be considered because it contributes to emotional and mental fatigue.

## *Crew Duty Times*

In an attempt to ensure pilots are properly rested, regulatory authorities established crew duty time limits. These are a one-size-fits-all attempt to ensure proper rest is obtained and crews aren't overworked. They are supposed to cover all eventualities, but often don't. Unscrupulous operators will also do everything they can to legally extract working time from a pilot.

Crew duty times, like any man-made rule, are not perfect. If you're not worried about the legal implications (who's watching anyway???), they can easily be broken without any immediate or obvious long-term effect. But you can't continue to break the rules of getting enough rest or good food or any of the other host of things that ensure alertness without paying the consequences. Fatigue can, and will, sneak up and bite you if you don't pay attention. The problem is, you probably won't know you should be paying attention - you'll be too tired!

As a way of getting into the spirit of this article, I deliberately overdosed on coffee and stayed up late and got up early. Initially, I didn't notice many mistaeaks in my wok, but as tiem wurnt on, it got wurser and wurser...

## *The Solution*

Be aware of how you feel. You manage and oversee your ship's status, so treat yourself as if you were another aspect to monitor and keep healthy to ensure safe flight. Most of us know the signs when we are getting fatigued, pay attention to them. Don't let yourself get to the point where you are too tired to notice.

Also, most of are not involved in the various wars going on, so it's never that critical if we have to cancel a trip. Don't be a wimp and say you can do it. It takes a real man to say no.

Some would say that my helicopter experience isn't complete because I haven't spent time in the bush, leaving me at a disadvantage when it comes to providing insight on overcoming issues of fatigue while living in the wilds. Fortunately for me, I'm now too old to be considered for a bush operation, even should I (shudder) want to go camping again.

# CHAPTER 57 *Down-Wind Takeoff*

Not Previously Published

*Comment: NO! Neither your eyes nor your mind are playing tricks on you! That is low-fuel' light associated with 'Downwind Take-off Dangers' related article. But why you ask?*

It's rather simple. It is a familiar setting that all of us have experienced; driving along on the highway when the infamous low-fuel light and the annoying beep or chirp activates to tell us we are nearing the end of yet another tank of over-priced gasoline. It is at this moment a couple of things take place: 1.) Your significant other usually reminds you of all the times and previous exits she reminded you that you should stop to fill-up, 2.) your mind starts playing games; 'how much fuel do I have when that light comes on' ?'How far did I drive last time when the light came on'? 'How many more miles to that next exit?'

So, what does this all too typical scenario describe? It describes another human being 'pushing the limits'. Many have found themselves coasting into the next gas station 'on fumes' or worse on the side of the highway because the limits were pushed by 'I'll just go a little more this time'. Sadly, this mindset is no different than the trap that we can fall into with a downwind take-off; "I had no problem with a 5-6 knot tailwind takeoff last time' or 'I've taken off with a 10 knot tailwind I don't know why another 5 knots would hurt anything' you hopefully get the point!

Our self-rationalization can get us in trouble in a hurry. What was a 5 knot tailwind takeoff one day will build progressively until you 'accidentally' find out just what that tailwind limit is! 'I'll just go a little more this time'. No different than the low fuel scenario we 'push the limit' in both cases; one leaves us with humiliation and the other leaves us with great potential for injury or worse. I'm not implying that a 3-5 knot tailwind takeoff will get you hurt or killed. What I am saying is don't fall prey to that 'I'll just go a little more this time' mentality that has been known to find its way inside helicopter cabins.

## *THE MECHANICS*

As my counterpart in Torque Talk often reminds me: 'a diagram is worth a thousand explanations'. So, let's take a look at the mechanics of downwind take-offs from a technical yet practical explanation with a basic graphic representation.

Looking at this 'generic' diagram we see three different helicopters each with a certain amount of power being used depending on the 'airspeed' of the helicopter or the 'relative wind' the blades are utilizing. At first sight of the diagram it should remind you of a basic power curve diagram and the fact that our wonderful machines are the only vehicle known to man that take more power to go slower. The power required curve could represent TQ (torque) required for a turbine helicopter or MP (manifold pressure) required. You will see at the 'bottom' of the power required curve we have the 'bucket-speed' or the speed at which we get the greatest airspeed for the smallest amount of power required. This 'bucket-speed' area should be familiar as it is normally the best autorotative speed range as well. Looking at Helicopter #1 we see a helicopter at or near 'max power' while in a 0 airspeed hover; in or out of ground effect, it makes no difference for this explanation. Granted, it will not always take 'max power' to hover but consider Helicopter #1 at or very near max power for this explanation. Following along with the example helicopters you will see that helicopter #2 now has 15 knots of 'forward' or headwind airspeed and the amount of 'power required' is substantially less than the power required for that 0 airspeed hover. This concept in and of itself is no (or shouldn't be) surprise to even the most novice students. It is helicopter #3 where we can get into trouble! Looking at helicopter #3 we see that we have 15 knots of 'reward' or tailwind airspeed. Looking at the power required we see that it is a 'mirror-image' of the power required for helicopter #2. That is correct! It takes the same amount of power, in theory, to hover with a 15 knot tailwind as it does a 15 knot headwind, but if you do bring your tap shoes! For the sake of aerodynamic argument tail rotor authority and increases in power required with use of the tail rotor are excluded from the equation. Another way to look at this explanation is that the blades don't care where the 15 knots of wind is coming from; in essence, with a 15 knot tailwind you could visualize the retreating and advancing blades (as you know them to be) have essentially traded places. I'm certainly NOT telling you to make a habit of hovering with a tailwind! A host of factors dictate why you shouldn't including; loss of tail rotor effectiveness issues - yaw stability, longitudinal stability issues due to wind getting under (or over) large stabilizer surfaces, as well as potential TOT and compressor stall issues in turbine machines.

So, if we have a 15 knot tailwind as seen with helicopter #3 and we commence a downwind takeoff the rotor system is starting with a -15 knots of 'support' if you will and therefore must outrun the tailwind and LOSE the translational lift that it had while stationary. Guess what? That takes more power! Essentially by taking off with this 15 knot tailwind you must use the power necessary to reach the power required area of a 0 airspeed helicopter as we described with helicopter #1. At this point you have a ground speed of 15 knots but the rotor system is experiencing a forward relative airflow of ZERO; you are getting NO help from translational lift and eventually (in a short amount of seconds) the helicopter will begin to descend. Remember where you are at this point; at or near max power. With the helicopter 'sinking' you add more power which increases the need for tail rotor which robs you of even more power. This is why I referenced 'at or near max power' above, if you were faced with this situation, heavy, and in less than ideal performance conditions you may not (and likely will not) have enough power and pedal to get you 'over the hump' of the zero airspeed point. This dangerous and often overlooked downwind takeoff condition sets the table for a hazardous cycle.

## *SUMMRY*

While many have fallen prey to 'pushing the limit' with the low fuel light in their car, one must realize that pushing the limit with downwind takeoffs can lead to disastrous results. We must resist the temptation to gradually increase our accepted risk level regarding downwind takeoffs. Obviously with the right power margin and ideal conditions taking off with a certain amount of tailwind speed gradient is possible and can be made safely. It is the human nature of 'pushing the limit' that we must avoid..

# CHAPTER 58 *Why are Helicopters Difficult to Fly?*

Not Previously Published

*Comment: I don't know of any helicopter pilot who immediately was able to master the control of the machine- every single one has had a number of hours of humiliation until enlightenment sunk in. Why?*

In order to understand this, it's necessary to look at how we control any vehicle or machine, from the point of view of control loop. This is shown in Figure 1 below.

There are many parallels to learning to ride a bicycle (except the falling off part)- somewhere, somehow, something clicks, and it becomes much easier. Helicopter flying is made more difficult by some particular aspects of both helicopters and the air, but the basics are the same. Since forward flight seems to present fewer problems in learning than hovering, we'll just look at hovering.

## *Hovering a Helicopter –*

The pilot wants to maintain his position, heading and height about the ground while someone hooks up an underslung load. To begin let's say the pilot can see the ground very clearly in front of him, and using a mirror, can also see the underslung load. Noticing the position to be slightly wrong, he makes an appropriate adjustment on the controls, which reacts through the flight control system and changes the tilt of the rotor disk slightly. This tilt changes the downwash a bit, causing the helicopter to move. The pilot assesses the movement and seeing it is not quite enough, makes another, smaller input. This second correction, when eventually seen by the pilot, is judged to be sufficient. The pilot waits until an another error in position before making another control correction, and so on.

The key element is the information fed back to the pilot in respect of the helicopter position, rate of closure to the underslung load, etc. There are many other items of information coming in as well - peripheral vision for roll and yaw rates, proprioceptive (seat of the pants) feeling for vertical speed, etc.

## *So what?*

Why go to the bother of writing all this? Of what use is it to the average helicopter pilot?

There are several very important concepts that need to be understood -one of these has been introduced as 'gain'. The next is to consider how the pilot fits into the loop.

To better understand this, return to the hovering example. If the pilot is trying to hover very accurately- to put the skids over a small landing pad, he will be working extremely hard. Why is this? Does the helicopter respond differently here than if the pilot were hovering 40 feet away? Does the helicopter 'know' something? Obviously not. The only part of the control loop that 'knows' anything is the pilot- he is aware of how accurately he must place the landing gear.

In this case, hovering over a small landing pad, information is fed back at a very rapid rate, and errors of even fractions of a inch are discernable. The pilot is trying to make very small, rapid control movements.

If the task requires this level of precise control, then it will be necessary to use close references (it would be catastrophic to try to land on the pad while looking at something else...). On the other hand, if the task does not require a high level of precision, using close references may lead to overcontrolling.

For most pilots, hovering at a low height with moderate precision requires the main area of regard to be about 20 to 30 feet in front of the helicopter. Looking closer (between the feet, for example) may lead to overcontrolling, and looking farther out (at the horizon) may lead to undercontrolling and a poorly maintained hover.

My experience of transitioning experienced pilots to new types of helicopters has shown repeatedly where the pilot looks is one of the major determining factors in ease and accuracy of hovering. The number of pilots who I have corrected was something that really surprised me.

## *Having explained how we fly, now it's time to look at why it's difficult.*

There is no doubt the first 10 or so hours of helicopter flying are among the most humbling experiences one can go through. Why is it difficult in the first place?

The helicopter is unstable, and takes a long time to respond to control inputs. Ask any control systems engineer to put the two characteristics together - an unstable control loop and a long response time, and he will question your sanity. The fact hovering is learned at all is more a credit to man's adaptability than to good handling qualities.

The instability of helicopters is a complex subject, and Ray Prouty's books and articles do a better job of explaining this in simple terms than I could. Basically if a helicopter was left to it's own devices, it would oscillate in an ever increasing manner to the point where it would crash. Measuring the time a helicopter takes to diverge from a steady condition is a task for the engineering test team, and requires a lot of technical training to understand and test. For us, it is sufficient to know that a helicopter without an Automatic Flight Control System (AFCS) will diverge, particularly in pitch attitude as various aerodynamic phenomena gang up on it.

The pilot's task is to stop these oscillations from developing. This is compensation for the shortcomings of the machine. Small, correctly timed inputs will stop the helicopter from diverging from it's hover attitude. If you look closely at how often control inputs must be made on a calm day in the hover in a typical light helicopter, it is about once every 5 to 8 seconds. Any other inputs are, strictly speaking, not necessary. A lot of helicopter pilots make unnecessary control inputs.

Note the word 'attitude'. In steady conditions, a constant attitude should hold the helicopter in the zero groundspeed hover. Unfortunately, things are never steady, and any disturbance from the steady condition will cause the helicopter to start it's divergent tendencies. Again, it is task of the pilot to stop those divergences from developing. More compensation.

## *Slow Response Explained*

The other complicating factor is the slow response of the helicopter. This is due to a combination of an actual slow response to the control inputs, and to the air we operate in. First the slow response.

The hydraulic system will introduce a small but measurable delay between the movement of the cockpit controls and the reaction of the actuators against the blades. Next, the blades themselves will take some time to react and get to their new pitch position. These two items take about 0.1 seconds. The blades must move to their final new position, which takes at least revolution to happen. At 360 RRPM, one revolution is about 0.15 seconds. Total time from input to blades moving is thus about 1/4 second. In control terms, this is a long time! The helicopter still has not moved from it's original position however.

Even with the new disk position, the helicopter still hasn't moved. While there may be a change in attitude of the helicopter following the input, there will be no movement over the ground1. This discrepancy between change in attitude and no change in position is disconcerting and takes a while for students to get used to. For movement to happen, the air has to be persuaded to react, which will take an additional, very perceivable period of time. A long time has passed between the pilot realizing he needs to make an input, with no movement of the helicopter. What would it be like to drive a car with this sort of delay between moving the wheel and changing position?

Consider our poor helicopter student- he sees he needs to make a control input, and so puts in a small correction, like he's told to do, but nothing happens. What does he do now? Right, he puts in a bigger input, just about the time the first input is taking effect, and things go rapidly downhill from there.

So there you have it, an unstable aircraft and a long time delay to control inputs- a potent recipe for disaster in any control loop, and part of the reason why helicopters are so difficult to learn to fly. We haven't even got into the cross coupling between the controls!

## What to Look At

The control loop explains many things about how we fly the helicopter, but another aspect needs to be considered- how did you learn to hover?

Do you remember the first time you tried to hover? It was undoubtedly done in a large, open field. (If you haven't tried hovering a helicopter yet, you probably will be put in a large open field–wait for it...) There are no obstacles to run into, and everything is uniformly green (or brown or white- depending upon the season).

How did you know you were moving up or down- there is normally nothing around to compare you height to, and without experience, us humans are not particularly good at judging height above the ground. In technical terms, vertical cues that are far away subtend very small angles and make it difficult to judge rate of climb.

What is the typical result for the student? - a lot of wandering around the field, with no real learning and lots of frustration. Why? Look again at the closed loop diagram. What sort of information is there to give visual cues about movement? Not a lot. Everything is the same color and not much different in texture, so there is very little real information about what the helicopter is doing. No matter where the student looks, he has no immediate information about how he is doing with regard to trying to hover. Why should he look 20 feet in front of the helicopter, when 200 feet or 5 feet all look the same?

There is also no real incentive to be accurate- one part of the field is as good as another and you won't run into anything...

The situation is made much better if there is something to look at- for hovering at 3 to 5 feet above the ground, the cues should be somewhere about 30 to 50 feet in front of the helicopter. I have used runway signs, marks on the runway, etc as cues, and had good success in having non-pilots hovering reasonably (within 10 feet of the spot using all 3 controls) within 30 minutes. A sign that could be run into provides some solid incentive to stay in one place, and when using it to compare to the ground behind it, also gives cues about height. The student has immediate cues, and can make corrections very easily.

1Even for those machines with fully articulated or hingeless heads- only an attitude change will happen immediately.

# CHAPTER 59 *Coordination and Co-Operation*

ALEA April 2009

*Comment: Crew co-ordination and co-operation doesn't just ensure the success of a mission, it ensures its safety as well.*

Several years ago, I had the pleasure of sitting in the back of a helicopter that was patrolling the night skies over a section of Los Angeles, Calif. Aside from the awesome spectacle of lights stretching from the sea to the mountains, the interaction of the ship's crew was a delight to watch. The two crewmembers, both police officers, seemed to have ESP regarding each other's intentions. At one point, after a radio call I barely understood, they turned toward each other and the question was asked: "Should we go there?" Before an answer could be verbalized, the pilot was already changing heading. They worked seamlessly as a team.

In another instance with this crew, the observer just said, "Orbit left," and the pilot rolled into a turn and kept flying — he didn't look at what the observer was interested in. The observer was there for observing and the pilot was there for flying.

## *Making it Work*

While riding in the jump seat of a business jet, there was some lighthearted banter amongst us as we started up on the ramp... until the captain said firmly, "Sterile cockpit 'til we pass 10,000 feet." For some reason, he later tried to apologize for the manner in which he said it. I had to tell him he was completely correct, that I was the one slightly out of line, and that I sincerely appreciated his words, which returned us to reality.

Another positive example of crew co-operation came to me from a very experienced news pilot. When asked what he did to keep himself safe and alive in relatively threatening scenarios, he said he rarely, if ever, orbited below 1,000 feet and 60 knots. When he did find himself in that situation, he was in continuous "talk" mode with the camera operator to tell him or her where he was going to go if they had any problems.

To find a negative example of crew co-ordination, I went back to an accident report I had read many years ago, where, in the midst of a real emergency that should not have been a problem, things went very wrong. The pilot directed certain things to be done, but the co-pilot decided he was going to do them differently. If this weren't bad enough, at a critical point it was discovered that a procedure that had been practiced by another crew member might not have been the optimum one. The result was, fortunately, only a slightly wrinkled airframe and lots of lessons learned.

## *Practice and Preparation*

One of the main issues with crew co-operation is who is going to do what and when. Like playing positions in any number of sports, it's important to know what your teammates are doing and going to be doing. To develop this knowledge, one needs discipline and practice... plenty of practice. But, when it comes to athletics, we rarely get to see the teams prepare. Remember this the next time you're watching a football game: the moves and formations are routine to the players because they've done them literally hundreds of times in practice — we should be so lucky.

So, where do we helicopter aviators practice? Too often, it only happens when doing the real thing. That is like putting together an all-star team but not allowing them to prepare and get used to one another before a big game. Even the bottom-of-the-league team with experience and discipline could probably beat them.

The fixed-wing world (here we go again, I can hear you say) has several advantages over us: their scenarios involve pretty routine tasks. Always taking off and landing on runways will do that for you. The scope of variations in their activities is relatively small. In the helicopter world, particularly the emergency medical service (EMS) world, where you don't know during takeoff where you're going to land, let alone what the landing site will look like, the need for flexibility and training is paramount.

The reality is I read accident reports all the time where it is obvious there was no crew co-ordination or co-operation. There are all sorts of instances where a front-seat occupant doesn't know: how to read the instruments and back up the pilot; ensure the altimeter on their side of the instrument panel is set correctly; read a map; know which books to get for the pilot; or even maybe question that the flight shouldn't be happening at all. All of these are examples of poor on non-existent crew co-operation.

## *The Head Magnet Syndrome*

Here's a question for all front-seat helicopter occupants, whether they are a pilot or not: how many times do you watch the other person change radio frequencies or enter GPS data, either out of curiosity or just to make sure they put in the right numbers? Don't you trust the other person? Didn't this distract you from your primary duties and put two heads down in the cockpit at the same time? Would wrong data entered into the radio or GPS be instantly catastrophic? Why not create a simple standard operating procedure where one person puts in the data and then calls the second to quickly check it after the first has their head back up?

It takes discipline to ignore something that's interesting, but it also takes confidence that other crewmembers are going to do things correctly.

## *Standardized Wording & Procedures*

Having had my share of interesting situations, and attempting to learn from the mistakes of others, during my more active flying days I used to brief that if we did have a real emergency, we were going to use the words "Mayday, Mayday, Mayday" in our radio call. I learned this from the United States Navy's P-3 crews, who, even if they had everything under control, following even a single-engine failure (ah, the dreaded three-engine landing), had to use those words in their initial contact with every air traffic control (ATC) agency until they landed. This was the Navy's way of ensuring everyone knew there was a problem and that the proper handling of the situation by was provided.

The looks of surprise from experienced pilots when I briefed this direction were always amusing, but I would explain that if we knew we were going to say that, there was a good likelihood we'd actually use it when the time came. If we practiced emergency procedures correctly — we'd do them correctly.

From this example of using of standardized words in emergencies comes the use of standardized words in other situations. If it was briefed that phrases like, "Taking off: heads out, sterile cockpit to 500 feet," or "Below 500 feet landing: heads out 'til we're on the ground," were to be used, then those words would get used every time. And if the pilot didn't initiate it, one of the other crewmembers should say it.

Standardized procedures and language helps. Everyone speaking the same technical words with clear knowledge of what the words mean is a big step forward. But, so is training and practice, and, dare it be said: monitoring. How many times does someone who is not a crewmembers go over a flight with all the crew to ensure that they all used the same wording and phrases? The advent of small data recorders, such as those developed by Appareo ***(see p.78, Vertical, Dec'07-Jan'08)***, could go a long way to helping with this, but it takes effort to monitor this kind of standardization.

## *Use of Simulators*

So, again we ask the question: where do helicopter crews get training and get to practice co-ordination and co-operation? Simulators ought to be the obvious answer, just like with our fixed-wing brethren. Unfortunately, there are few simulators for helicopters used in the public service/EMS/fire fighting world. And, there are fewer simulators (read none) that have a back end for a med crew.

Even if they did exist somewhere, it would take money, and time (another form of money), to send whole crews to a simulator that's not at a home base. The cry would go up that it's simply not affordable; and what's the problem anyway: we seem to be doing okay, aren't we? An ideal situation would be a full fuselage simulator in a trailer that could be moved from base to base.

For police crews, a simulator that incorporated all the mission equipment so complete crew training could be done in the simulator would help to develop procedures that take a lot of time to learn in the aircraft.

Crew co-operation is a beautiful thing when it happens properly, unfortunately, it's not easy to get to that point. But, it is necessary for the safe and effective operation of any helicopter when there is more than one person on board.

# CHAPTER 60 *Cockpit Demonstrator Evaluates System Concepts*

1994

*Comment: The first generations of military avionics represented a big improvement from visual navigation and bombing systems, but were hampered in the way that information could be displayed because of the severe limitations on the memory of their computers.*

The first generation of the Jaguar, for ex example.had no more than 32K of memory.

The fact that the avionics systems worked at all was a testament to the software engineers of the day.

With increased computing power available, systems engineers are now able to tailor not just the displays but also the way information is given to the pilot or navigator in some extremely friendly ways.

These human aspects of operating complex. multi sensor systems in a high pressure, low-level tactical fast jet aircraft are being addressed by many air forces and airframe manufacturers, and a va liety of techniques are being proposed.

*Avionics Magazine* was asked to have a preliminary look at one such system.

GEC Avionics' simulator has three distinct purposes, according to Jerry Fisher.

GEC Avionics' director of marketing and an ex-RAF test pilot. 'First of all. we set out to simulate algorithms of various components. using relatively low-cost software models instead of expensive hardware. We can quite closely duplicate the functions of a system, instead of having to physically build the system and then test it. This saves us a tremendous amount of time and money. For this reason alone, the simulator has been worthwhile.

'Secondly, we wanted to explore different ways of integrating the range of sensors and displays that feature in a modem aircraft. in an intelligent way, so the pilot didn't have to be the integrator and filter at the same time. Using a software model and commercially available hardware and software has streamlined this process considerably.

'For example, reprogramming a display in the C language is much easier than in Ada, and you can try lots more different ideas, in a much shorter time. This has permitted us to make rapid changes to suit the many suggestions we get from our likely clients. The touch-sensitive screens are commercially available screens rather than mil-spec systems, which makes them cheaper to purchase and easier to reprogram.

'Thirdly, we can display the work we are doing to potential customers in a very friendly way. Several people can stand around the cockpit and watch the displays and the HUD (head-up display) *(Continued from page 18)* symbology. We have had many different pilots, with a variety of backgrounds, use this system and had lots of feedback.

Since this is not a complex high-end simulator, we can afford to use it a lot more than a specialist engineering device.

'We recognize that there are definite limitations on the system-the HUD symbology for example, is not shown on the HUD in the cockpit, but is overlaid on the projected outside-world imagery in front of the pilot. The area on the screen matches that of the real HUD quite nicely, and accommodates changes more readily. Reprogramming the display symbol generator of a real HUD is no small task. This approach also lets several people at once see what the pilot should be seeing on the HUD.

'Part of our philosophy with that the tasks the pilot must complete are operationally realistic.

The HUD is representative of the European Fighter Aircraft HUD. but GEC was able to reconfigure it to other formats quite easily. The GEC team were projecting the HUD on the screen in red, which is easier to read than other colors with perform more simple. We only display what is needed when it is needed, we only control when control is necessary, and we let the computers monitor the aircraft systems.' The pre-demonstration brief by Dave Puleston. senior systems engineer at the GEC Technology and Systems Research Lab, and Andy Jones, senior software engineer at GEC's Guidance and Display Division, stressed that this simulator was by no means the full extent of their work, and had been rapidly produced in very short order to be ready for Farnborough. Several of the displays had 'systems' buttons for running the demonstration or to permit the engineers immediate access to the programming level of the system- they would not appear on the final version.

The simulator that was on display at Farnborough had recently been pulled out of the factory: engineers were working on last-minute connections and practical problems such as cooling and wiring. For the demonstration, the Direct Voice Input (DVI) part of the simulator wasn't working. and the loudspeakers for aural warnings were competing with the sounds of construction outside.

The HUD is representative of the European Fighter Aircraft HUD. but GEC was able to reconfigure it to other formats quite easily. The GEC team were projecting the HUD on the screen in red, which is easier to read than other colors with the current projection system. All that is being tested in the simulator are concepts of the HUD, not details.

There was no attempt at the Farnborough show to introduce the helmet-mounted display (HMD) that will be featured on new aircraft, since only the pilot could see how this works, not the rest of the audience. However. a full-binocular HMD is an integral part of the simulator and is being used to evaluate many human factors aspects in the Rochester laboratory.

The main part of the simulator consisted of three multifunction displays and a map display unit. plus space model mock-ups of the head-up display and other controllers. Jones said that some of the switches that were put in the simulator were only for show-they didn't do anything, but represented miscellaneous controls that would be required. A limited-displacement side stick and a full-motion digital throttle permitted representative low-level flying of the simulator. The stick had many buttons, but as this was not a simulator for displaying or trying HOTAS (hands on throttle and stick), many of the buttons were not typical, and the throttle had no switches at all. Given the state of the art on HOTAS. this simulator was an interesting demonstration of a different approach to using a complex avionics suite.

Three of the head-down multifunction displays were touch--sensitive, and featured icon driven menus. The photos show a sample of the various screen displays available. Again. because of the limitations of the mock-up for the show, not all of the choices were working, but that did not reduce the impact of the concept.

Part of the demonstration involved the use of the JTIDS (Joint Tactical Information Distribution System) and Sky Guardian self-defense systems.

The JTIDS transferred data about enemy aircraft, air defense sites, and targets from other (mythical) sources. such as AWACS. The Sky Guardian self-defense system integrated information from radar warning and other on-board sensors to indicate the position of pertinent enemy air defense systems. The lethal area of detection for one type of system is indicated in red-meaning our aircraft has been detected and this missile/radar may be a real threat to our health. A circle shown in green means we have been detected but the automatic Sky Guardian self-defense system has jammed the radar so that we are no longer in danger.

The top left screen showed the overall system operation, and had a variety of pages-the basic one, or index, let the operator select other screens such as navigation, communications, flight status, stores (or weapons). sensor operations, and DVI. The symbols were unique for each page, and the entire system was quite easy to use. For example, selecting the weapons display quickly showed the weapon system selected and the status of the rounds remaining for all weapons. Changing the selected weapon was as simple as touching its symbol.

Similarly, navigation and radio systems selection and operation were quite straightforward, and each page brought up appropriate sub-pages as well. The map display on the far right was a digital map unit under development, and no details of its operation.

So what does this all mean? In simple terms, the pilot will not have to carry around a lot of knowledge on how to use the system in day-to-day operations- and this can only be a good thing. A point that bears some consideration with such a system is to think of the single seat fighter pilot who is in less than-ideal conditions-it's 0300, pouring rain, he's been on a long mission, he has an aircraft problem, and he's trying to land in bad weather. Will were given during the demonstration.

The self-running demonstration was a quick (12-minute) flight through North Wales, where some enemy forces were threatening law and order. The demo was set up to show the various capabilities of the concept for the low-level air-to-ground attack mission. For example. the mission was pre-planned and already loaded into the computer.

After takeoff. an unexpected airborne threat was detected by the AWACS. Information on the threat was transmitted via JTIDS and immediately displayed on both the HUD and the head-down navigation display. The audio system alerted the pilot to the threat, and when the Sidewinder AIM9L was selected this was also confirmed aurally. Obviously. since this was a demonstration, the missile worked flawlessly and the enemy aircraft was removed. The quickest way back onto the pre-planned navigation route was shown on the HUD and navigation displays.

Normal navigation aspects like time and distance to waypoint were readily displayed on the head-down display. and the computer-generated head-down displays made it easy to see our location with respect to the target, navigation route, known enemy threats, and so on.

Closer to the target area (a bunch of tanks that were disrupting the peace and serenity of northern Wales, evidently). the Brimstone missile system was selected, and a salvo of four missiles were dispatched with a satisfying display of smoke and sound. In a more realistic manner, only three of the four hit the target, at least someone in the team wasn't being overly optimistic about things.

The main point of the demonstration was to show how easily the pilot could use such a system. In a nutshell, if this had been a full simulation and if the flight model and the visual system had been good enough, I could have programmed the mission and flown the flight feeling quite secure that the system was telling me what I needed to know about the aircraft and the environment. when I needed to know it. An interesting sidelight was the impression that even if the engineers had not been there to talk me through the system, I could have sorted out how to use it within a few moments-and I'm not a jet pilot.

To be honest, the voice warnings were audible saying that things were amiss.

but this was also evident from the other displays. The power of the voice-interactive controller was unfortunately not evident, but that will wait for another visit.

The rest of the demonstration was impressive enough, and the potential of DVI would probably not have stood out against the background noise. DVI is also such a leap in technology that some cultural adaptation would be worthwhile before attempting an assessment.

Twelve minutes was a taster for the possibilities of this concept-understanding the symbols was easy and the screens were well laid out. Rather than criticize the system, I had some alternative suggestions for controlling the displays that the GEC engineers were interested to hear. One of these involved the use of a rotary switch to scroll quickly through the radio channel selections rather than use the up/down switch that only changed channels one by one.

Similarly, navigation and radio systems selection and operation were quite straightforward, and each page brought up appropriate sub-pages as well. The map display on the far right was a digital map unit under development, and no details of its operation

So what does this all mean? In simple terms, the pilot will not have to carry around a lot of knowledge on how to use the system in day-to-day operations- and this can only be a good thing. A point that bears some consideration with such a system is to think of the single seat fighter pilot who is in less-than- ideal conditions-it's 0300, pouring rain, he's been on a long mission, he has an aircraft problem, and he's trying to land in bad weather. Will navigate.

and communicate safely? While the demonstration did not address this scenario directly, I am sure that it would offer convincing proof of the concept. Both Fisher and the engineers said that in this case a checklist would have appeared to step the pilot through the immediate actions and present him with options according to his flight plan.

Fisher had said that there were three reasons for making this simulator-I was not able to tell that the systems were not military standard. so the emulation using commercial software must work. Second, the integration concepts shown were new and different, and worked reasonably well.

Third, the system could be demonstrated to a great number of people at Farnborough.

On all counts, the project appears to have been successful.

GEC's efforts to use commercially available software and hardware and to integrate the various inputs with some intelligence appears to be paying off-fast jet pilots will find this sort of cockpit extremely easy to use, and let them get back to heads-up and out-of-the-cockpit flying. Even more improvements are on the way. -+-

# CHAPTER 61 *Policemen or Pilots?*

Not Previously Published

*Comment: Is it easier to make a Policeman a Helicopter Pilot or a Helicopter Pilot a Policeman?*

This article is guaranteed to generate a lot of controversy…

There are a lot of police helicopters operating around the world, working in a lot of different ways. A continuing argument has been whether you need to train a policeman to be a helicopter pilot or train a helicopter pilot to fly for the police department.

I'm not going to try to answer the question once and for all. There are a lot of different ways that police departments use helicopters- some carry SWAT teams, others act as primary or backup medical evacuation helicopters, still others do firefighting. I'm not going to consider those operations – just the police departments that use the helicopter as airborne support of ground operations, in a role that requires mostly patrolling from the sky.

## *Very Instructive Passenger Trip*

I'm basing this on flying with a police department that will remain nameless – mostly to protect them from being made fun of by their brother policemen.

It was a dark and mostly clear night – we takeoff after dark, and I'm sitting in the back of a well equipped, late model helicopter- Nightsun, FLIR, GPS street navigation system, more radios than you could shake a stick at – all the necessary toys.

We're operating in a pretty well populated urban area- lots of houses, but a fair smattering of industrial buildings and highways as well. Good cross section of what a lot of police departments across the country would face.

No sooner were we airborne, than were tasked to assist ground officers to find a gun that they thought had been thrown up onto the roof of a house. The house was minutes away from the base airport and we were soon orbiting, using the nightsun. After about 7 or 8 minutes of orbiting and not finding anything we were released and proceeded on our patrol.

The pilot was the driver, and the observer was really running the show – using the GPS and Nightsun and FLIR as needed. Not long after the rooftop search episode, as we were transiting to a patrol area, the observer looked down to the left and gave a terse 'Orbit left'. The pilot rolled into an orbit and after two or three times around – the observer gave the 'carry on' signal.

Following the Action

Now, up to this point I had been mostly able to follow the radios – The amazing part was the cacophony of noises that blurted, zapped, beeped and generally issued forth from the police band radios. Sure I'd missed something on the radio that was related to the orbit, I asked – Did I miss something on the radio?

Oh no, the observer quickly assured me – there have been a lot of drive-by shootings on this street, and I saw a couple of cars I didn't like the look of, so I thought we'd just check them out.

Immediately, I was struck by the years of experience that must have gone into the observer's decision making – you don't get that kind of experience from flying overhead – you get if from the ground.

The flight continued, mostly uneventfully, but with a background symphony of discordant radio bleeps and burps, which the two front seat crew had no trouble completely ignoring. Now I'm used to having a lot of radios (5) to deal with, but this was an order of magnitude more than I was used to – it wasn't just different radios, it was a whole host of noises that accompanied different types of messages as well.

## *Deciphering The Radios*

Somehow out of this discordant noise, the two front seat guys heard something and turned to each other – Should we go there? (Go where I wondered – I didn't hear anything). Turns out it was a burglar alarm going off, and we went to provide top cover to the responding ground units. (False alarm as it turned out, but it was a good demonstration of how attuned these folks were to the radios).

Since nothing much else happened that was particularly exciting, the rest of the stories came from talking to the crew about how the helicopter was used – providing top cover to officers on the ground by looking for obvious traps (the bad guys are hiding behind the next fence, just around the corner to the right, for example), or by following fleeing cars, or a host of other things that are much easier and safer from an aerial perch.

But what came out loud and clear was that local knowledge of the area was paramount- knowing which way a car was likely to go – where the parks and hangouts were, and so on – knowledge that could only be gained by several years of operating on the ground.

## *Translating 'Police Sense'*

How could you put this knowledge into someone who had years of flying helicopters in some other part of the world? Possibly by using a well trained observer to direct the pilot, but the observer seemed to be pretty busy working with the ground units...

Next, how long would it take to become familiar with something as seemingly simple as the radios? Air traffic radios are difficult enough, but are simple in comparison to dealing with all the different police radios- easier to learn air traffic radios than the other way around in my opinion.

Then comes police tactics – they operate at a different speed and discipline than aircraft. Getting used to that would take some time. And doing that task for quite a few hours at a time, when most helicopter operations are measured in minutes or fractions of an hour means a different discipline is needed by the helicopter pilot.

# CHAPTER 62 *Gaining an Edge*

**Vertical** 2012

*Comment: A brand-new blade tape design uses aerodynamic principles to improve helicopter performance, while simultaneously protecting main rotor blades.*

Rotor blades operate in a pretty tough environment. Whirling around at considerable speeds, they have to deal with dust, sand, rain and lots of other things that want to wear them down.

This is particularly true of a blade's leading edge, and even when metals like titanium are used to protect the leading edge, they're bound to wear out. Plus, replacing the leading edge is neither easy nor cheap, even if the disruption caused by having to take blades off and ship them away is ignored.

One solution to this problem is the Hontek sprayable erosion-protection coating system offered by Kaman. In recent years, this coating has been applied to more than 2,500 Sikorsky UH-60 Black Hawk rotor blades operating in desert environments like Iraq and Afghanistan

A more common solution is the sacrificial, replaceable blade tape. Unfortunately, while such tapes do protect the blade, many of these have the hidden side effect of reducing performance — by a measurable amount. The cause of this performance loss has been determined to be the trailing edge of the tape: even at one millimeter of thickness, the abrupt step from the tape to the normal blade surface generates a small vortex that rolls down the blade, disrupting the airflow and increasing drag. Since the engine has to overcome drag, this small increase results in reduced hover performance.

Another disadvantage of these tapes is that they normally have to be replaced along their entire length when they wear out, and this is not easy to do. I recall having to remove worn-out blade tape on a wet and cold day in England many years ago, after the rain had finally eroded the tape and the resulting vibration from the disrupted airflow had become quite unbearable. Fortunately, a pocket-knife was available to cut it off, but both blades had to be cleaned afterwards, and that's not easy to do with no stepladder!

The overall situation with blade tape — the trade-off between protecting the leading edge and the associated performance loss and maintenance issues — has stayed like this for a long time; until recently that is. What follows is the remarkable story of a man who took his very detailed knowledge of aerodynamics and combined it with technology to produce a blade tape concept that not only protects main rotor blades, but even improves their performance over unprotected blades.

## AN IDEA WITH LEGS

Over the years, I've been approached (and still get approached) by a lot of people with aviation ideas; some have potential, but most are merely novel with little practical application. Normally, asking a few detailed questions quickly reveals whether there's any substance behind the concept, and whether the proposer has any idea of the complexities facing him or her. So, when I was first approached by Peter Ireland about his concept, I was skeptical... but Ireland's answers to my increasingly difficult and detailed questions convinced me that his ideas were worth listening to.

In fact, Ireland — an airplane and helicopter pilot who has flown for, among others, the Royal New Zealand Air Force, the Royal Australian Air Force, Qantas and Korean Air — had already obtained a patent for his concept, which in itself was a good indicator that he was not some aviation version of the wild-eyed Dr. Emmett Brown from ***Back to the Future***. Then, he started talking about vortex generators on blade tape, and that really got my attention.

At this point, I must confess that I know more than most about vortex generators (which are protrusions that delay flow separation and stalling on an aerodynamic surface, thus improving its effectiveness). In fact, I have a company that produces a special type of vortex generator to reduce aerodynamic drag on trucks (which is a story in itself).

Curious about Ireland's concept, I started asking more questions about the tape design. He, in turn, told me about the data he had collected on his own Robinson R22 helicopter.

Now, I would expect any helicopter pilot who knew what he or she was doing to be able to measure a change in something like manifold pressure via the cockpit instruments, but Ireland also talked about fuel flow. A fuel flow gauge is not an instrument normally fitted to an R22, so his mention of this measure was intriguing. He then went on to talk about differences in collective position, and at first I thought he might have used something rudimentary like a tape measure for his data, but no, Ireland was talking about percentage of collective position. Here, I thought, was someone who probably knew what he was talking about, if he was measuring all of these variables to this degree of fineness.

When Ireland began to talk about tail rotor pedal position and cyclic positions, I knew that he was doing things correctly — very correctly. (In fact, to later obtain the data he needed to get a supplemental type certificate, Ireland had to instrument the blades on his R22 to measure stress and strain. His novel way of doing so without a slip ring would take too long to write about, but, suffice it to say, it was little short of brilliant engineering!)

Then came the data comparisons. Ireland said that performance in the hover with the traditional blade tape installed was four to five percent worse compared to clean blades. (It is interesting to note that such performance degradation is never mentioned in any flight manual supplement.) When he installed his BladeGuard "conformal vortex generator erosion protection system," however, the hover performance was around nine percent better than with clean blades, by all measures: at the same weight and height above the ground, his helicopter exhibited lower manifold pressure, lower fuel flow (which is an indirect measure of power) and lower collective position. For simulated hovering engine failures, the time from failure to touching the ground was increased. Also, he found rotor r.p.m. took longer to decay after shutting down the engine at flat pitch. In forward flight, meanwhile, tested at the same cruise speed and density altitude, the helicopter again required less manifold pressure, less fuel flow and a lower collective position. Finally, rate of descent in autorotation was lower than with the clean blades.

In other words, all of the data was pointing in the same direction. And, when Ireland explained the physics of how his new blade tape worked, the positive results all made a lot of sense to me.

## *The Right Kind of Vortex*

The major difference in Ireland's design — and the object of its patent protection — is the trailing edge of the tape. That edge is cut into a vortex generator pattern (although there's more to the patent than just that).

Of course, vortex generators have been around for a long time, and you'll see them on the wings of most airliners. In that application, they are designed to throw air up into the boundary layer. They create some drag, but for a large airliner wing they work in the conditions in which they're supposed to (low speed), and have a minor performance penalty the rest of the time. You don't see these same types of vortex generators on helicopter rotor blades, though, as the aerodynamic conditions in which rotor blades operate differ from those for seized-wing airplanes.

What makes Ireland's tape unique is that its vortex generators are conformal to the leading edge of the blade, and, rather than projecting air up, they suck the air back to the surface of the blade, behind the leading edge. So, instead of creating vortices that roll down the blade — as the performance-degrading blade tapes do — these vortex generators produce a series of vortices that spin at 90 degrees to the airflow and bring the air back down onto the surface, improving lift. (This effect can be clearly seen from the patterns left when Ireland's helicopter was hovered in a dusty environment.) By delaying flow separation, the vortex generators increase the effectiveness of the rotor blades, accounting for the performance increases Ireland has measured.

Ireland's tape also offers advantages from a maintenance perspective.

As previously mentioned, most blade tapes must be replaced over their entire lengths, even when — as is often the case — only the very outboard portion is worn. They also lack reliable indications of how much life they have remaining, so they are often replaced only when they are actually worn through (as evidenced in my own example stated earlier). Putting tape on can also be a pain, as any bubbles that get trapped under the tape can upset the airflow and provide a point for the tape to start lifting, especially because of rain.

To solve these problems, Ireland incorporated numerous small slits in his tape that permit any bubbles to be easily pressed toward a slit and dispersed. Alignment marks on the tape make it easy to bring it into line, and users are provided with information on how to recognize when it's time to replace the tape. To top it all off, the tape comes in short lengths, so only the worn pieces have to be replaced. Numerous trial installations have shown these features to be effective.

Ireland has been able to obtain worldwide patents for his concept, and has started a company called Edge Aerodynamix to market the resulting products. He has already obtained an STC in his home country of Australia for his BladeGuard blade tape on the R22, and it has the added bonus of being an approved "alternative means of compliance" there for the current airworthiness directive that addresses blade delamination in R22 main rotor blades ***(see p.40, Vertical, Aug-Sept 2011)***. Ireland will be pursuing an STC for the R44 next, followed by STCs for other popular helicopters (preliminary tests on a variety of other machines have shown benefits similar to those for the R22). Ireland also told me that a kit for tail rotor blades is under development, and that early tests have shown significant performance improvements there, too. STC's from Australia are normally quickly accepted by other countries, so there should be no need for additional certification work once an Australian STC is approved.

The only thing to note with Ireland's BladeGuard, however, is that no flight manual performance benefit is being claimed. To do so would take a lot of flight-testing, and that would only increase the price of the product and its time to enter the market. So, the performance benefits I cite here are not official numbers. Even so, it's nice to see someone take a fresh look at an old problem and find a creative — and effective — solution..

Figure 62-1 **typical Blade Tape Delaminating. Note how the tear is not from the leading edge, but farther back**

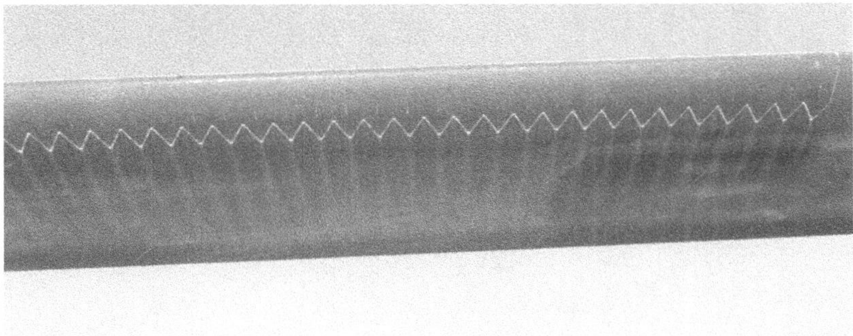

Figure 62-2 **Blade tape with VG shape. Note the streaks of dust from the vertices**

# CHAPTER 63 *Urban Aerospace X-Hawk*

ROTOR&WING INTERNATIONAL April 2007

*Comment: In my career in aviation, many concepts have briefly flashed across the monitor of ideas. Many that are out of the ordinary have had extremely brief lives, as they were patently impractical or so outlandish as to immediately dismissed. Some re-surface from time to time – a ducted fan car-type device springs to mind.*

Many are the brain-child of one person who it turns out has a fixed idea of the way things operate – and that idea is often at odds with reality. Other ideas actually have some serious design principles behind them, and bear a close second look.

## IDEA WITH MERIT

A really good indication of an idea that has merit is when a large company already established in the field decides to work with the idea. Large companies, with all the problems of large organizations and with shareholders to keep happy, don't work with whims unless there is some serious potential.

So, I was a bit surprised on a visit to Bell Helicopter's training center at the Alliance airport, to see a mock-up of the X-Hawk in the hangar. As I was busy with another project, I didn't pay too much attention to it at the time. On reflection, and knowing Bell's engineers, it should have been obvious there was something going on.

At the recent American Helicopter Society Forum in Montreal, I had the opportunity to speak with the design team from Urban Aeronautics, and it was a fascinating time. The first thing that needs to be said is that the concept is not new. Frank Piasecki produced a device called the Aerial Jeep 50 years ago, but like many of Frank's ideas, it was far ahead of the technology to be practical at that time.

**Figure 63-1 Artist's Conception of Urban's EMS Version**

## CHANGES OVER 50 YEARS

A lot has changed in 50 years – and for this concept, the major improvements that led the design team to re-consider the idea were in materials, engines and computing power. Advances in materials mean that significantly lighter composites can be used for the structure. Engines have much higher power-to-weight ratios compared to the early turbine Frank used, and computers can command an automatic flight control system that is custom-made for the idiosyncrasies of the design. Also, there have been significant advances in aerodynamics so that the issues of flow in and around and over and through the machine can be better understood and harnessed.

The time now appears ripe for this concept- a series of models have been built and successfully flown, demonstrating the idea is sound, and larger versions are in the works. Some of these versions are not manned – combining Israeli experience with UAVs is another piece of lateral thinking – but could be used for re-supply or even casualty evacuation.

One thing has to be stressed – this concept is not going to replace a helicopter in most missions – the inevitable compromises in design mean that it's not as efficient as a helicopter in hovering. Projected forward speeds match those of a helicopter, but with a much smaller payload. But it can do some things that helicopters cannot do.

Some of the unique capabilities are the ability to work very close to building and obstacles – with the lift producer encased in a ducted fan, you don't need to worry about hitting a fragile rotor blade against something. In spite of the high average downwash velocities compared to helicopters, Urban's model tests show that most of the high speed flow is contained in a very narrow (approximately 6 feet diameter) tube of air below each rotor, dissipates very quickly and thus avoids the helicopter's self-induced clouds of dust or snow.

But the ducted fan has another secret, and that's the vanes above and below the rotor which can provide direct lateral force. In a helicopter, you have to tilt the rotor to generate a side force, and this means tilting the fuselage. With Urban' 'Fancraft" technology, the vanes above and below the fans are adjusted so as to tilt the outgoing air, and move the vehicle sideways without tilting the body.

Imagine being able to bring a vertical lift vehicle right next to an opening on the wall of a building! Perhaps a wall of your own making. Even without the issue of hitting the rotor blades, this will take some getting used to! As the control system is unique, I'm sure there will be other things that this system will be able to that helicopters can't do. Another way to fly to be learned, or perhaps requires unlearning from how helicopters fly.

Another asset is that the machine can land in areas that are not much larger than size of the vehicle body. Not the rotor diameter of a helicopter, but the vehicle itself. And aside from the problem of hitting wires on the fuselage, there are no control rods to get severed. That's just what comes immediately to mind. I'm sure Urban (and Bell) has a list of other advantages to the concept they're saving for future marketing.

As far as engineering details, the man-carrying machines are being designed to meet Powered Lift requirements, including Category A performance. Powered lift is a combination of fixed and rotary wing transport category requirements, so the level of redundancy and performance is pretty high. What has been revealed is two turbines with 30 second OEI capabilities are being installed, as well as a ballistic recovery parachute. Details of the power required to hover are not revealed, but given the size of the fans, the engines will be larger than those on an equivalent weight helicopter.

A smaller vehicle called 'Mule' is being contemplated, which is unmanned and capable of carrying 220kg plus fuel for two hours. The primary role will be to carry equipment and supplies to the battlefield with the capability of flying back two wounded soldiers.

Obviously, it would have some sophisticated guidance system, and not be as simple as some folks would like to think it is, but is part of a process to gradually build up to a manned vehicle. Better to make small mistakes early than put all your eggs in one basket and discover that you've made a serious miscalculation too late!

What's the possible impact for the public use and EMS business? To start with, a machine like this would probably be more acceptable to the public due to lower noise. Secondly not having rotors slashing around above other workers (no matter how quiet the rotors, they still generate some anxiety level), or having to worry about walking into them will make the whole experience less worrisome. (in a perfect world, the rescue vehicle would just appear, and carry all the injured folks away in something like a magic basket, with no noise and no downwash – we're a long way from that, at least on this plane of existence....) Not having too pay too much attention to things like wires and poles will also reduce the stress for the crew as well.

Urban Aerospace will definitely be worth watching in the long run.

**Figure 63-2** **Two Early Piasecki Flying Jeeps**

# CHAPTER 64 *Need For Speed*

**Vertical** February March 2011

*Comment:* With three new high-speed helicopter concepts in development or testing, we decided to take a closer look at each design and what the pursuit of higher speeds will mean to the industry.

**Figure 64-1 A Trio of Speed Demons**

Taking a closer look at the industry's current high-speed concepts.

Pure helicopters have been hobbled by an upper speed limit since turbine engines gave us enough power to push to that limit of about 160 knots in level flight. Simply stated, using the main rotor to provide upward lift ***and*** forward thrust isn't that efficient. While some research projects many years ago pushed back the edge of the envelope, there were too many compromises to take these machines to either civil or military operational use.

The dream of going faster hasn't died, though, and recent advances in materials, knowledge and computing power have combined with the political will to produce something approaching a realistic possibility.

## Tilt Rotor

The main concepts currently in play are the tilt rotor (Bell-Boeing V-22 and Bell/Agusta BA609), the co-axial compound helicopter (Sikorsky X2), the single-rotor compound (Piasecki SpeedHawk) and the single-rotor plus propeller (Eurocopter X3). The Russians have their own solutions, but these are all slight variants on the four just mentioned, and so far only drawings and models have emerged. One of the interesting things about these concepts is that they all have slightly different approaches to the same aim, and competition will improve them all: the marketplace is a pretty tough proving ground.

Bear in mind that all these concepts retain all the necessary qualities of a helicopter — namely, the ability to maintain position with winds from any azimuth and to climb vertically.

All of the concepts are similar in that the main rotor is offloaded from the requirement to produce forward thrust. (Various forms of propellers are used to push the machines through the air, and to slow it down, as well.) When the rotor is not required to be tilted steeply forward, the blade pitch on the retreating blade can be reduced, with many benefits. The first benefit is the retreating blade now operates at much lower angles of attack and hence farther from the stall at the same airspeed as a normal helicopter. It means you can fly at a higher airspeed before you start to see the effects of stall. This has a huge effect on the loads placed on the blades, which is a much larger problem than most of us realize.

The Piasecki concept goes one step farther and recently added a large wing that stretches to nearly the full diameter of the main rotor, in order to further offload the main rotor. The Eurocopter X-cubed has a small wing, but it appears to be more to hold the propellers than to provide lift. The Sikorsky's co-axial rotor concept, meanwhile, reduces the lift that any one rotor disk has to produce.

Since there are competing designs in place, let's look at some of the trade-offs and technical challenges each may face. We'll leave out the V-22/BA609; the tilt-rotor concept has been around for quite a while and is reasonably well understood.

**Sikorsky X2**

Being a co-axial rotor obviously means having another set of whirling, rotating wings with all the attendant complexities of control, vibration, stresses and strains. And, it's still a rotor system, subject to all the issues that come with this.

While having a pusher propeller in the mix means the main rotors no longer have to produce forward thrust, they still need to produce all the lift, which means they must operate at the same pitch angles as other main-rotor-only systems. These pitch angles change a lot more than if the rotor were offloaded to a greater degree, and this requires more structure and induces more vibration that has to be eliminated one way or the other.

I attended Sikorsky's public demonstration of the X2 in October 2010 and found that the company had put a lot of effort into vibration control on the X2, as this was a serious problem on the much earlier XH-59A. The yaw control I saw via differential collective pitch on the two rotor heads is not a new concept, although all the other co-axial designs have featured much larger vertical stabilizers than the X2, which is just a proof-of-concept designed mostly for speed. Lastly, the rear prop can be used to slow the machine as well as push it, so there will be less pitch attitude movement of the airframe to change airspeed, and the cruise pitch attitude can be optimized for minimum drag.

Sikorsky also used the October demonstration to announce its follow-on development program for the X2: the S-97 Raider. This proposed model represents a sizeable investment to mature the design and establish a brand-new light helicopter. Sikorsky is targeting the S-97 toward the United States military as a potential light armed reconnaissance helicopter, and will build two more prototypes over the next four years for military evaluation.

**Piasecki X-49A SpeedHawk**

One of the advantages of using a wing to offload the rotor from the need to produce lift is that lower blade pitch angles can be used in all cruise conditions, which is the where the cyclical change in pitch and aerodynamic loads really create havoc.

I had the pleasure of talking with John Piasecki, president and chief executive officer of Piasecki Aircraft Corp. and the driving force behind the X-49A, to learn a bit more about the SpeedHawk, which applies the offloading concept to a modified Sikorsky H-60 Black Hawk. The first flight of the SpeedHawk occurred on June 29, 2007, and the aircraft has now completed its Phase 1 flight test envelope expansion.

The company's testing has already shown remarkable reduction in stresses and strains on the rotor hub and components compared to the baseline H-60. But, the disadvantage of the wing is that it sits under the main rotor and is subject to downwash in the hover, which hurts hover performance — which is the main reason for helicopters! (Piasecki's proposed solution is to have the wing tilt to a near-vertical position in the low-speed regime.)

The additional weight and complexity of the wing and ducted fan are about the same as the savings in weight that could be made in the rotor head compared to the co-axial concepts. Given that Piasecki is forced to use an existing airframe that is certainly not optimized for speed, it's unlikely the full advantages of the savings possible from a truly optimized wing/fuselage/rotor head will be seen in the near future. (John Piasecki, though, did confirm the large number of small improvements that could be made if they were starting from a clean sheet of paper.)

The movable, ducted fan/thrust bucket at the back end is necessarily heavier than just a propeller, but does provide a large moment-arm for yaw control and anti-torque. The interesting engineering challenge to integrate the fan / tail rotor (it needs a sexy name, too) into the control system appears to be well in hand.

Piasecki has also just installed a third engine (Rolls-Royce 250-C30) to provide additional power to the rear prop/thruster in order to permit all the normal engine power to go to the main rotor for hover performance — a challenge that was met with the typical ingenuity one has come to expect from good engineers!

## Eurocopter X3

The Eurocopter X3 "props-on-wings" concept adds some new twists and challenges to the discussion. The X3 first flight was on Sept. 6, 2010, and it was formally unveiled in late September at the French military secure Istres proving ground. The X3airframe comes from the Dauphin AS 365, the main rotor from the EC 155 and the main module of the main gearbox from the EC 175. It has two conventional five-bladed propellers in line with the five-bladed main rotor, all powered by twin Rolls-Royce Turbomeca RTM322-01/9 turboshaft engines.

Yaw control will be through differential propeller pitch, which will be interesting in side winds when one propeller is blanked by the fuselage. It will also mean that air is being blown forward and backward around the fuselage, which when close to the ground will make for some interesting flow patterns. The wing is relatively low, meaning any power changes in flight will affect the pitch attitude (an increase in power will tend to pitch the nose opposite to a reduction in power to a much greater extent than we see now). How these propellers would be used to slow the machine down without having a major effect on the airflow over the small wing is not known. (A rear-mounted prop such as Sikorsky and Piasecki have employed can be used in reverse with little effect on the rest of fuselage.)

The disadvantage of having two propellers means there is something else to fail. It's also assumed that the props would be shut down once on the ground — otherwise loading and unloading the aircraft becomes a real issue!

In its last set of tests for its Step 1 phase, Eurocopter reported that the X3 reached its speed objective of 180 knots of true airspeed in level flight "at a reduced level of engine power." In the Step 2 phase of testing, the next milestone the company hopes to achieve will be a cruise speed in excess of 220 knots.

In addition to speed, stability and handling characteristics have also been explored in the completed set of flight tests. "The flight envelope has been opened with and without autopilot to validate the basic hybrid demonstrator aircraft's stability and handling characteristics," stated the company in a Dec. 9 press release. "The X3 has reached an altitude of 12,500 feet and performed maneuvers with left and right turns at bank angles of up to 60 degrees."

## Some Additional Points

### Redundancy of control:

An interesting side effect of the Piasecki concept is that there is the possibility of redundancy of control — more than one control surface can be used to manage the helicopter. And, with the large number of possible controls, they can be mixed and blended to optimize performance for a mission: for example, the wing might be partly tilted for maximum lift at "low-ish" speeds to optimize the lift/drag ratio thereby reducing fuel flow and improving loiter time, if that's a mission requirement.

### Overcoming drag

Streamlining is an issue with anything attaining speeds of more than about 50 knots. Drag increases as the square of the speed, and anything that isn't sleek and streamlined is going to pay the price. Sikorsky is the hands-down winner on this front as it started from a clean sheet of paper and achieved probably the best drag reduction of any helicopter. Even the rotor mast is being given a fairing in the next stage.

Piasecki is working with a large handicap in utilizing a very draggy H-60 airframe. The SpeedHawk's next iteration will see a lot of drag reduction, but the large and complex rear fan arrangement will always add more drag than the Sikorsky concept.

The Eurocopter machine started with an already streamlined fuselage, so it's somewhere in between the other two main contenders.

## The Benefits of High Speed

What are the benefits of high-speed helicopter flight? The cruise airspeeds of the high-speed concepts now all comfortably reach into the low 200-knot region. For those already cruising at 150 knots — and there are not many civil helicopters that can do even this — that's a 30 percent improvement in speed. For those who are lumbering around 100 to 120 knots, this is nearly double.

This increase brings some interesting changes. That headwinds become a thing of minor inconvenience is one of the less obvious improvements. If you look at the table on p.xx, you can see the effects that a 20-knot wind directly along track has for an out-and-back trip. What should be a two-hour round trip for each of the highlighted boxes is affected by the wind. But the 200-knot cruise machine has less than one minute added to the trip. Unless you're a real glutton for punishment or have no alternative, most people wouldn't use a 100-knot helicopter for a 200-mile trip, regardless of the wind. (By the way, the numbers are even worse if there's a headwind both ways, which is what always seemed to happen to me!)

For short trips (less than 50 miles or so) there isn't much benefit to a high-speed helicopter, unless time is really critical. Those who say helicopter emergency medical services is an obvious market don't realize that most of the time the helicopter already gets there well ahead of when the patient is ready to transfer.

Time For Trip with 20 knot headwind

| | Cruise Speed | | |
|---|---|---|---|
| Distance | 100 | 150 | 200 |
| 100 | 2:05 | | |
| 150 | | 2:02 | |
| 200 | | | 2:01 |

**Not for Everyone**

Helicopters are useful for their unique capabilities of landing and taking off from very small areas. They're not typically used for long distance travel, as they are just too slow compared to any fixed-wing aircraft. This combines to make them "local" aircraft: they don't normally stray too far from home.

The speed improvement being sought will change all that. While helicopters won't become transcontinental machines, these compound ships will become regional aircraft. A radius of action of 200 miles will now (if you can justify it and afford it) be possible.

Of course, you'll need to be able to afford it — and initially the new users will be militaries, who also will open up new roles for the helicopters. Just as tactics are changing because the V-22 can lift troops quickly over long distances, a faster helicopter will have new roles and will only increase the military's use of rotary-wing aircraft (assuming the UAVs don't take it all away).

**We Don't Handle Change Well**

There have been lots of new concepts that have had teething problems. For example, the Learjet was well understood to be both a jet and a high-altitude machine when it came out, but there were still lots of growing pains not related to the design/technical aspects.

High-speed helicopters are not going to be different in this respect, and for insight into this I spoke with the United States Federal Aviation Administration's Hooper Harris, one of the few people (let alone government officials) I know with feet in both fixed- and rotary-wing camps. His comments were intriguing and insightful: "Pilots will have to worry about more than local weather, now it's regional weather that becomes an issue. To make maximum use of the range/speed improvements, it will probably be necessary to fly IFR [instrument flight rules] nearly everywhere, and the problem here is that helicopters don't always operate to and from airports, which is where the IFR infrastructure is set up. There are going to be challenges that go beyond the technical issues, and I hope both the FAA and the users can rise up to meet them safely."

**Helicopters Aren't Going Away**

Single-rotor helicopters aren't going to be replaced en-masse by these compound machines. There are some things the single rotor does much more cost-effectively than anything else. But, the changes are coming, and we need to be prepared for not just the technical challenges, but the myriad of other changes that will accompany any new concept.

# CHAPTER 65 *Sikorsky's X-2*

**Vertical** April / May 2008

*Comment: If you squint your eyes and look at the X-2 fuselage, the shape doesn't just speak 'speed', or 'sleek' or 'fast', it yells it.*

Figure 65-1 **X-2 un Flight**

Screams at the top of it's lungs – "I'll suck the doors off any other helicopter. I'll blister my own paint. I'll be gone before you know I was even here. Is there anything about me that doesn't suggest velocity???"

Overall, the fuselage is reminiscent of a bullet that happens to have some rotor blades on the top. Nothing sticks out. Not even the canopy release. You have to look hard to find the intake for the engine (it features a NACA intake – the most efficient way to get air inside an airframe at any sort of speed – I've not seen that before on a helicopter). It doesn't take much to ignore the main mast, as it's relatively small in diameter. You have to search to find the control rods for the lower rotor, and they are just not visible for the upper blades. (And this is all without the proposed fairings around the hub). The blades are skinny and elegant. The streamlining to feed air efficiently to the auxiliary propulsor (OK, the prop) at the back is superb, and the prop itself is big and bold – it screams 'I can put out more power than you can dream of - just watch me.' The end plates on the horizontal stab have a rakish look and the rudders are surprisingly small.

In short, this is a smokin' hot machine. You can almost feel it slipping through the air even standing still on the ground.

Shaking my head, I have to return to what Peter Grant and Steve Weiner, the two chief design and project folks on this machine are saying. Steve says that the last time Sikorsky did a co-axial rotor, (the X-59A) it was known for two things – speed and vibration. It used jet engines for the thrust. The X-2 is a departure from that design, and is entirely focused on two things – proving the concept works and development of the technology. And it will be fast and smooth, they insist.

## *Single Engine machine*

Research and development isn't cheap, and any way costs can be reduced while achieving the aim is used. Off-the shelf parts, like S-76 tires, and Comanche flight controls are used, as is a Blackhawk tail rotor driveshaft to power the aux propulsor. There was no need to go to a twin engine configuration, so a T-800 engine was shoe-horned in.

While we will probably see an offshoot of the concept in commercial or military operations within the next 10 years, you're never going to see the X-2 as a commercial machine – it doesn't have the payload or range to be anything except something that goes fast for about an hour with one person. It's to work out the wrinkles in the concept. If you wanted to put someone in the back seat both people had better be prepared to live in what they're wearing – there's not even luggage space for your mistress's negligee.

What does the aux propulsor do? It provides the ability to accelerate and decelerate without tilting the thrust vector – the main rotor can concentrate on providing only lift. It's estimated in high speed cruise that the prop will be using 90% of the power, and the rotor only 10%. From my one ride in an AV-8, I can attest to hanging in the straps with the nose 40° down and the airspeed staying constant.... While the civil version won't be doing this sort of maneuver, it will make the whole helicopter experience different for passengers.

This level attitude is going to present a small, but noticeable problem for helicopter pilots – pitch attitude won't be useful as a guide to airspeed – the fuselage should be flat throughout the airspeed range. I'm sure we'd get used to it.

Having only one engine raised the possibilities of having to do an engine-out landing. Should be about the same as an S-76 the engineers confirmed. A tailwheel hidden at the bottom of the aft vertical stabilizer was certainly going to help with that. I didn't consider whether the aux propulsor had a feathering capability, and it does. (This made me ask "Why aux? Is there some other 'propulsor'?" The answer was 'The main rotor...'. I responded – Why not just call it the 'prop'?)

## *More Technical Details*

The blades are obviously very stiff – Steve nearly did a chin-up at the tip of the blade, and it flexed down only a couple of inches. They are also quite complex internally- the spar is only ¼ of an inch wide at the tip. Since there is no need for the retreating blades to have to claw lift out the air, the root ends of the blades are smooth and double-ended. The aim is to reduce drag on the retreating side – the advancing side produces more than enough lift. As the blades don't have to produce lift when retreating, the range of blade pitch can be reduced compared to a conventional helicopter, and the amount of lead-lag and flap likewise smaller. The shape is very complex with both a lot of twist and taper. I thought I detected some forward sweep of the blade, but both Peter and Steve declined to comment, smiling broadly and obviously sharing an internal company secret.

There are pitch change rods on the top head, but they are inside the head, with the swashplate underneath the transmission. The necessary mechanical linkages are hidden inside the rotor shaft.

Active vibration controls as used on the S-92 are there to make sure this isn't a rough machine - there are 6 of 'em made by Moog. The single test pilot should have a pretty smooth ride. Engineering studies showed that 4 instead of three blades should be the smoothest configuration.

How is this sleek beast going to be controlled? After all there are not just helicopter controls to consider. The cockpit looked pretty standard – aside from the side-arm controller for pitch and roll, there was a collective and pedals. Everything between the cockpit and rotors was fly-by-wire in the interests of saving weight and complexity. (if you've ever seen the mechanical controls for any other co-axial machine, you'll appreciate the simplicity of fly-by-wire.) Oh, almost forgot, thrust on the aux propulsor is controlled by a small fore-aft button on the collective (see photograph). A rate-damping stabilization system is fitted, but nothing fancier - the aim was not to perfect the ways of controlling the machine, but fine tune the coaxial pusher configuration. Perfecting the flight controls for future versions will be done in the simulator – this machine is for research and development.

Noise was obviously an item of interest – how neighborly was this expected to be? The rotor and propeller would be slowed at high speed, which would help with noise. As the airspeed increases, the RPM of the rotor (and prop) is automatically reduced by up to 20% at the design cruise speed of 280 knots– that's right - 280 Knots!!! (we'll need a different airspeed indicator here folks!)

The exhaust stack already had soot on it, indicating that some progress had already been made in testing. Ground runs were to continue when the prototype gets back to the Sikorsky / Schweizer Skunk works.

Sikorsky's advertising brochures show a great number of possibilities for both military and civil use when this concept is perfected. It will really open up a whole range of missions where speed and hover capability are both needed.

Finally! Development with a capital D is happening in the rotary wing world –I don't wish to belittle the efforts of others who are making incremental improvements in existing concepts, but there is finally some pushing ahead with a different concept. Piasecki is developing a thruster/ tail rotor on a highly modified UH-60, and Sikorsky is branching into a concept that worked technically in the past and which now has the materials to be fully realized.

I'm looking forward to watching the engineers make this into a viable concept. My name is close to the top of the list for a ride when they're giving them, so get in line.

**Figure 65-2 What pushes it along**

# CHAPTER 66 *Eastern European Helicopters*

ROTOR&WING INTERNATIONAL 1995

*Comment: Stumbling at the Starting Blocks*

**Figure 66-1 Some Eastern European Helicopters**

The Berlin wall has been down for so long that it's no longer news. The Russian coup attempt isn't even mentioned anymore. We're still waiting for the flood of former Soviet helicopters into the Western market at cheap prices. What's happened?

Have you ever wondered why there is no information about these machines in the product reviews in the Western press, such as R&WI annual guide?

For starters, it must be said, that aside from a few minor quirks, there is nothing wrong with the technology, design or manufacture of these helicopters. Indeed, on a technical level, they are extremely good, and the designers rank with any comparable western designers. The quality of work in assembly is quite close to any Western build standard, despite a lot of very out of date equipment. Their design standards are different, as were their operational requirements.

Given the state of their economies, and the low cost of their materials and labor, the production and sales prices of these machines are far below those of the West. They should have been able to sweep the market clean and initially there were cries from the Western helicopter industry that this would put them out of business. Why hasn't it happened?

The reasons are both complex and simple. One simple answer is that 70 years of not just communism, but a way of thinking that stifled initiative, (except along carefully controlled guidelines) has effectively taken away the ability to do anything out of the line directed by central office. Central office has nothing to say anymore, and natural leaders are still not coming forward. Another reason is that 70 years of an unbelievably corrupt system of control has led to an nearly complete lack of ethics on the part of most managers.

Examples of this have been demonstrated to me several times. Lack of ethics shows when an Eastern helicopter manufacturer signs an exclusive agreement with one Western company, and then turns around and signs another exclusive agreement for the same product and area with another Western company the next day. Legally binding contracts are ignored. While Eastern European managers may claim they did not understand the fine points of law, more likely they don't care if an agreement is broken. 70 years of government that broke agreements with disregard showed them this was normal.

We don't hear much from the Eastern companies because they don't understand marketing and public relations. I have had some very interesting adventures traveling to Russia and Poland, and while I loved the people and was impressed by the technical accomplishments, I despaired of the organizations. In one case, I had arranged for an interview with the director of a helicopter manufacturing plant. There was no attempt to make sure I knew how to find the factory, and in Russia, that is no small problem. I can tell you that there are two similarly named streets in Moscow, at opposite ends of the very large city, and I arrived very late for the appointment. I was then kept waiting (which I deserved) but not offered a cup of coffee or tea in the whole three hours I was there. After the long interview, at which I wasn't sure the translator was getting my questions or the directors responses correct, I asked if it was possible to have a tour of their factory, which was at the same place. This was not possible, as I had not asked for this in the fax sent requesting the interview. A small point, but I'm sure if I hadn't been so eager for the interview, or so understanding, I might have painted a different picture of the company in the interview.

In normal fashion I returned the interview to the company for verification. Over a year later, and several faxes asking about the interview, it has still not been returned. Photographs I had requested of some interesting model helicopters in the directors office have never arrived. The article still hasn't been submitted. I'm not privy to the advertising rates of Rotor and Wing, but they were throwing away a lot of free advertising.

In another fit of enthusiasm, I offered my services to one of the large Russian companies to assist them with marketing. The price for my services was something even they would have been able to afford, however the response was that 'We don't need any help selling- we've sold 25,000 helicopters'. I wasn't perceptive enough (or maybe quick enough) to point out that they hadn't ever sold a single helicopter. They manufactured the helicopters, and someone took them from the factory, but they never had to sell one in the face of competition. Somehow, I doubt whether this subtle point would have made any impact.

In another example I asked the commercial director of another company why someone should buy their helicopters. They really were excellent machines- very well designed, with features not found on any western helicopter. His response was 'Because they're cheap.' No amount of work on my part would change his mind. This same company, by the way, having sold one machine in the West, has decided not to support it, 'because it's only one machine.'

I have been told, that despite what the enthusiastic press releases say, most joint ventures with Russian and Eastern European companies are bogged down, not in technical problems, but in financial wrangling and accounting problems. Who is getting what money and how is it accounted for- stories of funds disappearing into senior managers pockets are not uncommon.

The infrastructure that supports their industry is also drying up. Under the new systems in Russia and Eastern Europe, money has to change hands to get parts like hydraulic pumps, fuel lines and so on. With few hard currency sales from the West, and deliveries within the Russian sphere have virtually halted this isn't happening. The result is that the smaller companies who supply the thousands of parts needed are either going out of business, or turning to more rewarding products like fridges or toasters.

In the export market, it is not uncommon for the old Soviet style mentality to still be found. In one case related to me, a third world country wanted to buy some Russian helicopters. The Western company who was bidding in competition against Aviaexport found that the request for tender had been reworded on a minor technicality requiring a letter from the manufacturing plant so that in a strict technical sense, only Aviaexport could bid. The Western company was advised that they could not get a letter from the manufacturer, and in the unlikely event they would get such a letter, it would be declared a forgery at the worst possible moment. The only major difference between the two bids was that the Aviaexport price was 300% higher.

I could go on. The bottom line is that technically, the Russian design philosophy and manufacturing standards could inject some real competition into the Western helicopter industry. Realistically, it won't happen. Bell, Sikorsky, Eurocopter, Agusta can all sleep soundly. The Eastern machines will not sell, not for any technical reason, but because the people in charge of the system do not really understand the ethics and philosophy of business in the rest of the world.

# CHAPTER 67 *Hyperspectral Imaging*

Not Previously Published

*Comment: The very name of the subject will cause some folks to wonder – what does this have to do with aviation?*

## *HYPERSPECTRAL – MANY SPECTRUM*

Remote sensing of our planet ranges from photos from satellites and airplanes to radar and other exotic technologies. The explosion of relatively cheap computing power has caused what we used to view as nice pictures from above to transform into something limited only by our imaginations.

Explained simply, a black and white photograph contains different shades of Grey to make up its image. Color photograph typically combine red, green and blue colors to make an image. In reality, there is much more information given off by the surface of the earth or an object. If you could slice that into more accurate pieces, it would be possible to determine a lot of things. And this is without venturing into the areas of the electromagnetic spectrum that we as humans can't see, like the ultra-violet or infra-red.

The idea for this was borne from the concept that a spectrascope is used to determine the composition of material being tested. This is often used in criminal investigations or aircraft crash investigations to determine the composition of an unknown material. Applying this to airborne sensing required that spectrometers with very special ranges and high resolution be developed, and that specific computer programs be developed to use the mountain of information that could be obtained.

Essentially, a special diffraction grating splits the light into different spectra which are then captured by the digital camera. So far, this doesn't seem too far out of the ordinary. What comes next is incredibly complex, and probably really understood only by those who can use all the upper and lower Greek letters in their formula. Instead of just comparing say the red and green components, like you might in any commercial photo editing program, now the data can be really sliced and diced. Hyper-dimensional (many dimensions) mathematics comes into play. Comparing the red to the green is one dimension, but comparing the red to all of the other spectrum slices is multidimensional. `Let's just say the color content of any one pixel in one narrow band of the spectrum can be compared to the color content in any of the other bands. This means that a single pixel can be looked at in a whole variety of ways. And that's where the magic comes in – You need to know what it is you're looking for, and what the hyperspectral picture should look like, and then you can find it quite easily with the computer.

As an example, blue tarpaulins are used quite extensively in hurricane country to provide temporary roofing. If you were trying to count the number of blue tarpaulins manually, it would be very difficult and prone to error. However, the computer knows the difference between a blue tarpaulin and a blue pool liner, for example, and can quickly count the number of damaged roofs in an area – in fact, it can do it in real time as the aircraft flies over the area.

Some other points – works on reflected light, so there are no privacy issues as have come up with infra-red searches. Won't work at night (not that there was much night aerial surveying done anyway).

Can show differences – something that wasn't there yesterday, but is today, or something that was there yesterday, but is gone now.

Use for disaster relief, pollution monitoring,

## *WHAT DOES ALL THIS MEAN TO US IN AVIATION*

If you thought that all the aerial survey work was done and over, think again. Whole new applications will be emerging for this technology – everything from agricultural applications for optimum watering and fertilizing of crops, to accurately determining the effects of projects on things like groundwater flow. All of this will need not just one flight, but many flights to observe the effects of changes. Standby for lots more of this – we need to know and understand how to make best use of this.

To see how a crop develops, for example may require trips every couple of weeks.

**Search and Rescue –**

If you know the value of the reflected light of an aircraft's skin, you can spot it much more easily with an all-seeing eye. (Humans are not that great as searchers – we get tired, don't see everything, and so on – a computer will see everything and report on everything.)

**Exploration**

Minerals reflect light differently from one another. If you're looking for a mineral that is a good precursor for gold, for example, then you can have that mineral's signature tuned in to your imaging software as something to highlight. See Figure xxx.

**Agriculture**

How many different shades of green are there? From the times I've mused on the subject, looking at a forest, I was amazed at how many different subtle shades there were. Each tree is different. If you know the spectra of the leaves of the trees, you can easily do a survey to determine the tree population. Same with different crops – and I know what you're thinking – a way to find marijuana! Exactly, but it takes detailed knowledge of the spectra that each plant produces at different stages in development. For trees, the green will be different as the year progresses. And according to my sources, not all the spectra for marijuana are known, so spotting it at different stages of growth is quite there yet.

Resolution is obviously an issue – trying to measure this from space would not be as accurate as measuring from say, 2,500 feet above the ground. Speed of the aircraft also affects the resolution – you can only take so many frames per second without overloading the computer.

## *Real Time Detection*

The Civil Air Patrol has pioneered HSII for search and rescue. It makes searching less dependent on human eyes and senses, and is not subject to distractions, and the cameras can record everything.

For law enforcement and agriculture, it can identify crops at different stages of growth- think marijuana hidden in corn fields!

## *SUMMARY*

This technology will come galloping to the fore with faster computers- just wait!.

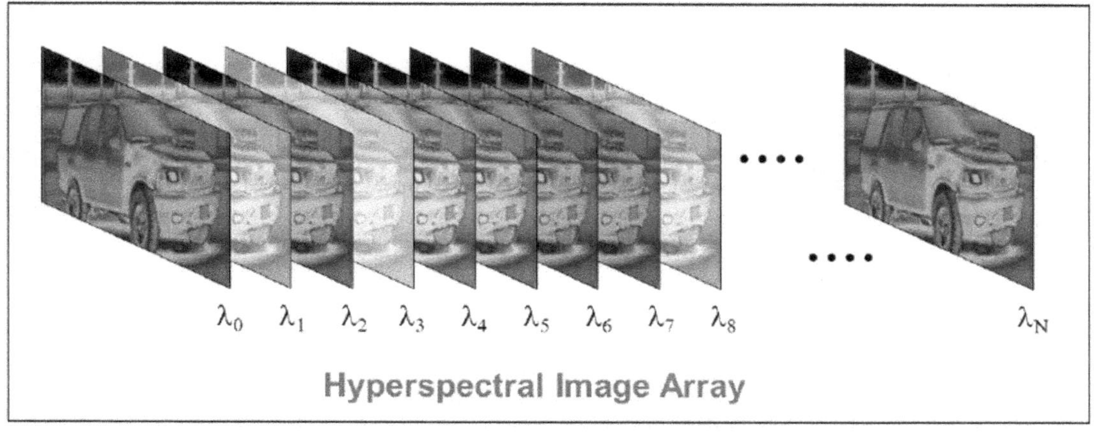


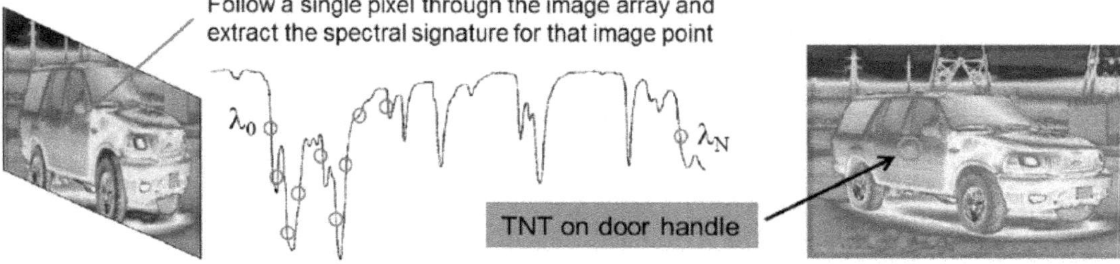


**Figure 67-1 A Brief outline of Hyperspectral Imaging**

# CHAPTER 68 *A Unique Navigation System*

ROTOR&WING INTERNATIONAL May 1995

*Comment: In a move that will catch many readers by surprise, Agusta Systemi, Agusta's avionics systems group, demonstrated a new military system for' helicopters. The system is called COPA-PLRS.*

COPA stands for (in Italian) Operational Airmobile Position Complex, and the system is a derivative of the U.S.-developed Position Locating Reporting System (PLRS).

PLRS grew out of the need for military commanders to know locations of units in a timely manner and to communicate on secure frequencies. The U.S. military uses PLRS to locate and track ground vehicles and soldiers but, so far, not helicopters.

By using advanced software and hardware, Agusta Sistemi developed COPA/PLRS into an accurate communication, identification, and positioning network with 3D navigation capabilities and jam-resistant encrypted communications. Specifically designed for airborne assets and their support units, COPA/PLRS is an autonomous part of the CATRIN system used by the Italian army for all-weather/day/night command, control, and communication.

COPA/PLRS was recently demonstrated to Italian army officials at Agusta's Cosina Costa factory. The objective was to guide three helicopters in simulated IMC along three routes to rendezvous at a designated location at a specified time. During the one-hour flight demonstration, the three helicopters (flying transport, scout, and attack missions) received directions from COPA/PLRS, and the pilots only had to follow a simple ILS-type display while 'under the hood.' COPA/PLRS basically consists of two units: a master station (MS), on the ground or aboard a command-and-control aircraft, and a user unit (UU), on the aircraft or vehicle being tracked./directed. (If the MS is on an aircraft, the crew does not need to be actively involved in its operation-that information can be transmitted to the MS from ground command and control.) At present, the MS is housed in a standard military air-transportable shelter. It contains special network communications facilities (including encrypted transmitters, ruggedized computers, displays, and other controls).

A single MS can work alone, or network with other MS as part of a larger system.

All software is written in ADA language.

The UU is a small device that can be man-portable or vehicle-mounted (ground or air); it consists of a transmitter/receiver and processor with a display. The man-portable and ground vehicle version has a user readout module, while the airborne version has an avionics unit composed of a keyboard and display.

In the aircraft, the UU is interfaced to the radio magnetic indicator or a multifunction display: the display looks and performs similar to an ILS. The UU's function is to transmit a positioning signal and send or receive information from the MS. COPA/PLRS provides three key functions: It stores flight-plan information and transmits this to aircraft; It calculates and tracks aircraft positions; and It transmits to and receives from tracked aircraft secure operational information reflecting real time mission needs.

## HOW DOES COPA/PLRS TRACK AIRCRAFT POSITION?

Simply put, it uses triangulation. The MS assigns an ID number to the UU and tells it to transmit a signal, in a data burst, at specified time intervals. The signal contains the UU's altitude (thanks to a built-in barometric-pressure sensor). To determine range between the UU and MS, the MS calculates the time difference between when the UU transmits its signal and when the MS receives it. Thus, the MS gathers positioning information on one or numerous UU equipped aircraft. With this data, it obtains a precise picture of where all the aircraft are in relation to it and to each other.

Another COPA/PLRS benefit: Any UU-equipped aircraft can act as an automatic relay station. It can receive signals from any UU and when it sends its signal to the MS, it includes the time it received any other UU signal. This capability opens up multiple paths for signals, increasing the global 'ruggedness' of the system.

The MS continuously monitors the whole process. When one UU, acting as a relay, drops out of line of sight or is in some other way degraded in performance, the MS automatically reconfigures another suitable UU to act as the relay. No operator action is needed.

To accomplish its multiple communication tasks, COPA./PLRS uses a synchronous common spread spectrum waveform, time-sharing a single frequency and managed by the MS. To service hundreds of UUs-as well as provide electronic warfare protection- COPA/PLRS employs frequency hopping and spectrum spreading, along with data encryption and interleaving. In terms of accuracy, Agusta Sistemi officials would only say that COPA/PLRS is similar to P-code GPS precision. The system could use GPS for the position of the MS if needed-and thus eliminate the need to calculate ranges between the MS and UUs. But it normally works autonomously-a capability certain to appeal to militaries that don't want to rely on the U.S. military's GPS.

Besides locating and tracking aircraft, the MS can direct the UU equipped aircraft. for example, should a need arise to change a flight plan, the information is easily transmitted by the MS to all aircraft affected. The MS can also transmit operational information to each aircraft's UU; this could include updates of enemy positions, changes in weather, etc.

System Offers For Military

What does a system like COPA/PLRS offer to the military helicopter pilot? The key benefits pertain to mission planning and flying. Flight planning a mission in a war zone takes a lot of preparation, often without the luxury of much time. A means to plan routes and no-fly zones expeditiously, precisely, and with up-to-date information would reduce the possibility of error. A system such as COPA/PLRS will permit centralized flight planning, ease flight monitoring, and expedite inflight rescheduling, while also giving line pilot a tool to fly the corridor accurately.

After a route is planned in a traditional way, it still must be entered into a navigation system, introducing more possibilities for error. Once in flight, the aviator must monitor the flight path to ensure the planned route is followed, plus attend to other tasks. If it is night or stormy, the flight may be canceled if no suitable low-altitude instrument navigation system is available.

GPS solves some of the problems, but it won't tell the aviator where the other helicopters are, nor will it support convoy activities on the same flight plan. Air traffic control in these situations becomes cumbersome.

Operating in a zone of conflict is doubly difficult when the air is congested with friendly traffic. The pilot has his hands full to navigate and fly through a complex three dimensional corridor without stepping on the toes of others. The matter is made worse in rapidly changing situations.

A system such as COPA/PLRS will permit centralized flight planning, ease flight monitoring, and expedite in-flight rescheduling, while also giving the pilot a tool to fly the corridor accurately.

When a lot of air traffic has to be handled, COPA/PLRS offers to increase safety and operational efficiency, by decreasing time and space intervals between aircraft operations.

COPA/PLRS opens the door for convoys of helicopters to safely operate in IFR conditions.Bottom line, Agusta's COPA/PLRS should be of interest to numerous military organizations.

Within the surface support vehicle, COPA/PLRS master station receives positioning signals from helicopters and support units to calcite where each unit is in relation to the master station and to each other. The master station also transmits encrypted navigation and operational messages.

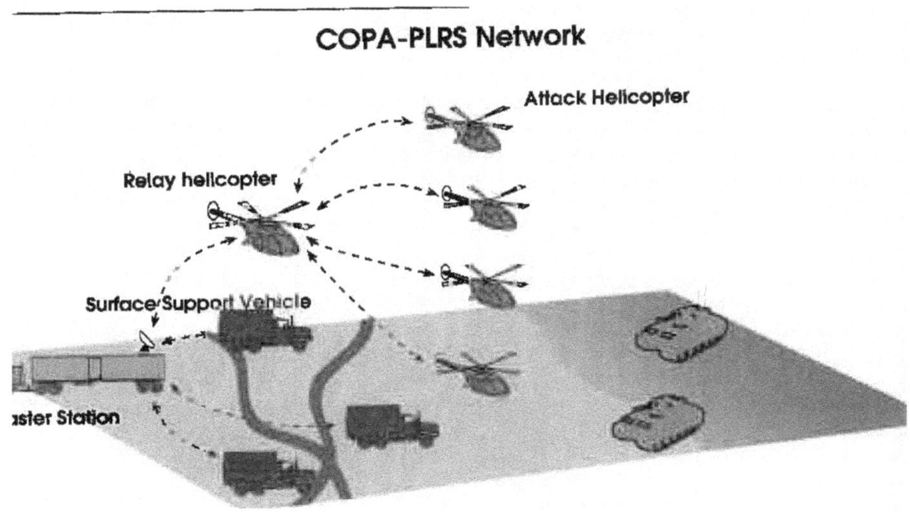


Figure 68-1 **COPA / PLRS Schematic**

# CHAPTER 69 *Early Moving Maps- Teldix KG-10*

Plane and Pilot 1994

*Comment: Despite the many pitfalls which await unwary pilots, global-positioning systems are catching on fast. looked on as 'Joe Bloggs' tried out a system accessory that shows you exactly where you are on the map*

Global Positioning Systems (GPSs) have radically changed the way we think of navigation. New ways to use this capability to determine posit ion accurately, repeatably and independently are frequently being found, leading to aII 'produced the nearest thing to a moving map available to the private pilot whole host of GPS receivers with myriads of features.

Limited panel space has meant that pilots have frequently to refer to the ops manual, even after regular practice. New equipment from Teldix - the CoPilot - takes a new approach, one which at first glance looks too simple.

Teldix, an established supplier of military map displays which use computer-driven dots of light and moving maps, started by asking: 'What does the pilot want to know?' It concluded that most want to know 'present position on the map', not a numerical display of latitude and longitude which must be related to an aeronautical chart.

A typical private pilot - let's call him Joe Bloggs - claims that flying causes him stress, because of the proliferation of air- traffic control zones which want him to report his position. Bloggs also says that the Decca-based navigation system in his syndicate's aircraft was removed because it was regarded as being too difficult to learn to

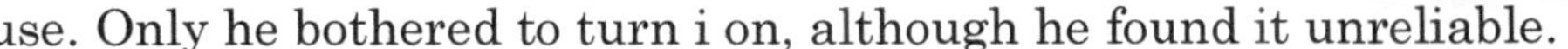
use. Only he bothered to turn i on, although he found it unreliable.

GPS, having seen advertisements for receivers.

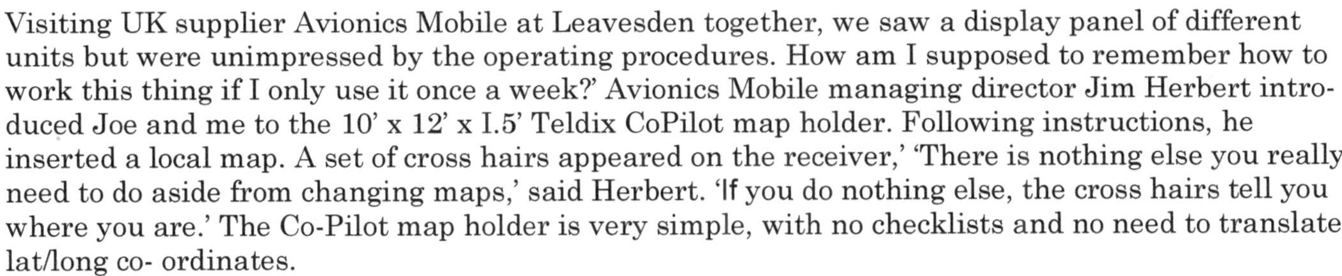
Visiting UK supplier Avionics Mobile at Leavesden together, we saw a display panel of different units but were unimpressed by the operating procedures. How am I supposed to remember how to work this thing if I only use it once a week?' Avionics Mobile managing director Jim Herbert introduced Joe and me to the 10' x 12' x I.5' Teldix CoPilot map holder. Following instructions, he inserted a local map. A set of cross hairs appeared on the receiver,' 'There is nothing else you really need to do aside from changing maps,' said Herbert. 'If you do nothing else, the cross hairs tell you where you are.' The Co-Pilot map holder is very simple, with no checklists and no need to translate lat/long co- ordinates.

Teldix uses an internal computer to move the cross hairs to indicate current position once a bar code on the cardboard- backed map carrier has indicated map scale and the location of the center of the 200mm X 200mm chart.

Maps for most of Europe and all of North America are available at 1:1,000,000 and 1:500,000, with details stored in the computer. The display can handle up to 50 so called special maps, which are required in the UK for copyright reasons. These can be approach plates, topographical maps (or enlarged photocopies), vertical aerial photographs or even a faxed copy, provided that they are to scale and provide lat/long information for two points at least 100mm apart on the map.

To set up a special map or points programmed through a small number of button pushes, initially or when details change.

## *Additional Features*

Additional features include the programming of up to 200 waypoints or as many as ten routes of up to ten waypoints each. To program the CoPilot map holder, Bloggs inserted the map and, with a few button pushes, was ready to position the cross hairs on the waypoint.

He wanted to go to a point one mile west of a nearby VOR beacon ('Don't go directly to the VOR - that's where everybody else is'). Although Bloggs had not previously seen the system, within two minutes the cross-hairs had marked the spot and the waypoint name was entered.

Since the weather was bad, Joe planned a route to a favorite pub with a landing strip and set up four waypoints, missing all control zones, and entered the route using two maps, all within five minutes.

Jim Herbert demonstrated how to reverse the route for the return flight by button- pushing until the Route number came up and changing to the alternative'.

Two buttons are pressed to verify the route, the cross hairs marching across the display to stop at the next waypoint. Press 'Enter' to move to the next waypoint. Thus, it is very easy to check the program at home or in the flight-planning room.

Well, we got to fly but did not get to the pub

It was easy to connect the system and we checked that the interface was set for the installed GPS system. Once the engine was started, we inserted the first map and took off. Joe pointed out that the display moved as soon as we started to taxi, the display indicating time and bearing to the next waypoint. Joe gave Herbert the heading to fly, correcting immediately for drift.

He did not need to keep a thumb on the map, but just glanced infrequently to see how we were doing. To see the next waypoint requires holding down a button, the cross hairs going to the new location and reverting when the button was released. After a short time, we put the display between the seats. It was brought out only when needed to check progress.

To demonstrate other features, Jim suggested changing the route, and passed me the unit. This would prove a good test, since I had watched Joe's handling of the CoPilot rather than taking note of how it worked. (If a pilot wants to write on the map during flight, he has only to withdraw it from the CoPilot.)

I found it extremely easy to determine position, verifying our location within ten seconds.Withouthelp,Ihad established the heading for the new waypoint.

When Joe misunderstood my · direction for a right turn, and continued turning to wander off course, it was easy to give him an accurate course to the waypoint.

We were able to provide air-traffic control with accurate distance and time-to-run when asked. without looking at the panel mounted GPS or performing mental arithmetic or doing finger/thumb-width approximations.

Back at Leavesden, it was time to ponder 'The Teldix CoPilot was a real break- through.'Joeenthused.'Therew as no stress in keeping track of where we were and finding position was almost instantaneous -you can't miss the cross hairs, when you pick up the display.'

If you wander off the map, the display prompts for the correct chart, the cross hairs only appearing when you insert a map that will show an (almost) foolproof position. Jim Herbert says that with the CoPilot one does not need to spend time translating lat/long or bearing-and-distance to a chart before verifying that with the view of the ground.

Avionics Mobile finds the system 'nothing short of a revolution in navigational concepts', claims Jim Herbert. 'An interesting point is that time and distance will only be given to the waypoint selected. There 1s no chance of the system lying to you about time-to-go to the final destination.'

So what does Joe Bloggs make of CoPilot? 'If I flew once a week, this would take no time to master. Without using the manual. It passes the test of ease-of-use with flying colors and it passes the test of usefulness, in the cockpit with the highest grade. It makes the whole experience of flying less stressful.'

I can only add that having used many different systems and spent more time than I wanted with my head inside the cockpit or looking on the margin of the map for lat/long, this is a superb solution to the navigation challenge.

Figure 69-1 The Teldix KG-10

# CHAPTER 70 *A Look at the Future of Rotary Wing Flight*

Not Previously Published

*Comment: What's the future of STOL / VSTOL Flight*

The last two years has seen the re-emergence of concepts that first saw flight in the 1960's and 70's. Tilt rotor, tilt wing, compound helicopters (both single rotor and co-axial), autogyros, tip driven rotors (Fairey Rotodyne) and even combination dirigible / helicopter are all not new. Pioneers such as Piasecki tried several concepts that flew successfully but were never put into series production. Bell has been working on the tilt rotor since not long after the dawn of rotary wing flight. Sikorsky was flying the Advancing Blade Concept in the early 1970's.

Nearly all of these concepts are now coming back to life – do they have a better chance of success now? What's changed in the last 30 years?

I took advantage of my contacts and polled them about what they saw as the potential. Some refused to guess- 'Been wrong too many times before' was heard several times.

It quickly emerged that the things that have changed since the 1960s were in the areas of computing, materials, and engines. Each has many impacts – computing means that more is understood on about aerodynamics and computational fluid dynamics, so we can now optimize rotor blades for a particular mission, for example. We know more about the dynamics of rotors and so can design for lower vibrations, among other things.

Materials advancements mean that we can get suitable factors of safety in structures with lighter structures – carbon fiber is everywhere for a good reason.

Engines are lighter, more powerful and have benefited from computers for controlling and recording everything.

Would you care to comment on what you see as the future for the developments that are re-emerging and capitalizing on these old concepts?

## *Unlocking the Potential*

Although technology appears to be old, it's the cutting edge for RW. Typical time to take a new technology from concept to operational use (whether civil or military) is 15 to 20 years. All these machines will take benefits that all new technology will give – weight reduction is one area that will immediately benefit. Technology is always introduced slowly.

Better aerodynamics from CFD code – we might be able to get a few more percent of lift from the rotors.

Most definitely tilt rotor technology will continue.

Remember if you don't buy the A model, you'll never get the B model.

What will help unlock the full potential of any of these technologies?

### Tilt Rotor

Let's start with the Tilt Rotor - the V-22 and AW-609 basically are taking 20 year old technology into flight. What would be done differently if those projects were re-started today?

### Compound Helicopters –

Any comments on the way forward for the Piasecki SpeedHawk?

One of the problems for the Speedhawk is that the main rotor isn't optimized for high speed – so right away it's a compromise. It still carries all that helicopter stuff. It is another demonstrator of how we can improve. If we took the concept further with optimized rotor blades for forward flight and combined it with the compound machine, it would open the envelope up more.

**Tip-Driven Rotors (Rotordyne)**

No to tip drive – unless you drive weight down

High speed rotor with propulsor at tip, with high drag. Noise was and will be a problem.

**Carter Copter –**

No hover capability, good forward speed.

**Pure compounding is well known –**

Applaud anyone who takes concepts and flies them.

Try to test for the technology for the benefits.

Two most prominent techs in 1960's were the ABC and tilt rotor

## *Other Peripheral Technologies*

Computing power in getting design right the first time.

Natural elastic modes can now be predicted – structures

Power – more power for less weight, especially for VTOL – each step increase in performance due to step increase in power to weight ratio

- 10lb/hp – Wright Flyer
- 1 lb/hp – helicopter now feasible
- 0.1lb/hp – first commercially feasible helicopter and also tilt rotor

Structures- light and strong – computing

X-2 is optimized for propulsed tech, but ABC wasn't.

Airfoil sections appear to be designed for high speed powered flight, ABC was high speed autorotative flight.

Get speed without fuel per mile – compromise from hover to high speed.

## *What technology isn't being Exploited*

**Ducted Fans**

The Urban X-Hawk is an interesting concept that appears to take advantage of all of the four advances mentioned above - any comment on the practical application of this?

**Co-axial rotors -**

Sikorsky has come out with some pretty advanced models for what still hasn't flown. This indicates quite a high degree of confidence in their concept.

**Tilt Wing -**

It's interesting to note that no-one has taken up a new tilt wing aircraft. Can you think of any reasons why this may be the case?

Moving primary structures with actuators –swing wing fighters were successful but the same benefits can be found without that complexity.

Two fundamental type of vehicles – those with lift at high speed from rotors, and those with lift from wings. Wings will probably get the L/D to the place. Wing affects hover performance and needs to be moved out of the way.

We've also pretty much reached the limits on what the pure helicopter can do - or it appears that way. Any thoughts for what we can do to make the pure helicopter more efficient / faster / cheaper / quieter?

Whole area of R&D – make operational capability of helicopter better. Helicopters are doing a great job, but need things that are more mundane, less snazzy.

Add to safety, and operational performance. Starting to happen.

Chip shots not long shots – we're always looking for new technology.

Helicopters have exploded worldwide because of ordinariness of good engineering and competition.

Keep it routine, safe, dependable.

Anything else you think might be worth discussing would be gratefully acknowledged.

## *ORDINARINESS OF HELOS*

Even as technologies mature – have to share with helo. 10 years before a technology gets accepted. .

**Figure 70-1 Scimitar rotor blades**

CHAPTER 71 *10 Commandments of Helicopter Flying*

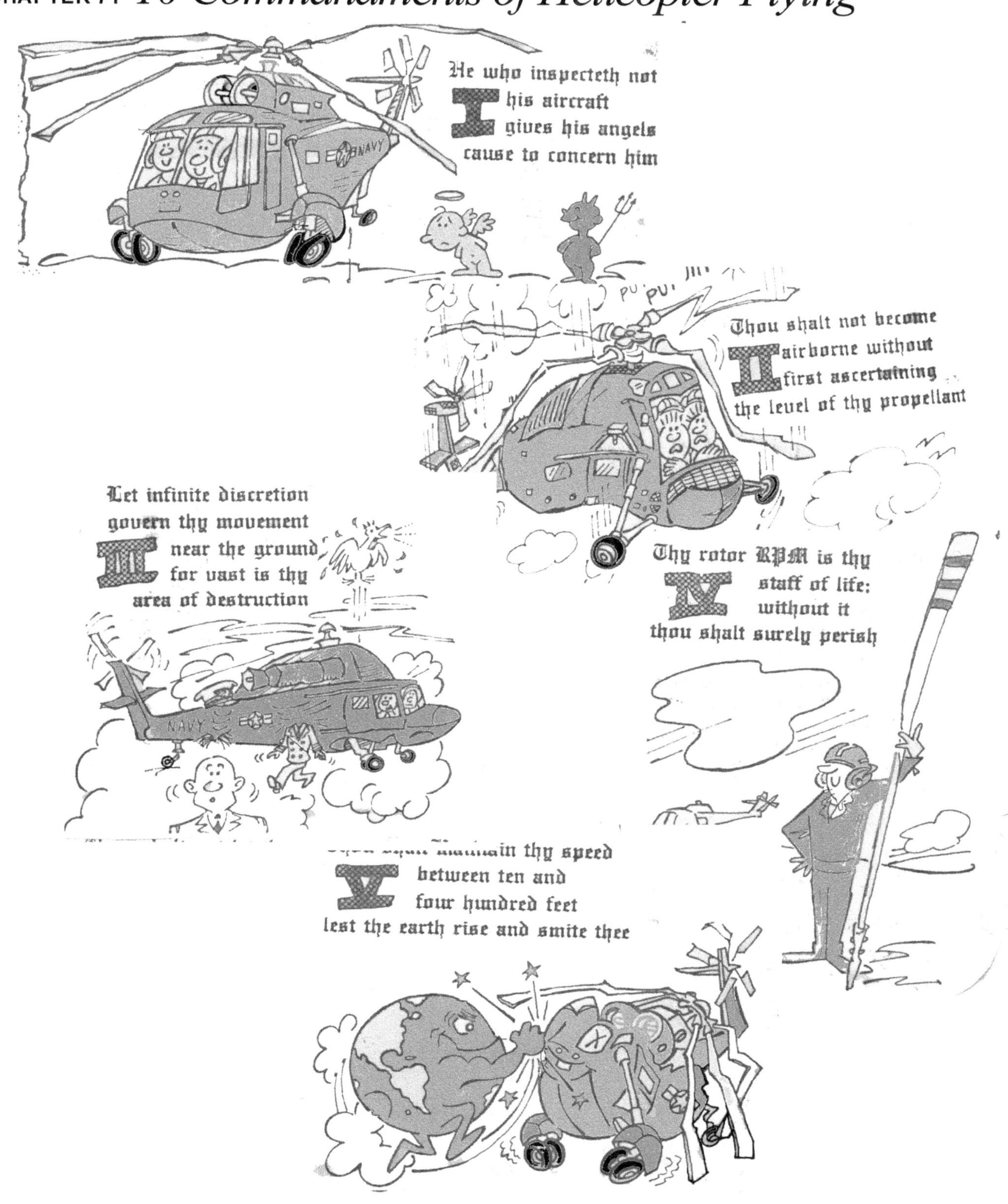

He who inspecteth not
I
his aircraft
gives his angels
cause to concern him
PU PU
Thou shalt not become
II
airborne without
first ascertaining
the level of thy propellant
Let infinite discretion
govern thy movement
III
near the ground
for vast is thy
area of destruction
NAVY
Thy rotor RPM is thy
IV
staff of life:
without it
thou shalt surely perish
thy speed
V
between ten and
four hundred feet
lest the earth rise and smite thee

Thou shalt not make a
trial of thy center of gravity
**VI** lest thou dash thy
foot against a stone

Thou shalt not let thy
confidence exceed thy ability
**VII** for broad is the
way to destruction

He that doeth his approach
and alloweth the wind
**VIII** to turn
behind him
shall surely make restitution

He who allows his tail rotor
IX to catch in the thorns
curseth his children
and his children's children
NAVY


Observe thou this parable
**X** lest on the morrow
thy friends mourn the

# CHAPTER 72 *Hymn of Flying Strain*

(with thank and apologies to Rudyard Kipling)

The manuals carefully tell us
In precise black and white
The load, the power, the speed of air
To use when we take flight.
So when a mangled aircraft
Lies spread across the ground
The blame for loss or error
Must eventually be found.
And laid upon a man.

The sensors carefully measure
The force, the speed, the strain
Of things that pull, push and spin
So all can read them plain.
To know within which careful bounds
We can operate sure.

The rule books solemnly tell us
In words of lawyerly prose
To avoid that went wrong before
But shows no sure certain paths
To keep us safe in all ways.
Yet in our daily dealings of
Things aeronautic we find
The gods put no numbers or rules
In view before mankind.

To no known regulation He made us
To no procedure bound.
To help us when we go
Beyond known ground.
Metal, fuel, plastics, electrons

We bend with bold imagining
And dare darkness and storm
Fly blind with trust implicit
In things of earthly form
Until our flaws of logic or strength
Show suddenly our weakness
In Nature's fiery furnace.

No child of Adam exists
who has not regulation bent,
Some limitation exceeded
And lived to laugh it off.
Consequence delayed, not seen.
Yet none of woman born can boast
Of breaking laws of physics
Without eventual cost.

The tomes of aeronautics,

Flight manuals, rule books as well
Can never show the line
Between written limitation and rule
And the stress that finally breaks
So we who fly can always
Stay within careful bounds

To take to the air in safety.
Know regulations to keep from trouble
With our fellow men,
And know those lines unwritten
Beyond which we cannot step
With wings of earthly measure.

# CHAPTER 73 *Aircraft Flown*

More or less in the order flown

OH-58D
Bell 222
Sh-2F
RH-53D
T-2
Beaver
Rockwell 114
OV-1B
pitts
Sea Fury
Alouette
Apache
P-51
S-76
TAV-8
T-34C
Mi-2
Mi-17
Rooivalk
Sw-3
Super Puma
PC-6
Speed canard
C-7
Dragon Fly
EH-101
Mi-28
A109
Brantley
Mi-26
UltraSport 331

King Air
Katana
A119
Bell 430
AS-350
Cheyenne
Bell 407
S-61L:
Bell 430
Bell 429
Eagle Single
H-19
H-34
T-38
E$nstrom
SW-4
Bonanza
Debonair
R-66
R-44
Bell 412
RGerman AF CH-53D66
Groen Bros Gyrocopter
Harvard

Aircraft Flown

www.ingramcontent.com/pod-product-compliance
Lightning Source LLC
Chambersburg PA
CBHW082109220326
41598CB00066BA/5893

* 9 7 8 1 7 3 2 5 4 0 9 3 4 *